A Harlequin

JANET DAILEY

Collector's Edition

Harlequin

JANET DAILEY

Collector's Editions

1 NO QUARTER ASKED
THE INDY MAN

2 BOSS MAN FROM OGALLALA
DARLING JENNY

3 DIFFICULT DECISION
ENEMY IN CAMP

4 HEART OF STONE
BIG SKY COUNTRY

5 ONE OF THE BOYS
BEWARE OF THE STRANGER

6 THE WIDOW AND THE WASTREL
SOMETHING EXTRA

A Harlequin

JANET DAILEY

Collector's Edition

Harlequin Books

TORONTO • NEW YORK • LOS ANGELES • LONDON
AMSTERDAM • PARIS • SYDNEY • HAMBURG
STOCKHOLM • ATHENS • TOKYO • MILAN

These books by Janet Dailey were originally published as
follows:

NO QUARTER ASKED
Copyright © 1974 by Janet Dailey
First published by Mills & Boon Limited in 1974
Harlequin Presents edition (#124) published January 1976

THE INDY MAN
Copyright © 1977 by Janet Dailey
First published by Mills & Boon Limited in 1977
Harlequin Presents edition (#223) published
February 1978

ISBN 0-373-80601-9
First edition October 1982

CONTENTS

NO QUARTER ASKED 9

THE INDY MAN 193

NO QUARTER ASKED

"JUST WHO DO YOU THINK YOU ARE?"

Stacy's voice was shrill. "Humiliating me like that in front of your cowboys! Well, I'll show you, Mr. Big Shot. I can take anything you can dish out!"

"Oh, can you?" Cord murmured savagely. His mouth descended on Stacy's in a kiss meant to hurt, to punish, to master her completely. Then he pushed her away.

Stacy was stunned by her passionate response to him. "All right, you've proved your point," she said finally. "You know you can always force me to 'behave.'" Her eyes darkened with emotion. "But you will never, ever be able to make me feel anything but disgust for you!"

CHAPTER ONE

STACY stared out the window at the traffic rushing between the concrete buildings below. The sombre grey and brown tones of the towering structures reflected the depression that hung so heavy on the young girl's shoulders. A little sigh escaped her as she let the curtain fall back in place and turned to face the ageing man behind the desk.

'Mr. Mills, you were Daddy's friend. You should understand more than anyone why I have to get away by myself to sort things out. Why does it have to make any difference if it's in a New York apartment or a cabin in Texas?'

'It's because I was your father's attorney and closest friend that I wish you would think it over a little more,' the lawyer replied, removing his black-rimmed glasses and absently wiping them with his handkerchief.

'I'm not trying to run away,' Stacy ran a gloved hand nervously over her arm. 'I just need time to see where I fit in again.'

'Look, Stacy, any other young girl in your shoes would be going to Europe or the Islands. You're a wealthy girl now. I can understand that you aren't particularly happy with the way you acquired your money, but the death of someone dear always involves a difficult adjustment. You've always been so independent, even headstrong, that I don't see why you insist on burying yourself out in the country.'

Stacy Adams looked hesitantly at Carter Mills, Sr., wondering how she could make him understand why she had to go. Her father, Joshua Adams, had respected this man and trusted him as few men are ever able to in their lifetime. *Her father.* The words caught in her throat. Stacy glanced down at her blue suit and the gloved hands clenched so tightly in her lap. Her mother had died shortly after Stacy was born, leaving her globe-trotting husband with the unfamiliar and frightening task of raising their child. Refusing the generous offers from friends to care for Stacy, Joshua Adams had filled another suitcase with nappies and powder and carted the year-old girl off on his next foreign assignment. Life for father and daughter had been one long world tour with brief respites in New York to catch their breath before starting out again, as he built his reputation as a freelance photographer.

Loving memories whirled through Stacy's mind, most vividly, her seventeenth birthday three years ago, when her dad had smuggled a puppy into a plush New Orleans hotel. Cajun, he had called the pup, in honour of the Creole country of his birth. The wiggling, playful dog had swiftly grown into a husky German Shepherd, devoted entirely to his young mistress. Her father predicted that Cajun would protect Stacy better than any guardian angel. Stacy wondered if her father knew how right he had been, because it was Cajun who had pulled an unconscious but unharmed Stacy from the wreckage of the chartered plane before it burst into flames. The pilot and her father didn't make it.

As she tried to blink back the tears that clouded her eyes, Stacy raised her head to meet the lawyer's affectionate gaze. Her brown eyes grew misty with the threatening tears, as her mouth curved into a painful smile.

'I take it back, Stacy. Perhaps going out there will help you face your problems. Joshua loved the West and never turned down an assignment that would take him there.' Carter Mills, Sr., rose from his chair and walked around to where Stacy was seated. 'But remember you're still a young woman, barely twenty, with a lot of the world ahead of you. He wouldn't have wanted you to miss any of it—not the good and definitely not the bad.'

Stacy grasped the hands he offered and rose, her trim, tailored suit enhancing the feminine figure underneath. 'I knew you would understand and see why I have to do this.'

'There's at least one young man that I know of who's rather upset about your leaving,' Carter Mills commented. 'But you can't blame my son for wanting to escort you around our more fashionable clubs. And you can't say you don't belong there, not with the inheritance your father left you.'

'I'm afraid I haven't accepted the idea that I'm comfortably wealthy yet. Before I was happy just to be with Dad, travelling wherever the wind blew—maybe I inherited his itchy feet. Out there with just Cajun, Diablo, and miles of space, I should be able to decide about the future,' Stacy concluded as she reached for her purse.

'Are you taking that fool horse, too? I had hoped you'd sold him long ago,' exclaimed the lawyer with no attempt to hide his concern. 'I don't mind telling you that I think you're making a grave mistake taking him.'

'Oh, Diablo isn't as vicious and unruly as you would like to believe. He's high-strung, that's all!' Stacy smiled. 'You know very well that I'm an excellent horsewoman. Dad would never have allowed me to have Diablo if he didn't think I could handle him.'

'I realize that, but I'm sure it never occurred to him that you would be taking that horse out in the wilds with you,' Mr. Mills replied gruffly.

'No. I'm sure Dad probably hoped that I would settle down and take my place in society, so to speak. But I'm not ready for that yet. Maybe I never will want to be, who knows?' she said, then added, 'I really should be going.'

'What are you doing with the apartment while you're gone?'

'I decided to just lock it up rather than let it go,' answered Stacy, a shadow of pain clouding her eyes momentarily.

'Just as long as you know you're always welcome at our home. And if there's ever anything you need, don't hesitate one minute,' Carter Mills said.

'I won't. Carter Jr. is taking me to dinner tomorrow night for one last fling with civilization. He seems to think that I'm going to the darkest regions of Africa,' Stacy smiled, touched by the sincere concern extended by the lawyer. 'Thanks for everything, Mr. Mills.'

Stacy smiled as she walked out of his office into the reception room. Mr. Mills couldn't help but have misgivings about her impending trip. She wasn't going to an exactly remote area, but she would be reasonably isolated. When his son Carter had told him about Stacy's decision to rent a hunting cabin in the Apache Mountains of Texas for the spring, he had immediately checked into the situation as a personal friend. But he honestly could find no real flaws with her plans, except that she was going alone.

Stacy entered the lift with a lighted 'down' arrow

flickering above it. Mulling over her plans, she was unaware of the interested looks she received from some of her fellow passengers. The sprinkling of freckles across a too-straight nose usually dismissed her, in a stranger's eye, as average. But second glances noticed the gleaming brown hair framing her oval face and the dark brown eyes, now shadowed by her grief, with their naturally thick lashes that combined to give her a refreshingly wholesome aura.

On the ground floor, Stacy proceeded to the street where an incessant tide of pedestrians awaited the commands of the red and green globes. Swept along by the flow at the crosswalk, she let herself be led by the steady stream until she reached the parking lot where she had left her car. Preoccupied with her memories as she was, her hand caressed the steering wheel for a second before accelerating into the traffic. The luxurious sports car had been the last present her father had given her.

Looking back, Stacy realized she should have recognized the import the expensive gift carried. She had always assumed that, although she and her father lived very comfortably, their financial condition was dependent on her father's income. The discovery that her father's death had left her independently wealthy still seemed a dream. Stacy didn't know what she would have done if that had not been the case. She possessed a smattering of knowledge about everything, but she had forgone any further schooling to travel with her father.

Arriving at her apartment building, Stacy entered and took the lift to the fifth floor. Silently she walked down the corridor to her apartment and hesitated as she reached her door. Depression spread over her as she inserted the key and opened the door. She was immediately greeted by an ecstatic German Shepherd yelping his pleasure at her return.

'Cajun, you brute, did you miss me?' Stacy smiled sadly, cradling the enormous head in her hands as she looked at the unmasked adoration in the dog's eyes. 'What would I do if you weren't here?'

The telephone jingled dimly, stirring Stacy out of her thoughts. Bending a nyloned knee on the flowered couch, she picked up the receiver.

'Yes?'

'Stacy? Carter,' came the masculine voice on the other end. 'Dad said I just missed you.'

'I left there around four,' Stacy said, glancing at her watch as she sat on the couch.

'How's everything going?' A touch of concern peeped out of the light tone.

'Fine, really. I was just going to finish up the last of my packing, except for the few odds and ends that will have to wait,' Stacy said, adding with a little laugh. 'I even packed some dresses in with all my riding clothes. I'm planning to live it up in some little cowtown!'

'Just as long as you don't meet some tall, dark, handsome cowboy and ride off into the sunset on his trusty steed,' Carter mocked, 'I won't mind.'

'I wouldn't worry. They don't make cowboys like they used to,' Stacy chuckled. 'On our last trip west, all I ever saw were sunburned, middle-aged men with families to support.'

'Are you still driving down?'

'Just Caj and me. Diablo's going by train as far as Pecos. I'll pick him up there and go on to McCloud. The cabin's about thirty miles from town, so I'm really not too far from civilization.'

'I'm glad you didn't ask me to go along. All that solitude would drive me up the wall. I don't see how

14

you'll be able to take it for more than a week. How different can one mountain be from another?' Carter teased.

'Maybe you're right, but I'll have to find that out for myself.'

'Can't talk you out of a thing, can I?' the voice in the receiver said. 'Listen, I have a brief to work on tonight, so I won't be able to come round. We still have a date for tomorrow night. Seven sharp, right?'

'Right,' Stacy agreed.

'Okay. Take care and I'll see you tomorrow. 'Bye!'

'Good-bye, Carter.'

The click of the phone echoed forlornly in the crushing silence that followed. Refusing to give in to the melancholy that the empty room emitted, Stacy rose from the flowered couch to enter her bedroom. She would do that last-minute packing she had mentioned, filling the void intensified by the phone call with a bustle of activity.

The next night Stacy was just fastening the clasp on her onyx pendant when the doorbell rang. She surveyed her reflection one last time in the mirror. The sleeveless, peach-coloured dress with its V-neck and pleated skirt set off the copper tan of her skin and the golden highlights in her hair, that was pulled back in ringlets, Grecian style. Taking a tissue, Stacy blotted her peach-tinted lips and applied a little gloss before allowing a satisfied smile to light her face.

When she opened the door to admit Carter, her dark eyes were flashing with pleasure. 'I didn't keep you waiting too long, did I?'

The tall, fair-haired man grasped her hands and pushed her away from him. His blue eyes answered her sparkle with a shine all their own. 'May I say what

15

you already know? I wouldn't have minded waiting longer if I'd known what a vision I was going to see. Shall we go?' he asked, placing the crocheted stole Stacy handed him around her shoulders while brushing a light kiss on her hair. 'I've made reservations for eight at the Meadow Wood Country club.'

'Marvellous,' Stacy smiled.

The two chatted amiably on their way to his car, but once inside the conversation abated. Carter gave his full attention to the traffic around him while Stacy unobtrusively studied his silhouette. He was a good-looking man with light brown, almost blond hair and clear blue eyes. Six years older than Stacy and just entering his father's law practice, Carter was considered quite a catch by many of her acquaintances. His attractive fair looks were a perfect foil for Stacy's brown hair and eyes.

There had never been any avowals of love or promises to wait between them. When Stacy had accompanied her father on his travels, she had sent Carter funny postcards of wherever she was and called him when she got back in town. Carter dated other girls when she was gone, but never anyone as regularly as Stacy. The two families had been pleased with the budding relationship of their children, nurturing secret hopes of an eventual marriage.

Stacy smiled, watching the competent hands manoeuvring the car into a parking lot. Their relationship could never be considered as brother-and-sister, she thought, even if it hadn't reached the heart-pounding passionate stage yet. They were both enjoying the other's company while waiting for love to come their way. Some day, she supposed, they would marry. They would have a good life. They got along together too well for it to be any other way. But not yet, not yet.

'Besides,' Stacy thought, 'I'm still naïve enough to wish for a love that will sweep me off my feet, even if it is only fairy-tale stuff.'

'Dreamer, are you going to get out of the car or just sit there?' Carter asked, laughing down at the girl as he stood holding the car door open for her.

'I'm sorry—I was off in another world.'

'Well, come back. Tonight is my night and I plan to make the most of it,' he smiled as he escorted her to the club entrance.

His arm rested lightly around her waist as he opened the elaborately scrolled doors of the private club. Carter ordered their drinks while Stacy gazed at the unique furnishings. The bar was decorated in an exotic jungle-type atmosphere with leopard and zebra skins adorning the walls.

When the waitress returned with their drinks, Stacy caught Carter looking at her with a sombre expression on his face.

'Why so grim? I thought we were going to celebrate tonight?' Stacy chided.

'Sorry, I was thinking about that vacation you're taking. Stacy, Dad isn't too happy about it, and neither am I. If anything happened to you out at that godforsaken cabin, it could be weeks before anyone finds out,' he said earnestly.

'Please, let's don't talk about it tonight. I've made up my mind that I'm goin- and that's all there is to be said,' she replied a litt'e sharply because of her own apprehension. 'It seems everyone knows what's best for me but me.'

'Did it ever occur to you that this time they might be right?' A hint of disgust was in his voice. 'You seem to think that because you've travelled all over the world you can handle anything that may happen.

17

Why, you're no more experienced than some country girl! All your father showed you was the world from the sheltered side of a camera lens. You have no idea what it's like to be on your own.'

'Just because I've seen war and hunger and famine from his view, does that make it any less real? I know what life is about. And I know what I'm going to do with mine, so there's no need of discussing it any further,' Stacy retorted.

'Will you stop being so stubborn for once and listen to reason?'

'I told you the subject is closed.'

'Then let's dance,' Carter suggested roughly as the combo started playing a slow tune.

Stacy rose, pushing her chair back from the table. Carter held her elbow firmly, directing her to the dance floor. When he took her in his arms, both expressions were a little grim.

Stacy laughed, 'Oh, Carter, I'm sorry. I really didn't mean to lose my temper. Please don't let's argue tonight.'

He smiled down at the girl's pleading eyes. 'Okay, we'll consider the subject closed. We'll just enjoy our evening together.'

Later when their reservation for dinner was called, the couple entered the dining room and were escorted to a small table for two secluded from the rest of the diners. When the final course was over, the couple settled back contentedly with their coffee.

'That was a delicious meal,' Stacy said, accepting the light from Carter for her cigarette.

'Umm. But the partner is even more delicious.'

'Thank you, kind sir.'

'Did you want to go back into the bar and dance, or would you rather go somewhere else?'

'No, let's stay here. I really enjoy this atmosphere and besides, I don't feel in the mood for a discotheque tonight,' Stacy replied.

'Good, neither do I. There's some talking I want to do and I'd hate to shout it over the din of some rock band.'

'Please, not another lecture about my trip,' she begged. 'You promised there'd be no more discussion about my going to Texas.'

'And I have every intention of keeping my word. This is something entirely different. Shall we go?'

'Yes.'

Stacy waited for Carter at the entry way to the lounge while he paid the bill. They found a table over in a corner and ordered drinks. At the beginning of a slow ballad, they wound their way on to the floor. Holding Stacy a little away from him, Carter gazed down into her brown eyes and smiled gently.

'Remember after your father's funeral the comment Dad made about you being one of the family?'

'Yes,' said Stacy, returning the serious look on her partner's face.

'I want to make it legal. I want you to be my wife,' he said, their steps almost ceasing. 'I'm not trying to talk you out of your trip, but while you're thinking about the future, I want you to include me. Stacy, I care about you—I love you and I want to watch over you for the rest of my life. We've never talked about the future before and it's time we did. Before, we were both too young. I still had law school to finish and you still had some growing up to do. Well, they're both done now and this is the time to start planning the rest of our lives.'

'Carter, I don't know what to say. I don't know if I'm ready to settle down. I don't know——'

'Don't say anything. I know it's awfully soon after losing your father. You're bound to be confused, so I'm not asking for an answer yet. When I think you're ready, I'll ask you again properly. Until then I'm just asking you to remember that I love you and want to marry you while you're out there in that Texas refuge,' Carter said quietly, gently kissing the top of her forehead.

He drew her once again into the circle of his arms, and they continued their dancing in silence while Stacy mulled the proposal over in her mind. She shouldn't have been surprised by it, but she was despite her earlier thoughts on the same line. Returning their table after the song was over, they sat quietly without speaking.

'You mentioned you were shipping Diablo to Texas. as going to ask if you wanted to take my grey,' said ter. 'He's definitely more manageable than that red vil of yours.'

'I don't expect to have much trouble with Diablo, but thanks for offering,' Stacy said, smiling at her date. 'Besides, he's already on his way to Pecos, so I'll just stick with my original arrangement.'

'What time do you plan to leave tomorrow?' Carter asked.

'I hope to get started by midday.'

'It's rather late now. I don't want it to be said that I kept you from your beauty rest. I think you'll have plenty to think about tonight. At least I hope so,' said Carter, casually referring to his earlier proposal.

They talked little on the way home. Stacy nestled down in her seat and gazed out the window at the neon world before her. Pulling into the parking lot of Stacy's apartment building, Carter turned the car motor off, then instead of getting out of the car, he sat quietly in his seat looking at the brown-haired girl beside him.

'I won't be able to come over tomorrow and tell you good-bye, so I'll wish you my good luck now,' he said, drawing her over into his arms.

Stacy tilted her head back and awaited his kiss. His lips were firm and gentle as they pressed down upon hers. He held her body close to his as his hands caressed the tanned shoulders underneath her stole. Stacy's heart increased its tempo with the growing urgency in his kiss.

'Take that with you, Stacy, and let it plead my cause,' he finished.

Reluctantly Stacy stepped out of the car when he came around and opened the door for her. In silence, they walked into the building to the elevator.

'I'll leave you here. Stacy, come home soon,' Carter whispered to her, looking down affectionately at the freckled nose and wide brown eyes. Softly he dropped a kiss on her forehead and walked away.

Watching the slender, but muscular man leave, Stacy felt a cold emptiness chill her heart. She turned uncertainly to the yawning doors of the lift. Quietly she let herself into the apartment, questioning her decision to leave the only home and friends she had.

An hour later she had fallen asleep, once again resolved to carry through with her plans to journey to Texas.

CHAPTER TWO

'McCloud—10 Miles,' the sign read. Stacy arched her back, stretching the cramped muscles. Two and a half days of steady driving were beginning to tell. But she was almost there and the excitement of finally reaching her destination was starting to flow through her. She glanced briefly at her reflection in the rear view mirror. Only her eyes showed the weariness she felt from the long drive. The pale, lemon-yellow top that complemented her olive-green pant-suit looked as fresh as when she had put it on that morning. The matching jacket lay over the back of the passenger seat where Cajun was sleeping, his huge body contorted by the limited space.

The two-horse trailer specially designed for the Jaguar was pulling easily. Diablo had raised quite a fuss when she loaded him in Pecos, but had since settled down nicely.

The afternoon sun was glaring through the windshield of her car as Stacy reached for the sunglasses lying on the dash. It wouldn't be long now before she'd be in her Texas retreat. First she would stop in town to look up the Nolans, so they could direct her to the cabin and then pick up some groceries. With luck she should be cooking her supper by seven.

Ahead she could see the growing outline of the small town. As it drew closer, Stacy lowered her speed, taking in as much of the surroundings as she could.

She pulled into a petrol station on the outskirts of town. Stepping out of the black sports car, she snapped her fingers to the waking Shepherd to follow. Stiffly and a little sleepily, he joined his mistress on the concrete paving. Stacy glanced appreciatively around the station, noting the lack of litter and usual car parts. Although the building wasn't modern, it was in excellent repair.

A teenage boy walked out of the office area towards the Jaguar. His admiring glance at the lithe figure passed unnoticed by Stacy as she surveyed the town ahead of her, shimmering in the afternoon sun.

'Fill 'er up, miss?' the young voice drawled.

'Please. Check under the hood, too,' she replied, smiling at the gentle Southern accent.

Cajun went off to investigate a grassy lot next to the station while Stacy walked into the office to escape the sun. Inside, it took a minute for her eyes to adjust to the absence of the blinding sunlight. There were two men inside. One, the older of the two, was dressed in an attendant's uniform. The other, who had his back to Stacy, was dressed in blue Levi's and a faded plaid shirt. His dark, almost black hair was barely visible under the sweat-stained brown Stetson on his head. His tall, muscular frame blocked the attendant's view of Stacy until she stepped over to the counter where there was a selection of sweets.

'S'cuse me, Cord. Can I help you, miss?' the man inquired.

Stacy glanced up at the man facing her, taking in the smiling hazel eyes and his creased face, leathered by the Texas sun. She couldn't help but return the smile offered by the stocky man.

'Yes, I'd like one of those chocolate bars,' Stacy said.

'Sure thing,' the man nodded, turning towards the cash register with the coins Stacy had handed him for the bar. 'Don't think me nosey, ma'am, but from your accent, I take it you're not from around here?'

23

Laughing, Stacy replied, 'I never realized I had an accent, but I suppose to you I do. Actually I'm from New York, but I'm staying here this summer. I was wondering if you could tell me where I might find a family named Nolan. I've rented their hunting cabin,' she explained.

It was then that the second man turned to face Stacy, and she was surprised by the seeming antagonism in his eyes. Puzzled, she heard him mutter a goodbye to the man behind the counter and stride out the door to a jeep parked beside the station. Turning back to the counter, she attempted to shake herself free of that haunting expression in his eyes. What had she done?

'I'm sorry, what did you say?' she asked, realizing the attendant had been addressing her.

'I said the Nolans run the grocery store in town. You turn right at the next block, then straight for two more, then left. Theirs is the second shop from the corner,' he smiled.

'Thank you.'

'Miss, you were a quart low on oil, so I put some in. Boy, that's some car you got,' the young boy commented, coming inside, his allegiance switching from the attractive girl to the black sports car. 'I'll bet she really leaves 'em behind on the straight-away!'

'That's enough, Billy,' the older man put in, taking Stacy's money for the petrol and oil. 'I'm sure the lady appreciates the fact you like her choice of cars.'

Stacy laughed in return. 'Right now I'd better look up the Nolans or it'll be dark before I get to my new home.'

'Well, you just follow the directions I gave you and you can't miss it. Molly Nolan is always there in the afternoons, and I imagine she'll know where to run

24

down her old man,' the attendant said as he walked along with Stacy to her car.

She whistled to Cajun and waved a good-bye to the two attendants as she drove out on to the highway. Stacy smiled to herself as she turned right at the next block. The people seemed friendly anyway. At least two of them were, she qualified. And she wasn't going to let a dark-haired stranger's seeming hostility spoil her first visit to the town. If he hadn't seemed so disagreeable, she probably would have considered him handsome, she reflected.

He certainly had the requirements—dark hair, brown eyes, and a tall, muscular build—but he had acted as if she carried the plague. There really wasn't any reason for her to keep dwelling on those unfriendly dark eyes; chances were she probably would never see him again. It was the clear-cut features of his face with their straight lines outlining his jaw, cheekbones, and chin that gave Stacy the feeling there was no 'give' in the man.

Reaching the corner of the second block, she spied the grocery store. Ahead of her was a space just wide enough for her to park her car and trailer. Cajun attempted to join her when she hopped out of the car, but she ordered him to stay. She glanced into the horse van at Diablo before continuing on her way to the shop.

It was a quaint little main street, covering all of two or three blocks. There was a drugstore on the corner, the grocery store next to it, a little brick post office after that, followed by a clothing shop and a café. 'It isn't a big town,' Stacy thought, 'but it's probably sufficient to serve the ranch community surrounding it.'

Pushing the door open, she entered the grocery shop. Behind a narrow counter was a small, matronly lady

Stacy guessed to be in her late forties. Her hair was peppered with grey which made her seem more motherly. The simple house dress covering the plump figure reminded Stacy of a kitchen filled with the aromas of fresh-baked cakes. When the customer the woman was waiting on left, Stacy stepped forward.

'Excuse me, are you Mrs. Nolan?'

'Yes, I am. Is there something I could help you with?' the woman asked.

'I'm Stacy Adams. I made arrangements to rent your cabin for the summer,' Stacy explained, smiling at the jovial face.

'Of course, how silly of me. I should have recognized you right off. We don't have many tourists stop in our store. You did say you'd be here on the first part of May, but it had completely slipped my mind,' apologized the older woman. 'I imagine you're anxious to get out there before dark.'

'Yes, I had hoped to stay there tonight, Mrs. Nolan.'

'Oh, goodness, call me Molly or I'll think you're talking to someone else,' she laughed. 'My husband will be here shortly and can drive out with you. We cleaned it all up last week, but it's still a little barren. You know how men are, if they got somethin' to sit on and a place to cook food, it don't matter if there's curtains at the windows or a cloth on the table.'

'I'm sure it will be fine. I hope you didn't go to too much trouble just for me,' answered Stacy, recognizing that the woman had noticed her city clothes and was concerned that Stacy was expecting something fancier.

'Excuse me,' a voice from behind Stacy said.

As she turned to move away from the counter, she found herself face to face with the broad shoulders of the stranger from the petrol station. Involuntarily her eyes rushed up to meet his. There was no flicker of recognition in the dark eyes, no spark of interest.

'Oh, Cord, I'm so glad you're here,' said Molly Nolan, coming around the counter to take his arm. A faint smile tickled the corners of his mouth as he looked down on the motherly figure. 'I want you to meet Miss Stacy Adams. She's rented the hunting cabin in the foothills of the east range for the summer. Stacy, this is Cord Harris, your official landlord. The Circle H headquarters is about ten miles from the cabin.'

Surprised by the unexpected encounter with the stranger a second time, Stacy murmured a polite reply to the introduction and managed to raise her eyes to meet his stony gaze again. This time there was no doubting the hostility and contempt in his eyes. Deliberately they searched her face and continued their way over her yellow top to her creased slacks and fashionable buckle shoes, before returning derisively to her face. The pant-suit that Stacy decided as being practical for travelling before suddenly seemed too chic, too elegant for this rough country.

Embarrassed, she felt the growing heat burning her cheeks. Angry that this Cord Harris had managed to make her feel artificial and cheap, she thrust out her chin defiantly.

'I hope you won't find our country too desolate and isolated for you,' the man went on, a trace of sarcasm in his voice.

'I'm sure I'll enjoy my stay here. Almost everyone has made me feel very much at home,' Stacy replied, attempting to curb the anger that trembled on the edge of her words.

'I'm sure they have,' inserted Mrs. Nolan. 'We don't have many pretty young things like you around here. Why, once the word gets around that you're staying for the summer, our young men will beat a path to your door!'

'I doubt that,' Stacy smiled, 'but it's nice of you to say so.'

'Not worried about staying alone at that deserted shack, are you?' Cord Harris interposed. 'After a few nights alone out there, you'll probably welcome the company of our young men.'

'It's possible, but unlikely. You see, Mr. Harris,' Stacy was now indignant at the veiled cynicism, 'I came here to be alone. I do intend to make friends, but I don't intend to enter the social set.'

' "Intend," very cleverly stated,' the dark-haired man drawled, meeting Stacy's flashing eyes with a cool gaze. 'It leaves you wide open to do whatever you please. And somehow you don't seem the type to isolate yourself for any amount of time.'

'Now, Cord,' Molly Nolan put in, trying to quench the unexpected friction between the two. 'I don't think it's our place to judge Miss Adams or her plans. You apologize for your rudeness.'

'If what I said was unfounded, I certainly do apologize.' His hand touched his hat brim, mockingly. 'I do hope you enjoy your stay here, Miss Adams, however long it may be.'

Nodding a good-bye to Mrs. Nolan, the arrogant rancher picked up his sack of goods and went out the door without allowing Stacy time to reply. Her fury had reached the peak where words failed her. Never had she met such an overbearing, insolent, and sarcastic man! Turning to the astonished woman beside her, Stacy vented her displeasure.

'Who does that man think he is?'

'Oh, you mustn't mind Cord,' soothed Molly absently. 'He has a tendency to voice his opinion. Underneath all that bluster though, he's really quite charming.'

'You could have fooled me,' Stacy exclaimed. 'I wish he lived ten thousand miles away instead of just ten. What in the world did I do to warrant such an attack?'

'Nothing, dear, I'm sure. Maybe you just reminded him of someone else,' the woman replied bustling around to the other side of the counter. 'I imagine you'll want to do some shopping. My husband ought to be here any time now.'

Still fuming inwardly, Stacy took a trolley and started down one of the aisles. 'He may be my nearest neighbour,' Stacy thought, 'but I'll make a special point to avoid him from now on, though I would like to see that infuriating coolness of his upset once!'

After picking up all the supplies she felt she would need, Stacy returned to the check-out where she found Molly Nolan engaged in a conversation with a thin, balding man. Guessing that it must be Mr. Nolan, Stacy joined them.

'Well, dearie, did you find everything you needed?' Molly inquired, then turned to the man by her side. 'This is Miss Adams, Harry. This is my husband. He'll drive up to the cabin with you.'

'I'm happy to meet you, Mr. Nolan,' Stacy said, extending her hand to the little man before her.

'Molly said you was a pretty thing, but she didn't say you was this pretty. Ya shore are going to light this little cowtown up,' the bright-eyed man replied, eagerly shaking her hand. 'I hope the cabin will suit you all right, 'cause it shore ain't very fancy.'

'I'm sure it will suit me. I'm used to roughing it with my dad,' Stacy said, smiling at the man who was an inch shorter than Stacy's five-foot-four.

'Oh, is your father coming to join you?' Molly asked.

29

'No.' A flicker of pain haunted her face momentarily. 'He was killed in a plane crash a month ago.'

'Oh, I'm so sorry. I didn't mean to——' Molly started.

'No, you couldn't have known,' interrupted Stacy.

'What about your mother? Is she still back East? Does she approve of your gallivantin' off by yourself?' Harry Nolan asked.

'My mother died shortly after I was born, so I'm pretty much on my own now. But you needn't worry about me being alone, I brought my German Shepherd along with me. I'm sure he can handle any four-footed animal that would wander in, and the two-footed variety as well,' Stacy laughed, thinking about Cord Harris with a malicious satisfaction.

'Good dogs, them Shepherds,' the old man agreed. 'He'll watch out for you real good.'

'Naturally I hope he won't have to,' Stacy said, reaching in her purse to pay for the groceries. 'Well, Mr. Nolan, I'm ready to go whenever you are.'

'Where'd you park your car?' he asked.

'Across from the drugstore.'

'I'll meet ya in about five minutes with my jeep and you can follow me out,' he nodded, moving towards the door.

'Now if you need anything or get to feelin' you want some company, you just hustle yourself into town. Me an' my husband would love to have you any time,' said Molly after her husband had left.

'I'll remember. But I think for a while I'm just going to enjoy the peace and quiet,' Stacy replied, touched by the motherly concern.

'The folks around here are all pretty friendly and would be more than glad to help you out if you have any kind of trouble, so you just don't hesitate to ask anybody,' instructed the matronly woman. 'Peace and quiet's fine, but you mustn't shut yourself off completely. You just remember that you're always welcome here and don't be ashamed to ask for help.'

'I won't be. Thank you again. You'll be seeing me.' Balancing the sack of groceries in one arm, Stacy pushed the door open with the other. It was nice to feel so at home with people she had only met a few minutes ago. With the exception of a certain man, everyone had gone out of his way to help her.

Reaching the car, she put the groceries in the back, quieted the excited dog, and looked around for Mr. Nolan. In the van Diablo was starting to raise a little fuss. Walking back to the trailer, Stacy entered the van by the side door of the empty stall. The sorrel turned his blazed head to her and blew gently on her face. Softly she talked to him, trying to quiet him down. His ears flicked back and forth catching her words, but his eyes still rolled with unease.

Glancing up, Stacy saw Mr. Nolan drive up beside the Jaguar. As she emerged from the van, the wizened old man crawled out of his jeep and joined her beside the trailer.

'All set to go?' he asked.

'Yes, just making sure everything was secure in the trailer. I'm afraid my horse is a bad traveller,' Stacy explained, glancing at the tossing head of the sorrel.

'Mighty flashy-lookin' horse,' commented her companion. 'What breed is he?'

'Mostly Arabian,' Stacy answered, walking over to the driver's side of the sports car.

'Never cared much for them. Too flighty actin'. Give me a steady quarter horse any time,' the man answered a little gruffly. 'Well, we best get goin'. The road's not in too bad a shape, so you should be able to keep up

31

with me easy.' He started the jeep and moved off.

It wasn't at all difficult to follow him. They drove through a few blocks of homes before taking a gravel road heading north from town. The road soon entered the foothills and finally into the mountains themselves. After they had gone about twenty miles, the jeep turned on to a side road that was little more than a worn track. Stacy refused to let herself dwell on the jolts her Jaguar was taking and prayed that the low-slung sports car wouldn't get hung up in one of the ruts, while she was trying to concentrate on the bouncing rear end of the jeep in front of her. She glanced in the mirror anxiously at the horse trailer behind her. Diablo would really be a bundle of nerves by the time she got to the cabin.

The pine woods were so thick that she couldn't see to either side and with the sun setting, the rays filtered through the trees only in patches. The trees thinned out ahead as she watched the vehicle in front go down a small hill into what looked like a clearing. Reaching the top of the hill, Stacy saw a luscious green meadow before her with a stream cascading through it. Off to her left against the back of a canyon wall was nestled a small wooden cabin with a corral and lean-to beside it. Looking to her right briefly, Stacy could see the mountain meadow wander into the arroyos beyond. Why, it was a valley, but more beautiful than any picture she had ever seen.

Harry Nolan had parked his jeep and was standing by the wooden porch of the cabin when Stacy pulled her black sports car to a stop in front.

'It's beautiful!' she exclaimed, as she got out of the car to gaze at the surrounding mountains.

'Yep,' the man replied, removing his straw hat to wipe his balding head with a kerchief. 'I'll show you around the inside. I think you'll find it comfortable.'

Smiling, Stacy followed the wizened figure into the cabin. The main room housed a fireplace with a large, stuffed deer's head above it. The hearth was filled with firewood with an ample supply piled beside it. There was one sofa in the room and an old rocker. The kitchen, consisting of a few metal cupboards over an old-porcelain sink with a pump-type hydrant, covered the west wall. Luckily there was a propane gas stove to cook on; Stacy was sure she could never have managed one of those wood-fired ranges. The table with its two chairs sat in the middle of the room. She could see Molly Nolan's touch in the red-checked tablecloth and matching curtains at the window.

The motherly woman was probably responsible for the pillows on the sofa and the horsehair blanket hanging on the far wall, too. Harry Nolan explained to Stacy how to light the kerosene lanterns and adjust the wick to give off the right amount of light without smoking the glass before he showed her into the bedroom. A big four-poster bed dominated the small room. The bed was covered with a large patchwork quilt that Stacy knew had come from the Nolans. Squeezed in a corner was an old set of chest of drawers. Behind the door was a place to hang her clothes.

'Oh, this is perfect,' Stacy smiled, surveying the two rooms excitedly. 'I can't think of anything that isn't already here.'

'Well, I'm glad it suits you. The missus will be happy to hear how much you like it,' said Harry, his bright eyes glowing at Stacy's enthusiasm. 'Now, if you'd like, I'll help you unload that horse of yours in the corral.'

Accepting Mr. Nolan's offer, Stacy manoeuvred the car so the back of the trailer was over to the gate that the short man had opened. Stacy set the brake and walked back to let the tail gate of the van down before she entered the empty stall beside the restless horse. Anxiously, the sorrel pulled at the rope that held him, interfering with Stacy's attempts to loosen it. She tried to quiet the nervous horse, but his feet increased their tattoo on the trailer's floor as his ears flattened against his head. Finally the knot on the end of the lead rope was loose. As soon as he found himself free, the red stallion half-reared, pulling the girl along with him out of the van. The whites of his eyes flashed menacingly as he danced down the ramp on to the solid ground of the corral. As quickly as she could, Stacy turned the horse loose to gallop around the corral.

The flighty Arabian circled the corral warily, his flaxen mane and tail whipping in the wind. Then his attention was caught by the stranger leaning against the fence rail near his mistress. Instantly he bore down upon the man, his teeth bared and his pointed ears snaked back. With surprising agility the lean man leaped away from the fence and the savage attack.

'Does he do that often?' Harry muttered.

'Fortunately, no,' Stacy apologized, waving the horse back to the centre of the pen. 'Once in a while he does strike out without any apparent provocation, though.'

Studying the spirited horse pacing up and down on the opposite side, head held high into the wind catching the various odours carried by the mountain breeze, Harry turned to Stacy. 'What's that scar on his neck? A rope burn?'

'I don't know,' she answered, noting the faint white line barely visible under the full mane. 'He had it when I bought him.'

Eyeing the slim figure speculatively, Harry de-

34

manded, 'Just how the devil are you able to handle him? He could walk over you like you was air.'

'Evidently we have some sort of understanding. Although sometimes I think he just tolerates me,' Stacy laughed, shrugging off the concern in the man's voice. Changing the subject quickly, she asked, 'Are there many trails around here accessible by horseback?'

'Plenty. Most of them either lead deeper into the mountains or into the valley, and a few of them branch out over to the Circle H,' replied Harry, gesturing towards the west.

'Where is the Circle H exactly?' Her hands shaded her eyes from the setting sun. That was one place she intended to avoid.

'This here's Cord's land that the cabin sits on. We just got a lease. It's an abandoned line shack that me and some of my friends use when we go huntin' and fishin'. But if you're referring to the ranch house, that's about nine, ten miles from here. Yep, he's got himself quite a spread. Runs it with an iron hand, he does. But the men don't mind 'cause they always know where they stand with him. He pays good money and expects a good day's work for it.'

Stacy could believe that. He probably rode around with a whip in his hand.

'Molly said you met him at the store,' the ageing man added. ' 'Course, you know he ain't married.'

Stacy made no reply as she watched the sorrel paw at some hay in the lean-to. 'Who could stand him?' she thought to herself.

' 'Bout six years ago, we all thought he'd got himself caught, but the girl up and ran off with some oilwell man. Never did much like the girl. She always thought she was so much better than the folks around here. He's better off without her,' nodded Harry, ignoring the bored look on the girl's face, and kept on talking.

Secretly, Stacy couldn't help but applaud the girl who had managed to set that arrogant cowboy back on his heels, but she didn't show it.

'He fixed up his grandma's hacienda on the place for her, piled a lot of money in it. He lives there alone except for his housekeeper.' Moving away from the fence, Harry started towards his jeep. 'Well, if I want to get home 'fore dark, I'd better mosey along. If there's anything you need, you be sure to let us know.'

'I will, Mr. Nolan. And thanks for all you've done. I really appreciate it,' Stacy said, shaking his hand warmly.

She stood in front of the cabin and watched the jeep drive off on the faint trail into the stand of trees. The solitude encompassed her as she lost sight of the jeep in the gathering shadows. Cajun came up behind her and shoved his moist nose in her hands. Kneeling down, she rumpled the hair on his neck roughly.

'I'm not alone, am I? Not as long as I have you around, huh?' Stacy smiled, and looked towards the cabin door. 'Let's go fix us something to eat.'

CHAPTER THREE

THE sun was streaming over the meadow when Stacy walked out of the cabin door to watch the golden haze cover the meadow. The valley was filled with the songs of birds trilling their greeting to the new day. The sun's rays were striking the rippling brook, turning it into a ribbon of shimmering quicksilver. Inhaling the brisk, clear air, Stacy emitted a satisfied sigh. Then, clicking to the Shepherd standing beside her, she walked over to the corral.

Two days had passed since she had first came to the mountain cabin. The first day Stacy had spent unpacking and settling in. The tack had to be cleaned, as well as the horse trailer and sports car that was dusty from travelling over the gravel roads. She had taken an evening ride down the meadow to give the moody sorrel some exercise and accustom him to the change of climate. The second day she explored the mountains to the east of her, spending most of the day away from the cabin. The scenery continually took her breath away. Never had she travelled so far without finding any trace of civilization except an occasional herd of cattle in the valleys below. Surprisingly enough the evenings had passed rather swiftly for the young girl. After cooking her meal, feeding the horse and dog, she had sat out on the porch until the evening light faded.

It was so restful that, for the first time in several weeks, Stacy felt at peace. Surrounded by the natural serenity of the valley, the worries and grief that had plagued her before seemed non-existent. Nothing mattered but being alive. She knew she had done the right thing in alienating herself from the rest of the world. But part of her never wanted to leave, even though she knew she would have to eventually.

Last evening she had written Carter a letter letting him know she had arrived safely and was settling in. This morning she planned to ride along the main road to find a rancher's mailbox so that she wouldn't have to go into town to post it. She hadn't noticed one on the drive to the cabin, but then she had been concentrating on the road and the vehicle in front of her.

Entering the side gate of the corral near the lean-to,

Stacy got the bridle out of the shed and started to approach the red horse who began retreating to the far side of the enclosure. Ignoring the flashing white feet and the small pointed ears that kept flicking back and forth, she walked up to the horse. Snorting, the sorrel lashed out half-heartedly with his front hooves and dashed to the other side of the pen. Arrogantly he looked back at Stacy, tossing his head defiantly.

'All right, Diablo, let's don't play hard to get this morning,' Stacy said, walking slowly towards the horse. 'It's too lovely a morning to work up a sweat catching you.'

The horse stood uneasily as she approached, still talking to him in her soft voice. He eyed her apprehensively as she stopped in front of him and extended her hand. Diablo stretched his small muzzle to her hesitantly and after a little investigation, blew into her hand gently. Docilely he submitted to the bit and bridle and stood quietly, the reins dangling on the ground, while Stacy fetched the blanket and saddle. Stacy never knew how Diablo was going to react to the saddle, sometimes he accepted it calmly and other times he acted like a yearling that had never seen one before. Cinching up, Stacy led the quiet horse out into the yard before mounting. Whistling to Cajun, she started her mount down the trail towards the main road. The sorrel pranced a little as the Shepherd ran alongside, but offered Stacy no trouble.

The sun's rays peeping through the cover of branches danced on the coppery red coat of the horse accenting the whiteness of the rider's blouse. Cajun raced ahead investigating all the sights and sounds of the trail. Acknowledging her sorrel's desire to run, Stacy nudged the horse into a canter. They continued at a ground-eating lope until they reached the main

38

road. Here Stacy slowed the horse to a trot, turning him in the direction of town. Diablo resented the slowed pace and began side-stepping and pulling his head in an attempt to loosen the tight rein. She was unable to admire the scenery as she fought to control her horse. Cajun still led the way, but checked back to make sure his mistress was with him. Stacy's whole attention was devoted to her mount that had begun to rear and plunge around. It was then that she noticed the saddle slipping. The cinch had loosened during the ride from the cabin.

Pulling the horse to a stop, she dismounted. But Diablo had abandoned the earlier docility at the cabin and refused to let her near him. His white feet lashed out, preventing her from approaching him. Slowly Stacy tried to edge her way up the reins to the horse's head, only to have him pull away with his superior strength. Concentrating on trying to quiet the fractious horse, she didn't hear the car coming down the road behind her until it was within a hundred feet. As she turned to see where the vehicle was, Diablo bolted past her, but was pulled up short by the quick thinking of the girl as she yanked the reins hard, forcing the horse to turn in a half circle.

With the noise of the car and the normal misbehaviour of the animal, the sorrel became completely unmanageable. Ignoring the car that had stopped just a few feet away, Stacy concentrated on preventing the horse from breaking away. With the endless open space before her, she knew she would never be able to catch him once he escaped. In the mood he was in now, he would run for miles before stopping.

From the corner of her eye, Stacy recognized the dark, towering figure that had climbed out of the car and was walking towards her. Of all people it had to be Cord Harris. He was the last one she wanted to see just now.

'Looks like you're having a little trouble, Miss Adams,' the low-pitched voice drawled.

'Brilliant observation,' Stacy said sarcastically, puffing from the exertion of holding the high-strung animal.

Walking up behind her, the man took the reins out of her hands and motioned for her to move back. At the sight of a stranger on the other end of the reins, Diablo renewed his battle for freedom, but he was no match for the determined man. Dodging the flying hooves, Cord grabbed the cheek strap of the bridle and hauled the horse down on all four feet. Gradually the sorrel settled down, tossing his head and snorting occasionally.

Stacy gazed at the broad, muscular shoulders underneath the tan jacket the man was wearing and watched as he ran his hand down the horse's neck. She couldn't imagine anyone being able to win in a fight with this forceful man. Just then he turned his head and met her searching gaze. As much as she wanted to, she couldn't keep from staring into the dark eyes that smouldered with a strange, deep fire. He was the one who broke the silence.

'I would recommend you get yourself another horse. He's more than a slip of a girl can handle.'

'Thank you, but I didn't ask for your advice, nor did I ask for your help,' Stacy retorted, hating the fact that she was beholden to this man.

'It didn't look to me like you were doing a very good job,' he replied coldly, his mouth turning up in a mocking smile. 'But then, maybe I had the wrong idea.'

'I would have been able to handle him if you hadn't

40

driven up in that noisy thing,' she said, gesturing defiantly at the sleek gold and brown Continental behind her, 'and worried him more than he already was.'

'I didn't realize I needed your permission to drive
down a public road,' drawled Cord Harris, the sarcasm
heavy in his voice as his eyes flashed at her. 'If your
horse is scared of traffic, perhaps you shouldn't be riding him where he's bound to meet it.'

'I'm sorry, I shouldn't have said that,' Stacy said bitterly. He had done her a favour and she wasn't exactly
behaving properly. 'He's a little temperamental sometimes, and this happened to be one of those times.'

'I hope they don't happen very often or I'll be finding you lying dead somewhere out on the range the
next time he throws you.'

'Oh, he didn't throw me,' Stacy corrected. 'I got off
to tighten the cinch.'

'Oh,' he said, a frown creasing his forehead as he
turned to the saddle. 'I apologize to your horseman-
ship, then, because I assumed the two of you had
parted company a little more dramatically.'

'No,' Stacy laughed, 'though I admit we have a time
or two!'

She walked up to fondle the horse's head while Cord
proceeded to tighten the girth on the saddle. Turning
back to face the girl, he rested his arm on the saddle-
horn. Self-consciously, Stacy felt his eyes on her and
turned to meet them, but he turned away quickly before she could read the expression written there. When
he looked back, his face revealed nothing of his
thoughts and Stacy looked away this time, feeling herself redden under his eyes.

'Where were you heading, any place special?' he
asked.

'I was looking for a mailbox,' Stacy replied hurriedly, trying to cover the sudden unexplainable blush.

'A mailbox!' Cord laughed scornfully. 'Just where did you intend to find a mailbox out here?'

'No, I mean a mailbox for a ranch where the mailman delivers and picks up their mail,' defended Stacy, her dislike for the arrogant man returning once more.

'Well, I'm sorry to disillusion you, Miss Adams, but there aren't any between here and town,' he said, one side of his mouth curling up in disdain. 'You forget that this part of the country lacks a few of the luxuries that city people consider necessities.'

'I didn't know,' she said hotly, her temper rising, 'and I don't think it's very amusing of you to degrade a person because of their ignorance.'

'I'm not trying to degrade you,' Cord said calmly, unruffled by the fiery figure standing defiantly before him. 'I'm merely pointing out that you would be more comfortable if you would go back where you belong.'

'Mr. Harris, I don't think it's any of your business where I may or may not belong, and I would appreciate it if you would get out of my way so that I may have the pleasure of bidding you good-bye!'

Glowering down at her from his greater height, Cord Harris seemed about to say something, but clamped his mouth shut in a grim line. Although already regretting her hasty words, Stacy felt compelled to raise her chin to emphasize her stand. They stood glaring at each other for a few minutes and then, without warning, the rancher swooped her up in his arms.

'Allow me the privilege of helping you on your way,' he said fiercely, holding her in an iron grip against his chest.

So astounded was she by his action that Stacy didn't even attempt to struggle but lay in his arms, her heart beating wildly. She realized that she was playing with

42

fire, crossing this man. Effortlessly, he deposited her in the saddle of the sorrel, tossing the reins over the horse's head. Catching them, she looked down at his blazing eyes.

'That's what you wanted, wasn't it?' the mocking face said darkly.

Regaining some of her composure, Stacy retorted, 'As I said before, Mr. Harris, I didn't ask for your help.'

'You'll find people around here don't ask—for anything. If they want to do something, they do it.'

Diablo, sensing the tension in the air, began dancing about. Stacy could think of no answer to Cord's cryptic words and felt sure that anything she said would only make the situation worse. She didn't want to incur his wrath again. The consequences were too unpredictable with a man like him. With as much poise as she could muster she reined the sorrel around the imposing figure. She could feel his eyes on her as she urged the horse into a trot back up the road she had just come down. Burning in humiliation, she longed to gallop away from those haunting eyes, but her pride insisted on an orderly retreat.

Stacy had to steel herself to keep from looking back. Finally she heard the car door slam and the motor start. Immediately she kicked the sorrel into a gallop. She didn't allow the horse to slow down until they had reached the turn-off to the cabin.

By the time the three reached the house, Stacy's humiliation had turned to anger. He had no right to treat her like that! His overbearing manner was outrageous and interfering. He acted as if he had a right to tell her what to do. Fuming, she unsaddled the fidgety horse, flinging the saddle and bridle in the shed with an unusual disregard for their care. She

43

stomped out of the corral, closing the gate vehemently, and continued her pace to the porch of the cabin. The dog sensed the mood she was in and scurried off to a corner of the building under the shade.

Disgustedly, Stacy sat in the chair on the porch and gazed moodily at the quiet meadow. She shuddered as she recalled Cord's arms around her. She could still smell the masculine odour of his cologne that was clinging to her blouse. If only she had struggled or fought with him or done anything instead of just lying so passively in his arms, submitting herself to his will! She could have at least scratched those rugged features or pulled his dark hair. Never again would she allow herself to be so weak-kneed in his presence. If she ever met him again, she vowed, she would tell him exactly what she thought of him.

The serenity of the valley meadow failed to comfort her wounded pride. The peace she had felt earlier in the morning was gone and the inactivity of just sitting only increased her agitation. Finally she rose and entered the cabin. It was almost noon, but she had no appetite. Grabbing her swim suit, she changed clothes and, with a terrycloth jacket over her shoulder, started down to the brook that ran through the meadow. Perhaps an icy dip in the mountain stream would cool her temper.

Not far from the cabin the stream widened just deep enough and wide enough to enable her to swim. Kicking off her sandals, Stacy dived into the water. Cajun had followed her at a safe distance and settled himself under a shade tree to watch over his mistress. She splashed around for nearly an hour before pulling herself exhaustedly on to the bank. Propping herself up against the tree with Cajun, she lit a cigarette and relaxed. The afternoon sun started making its way across the sky, but still the two sat under the tree. The exertion of her swim had calmed her nerves, but it hadn't taken away the loathing she felt for the arrogant rancher. She toyed with the idea of returning home, but dismissed it quickly when she remembered Cord Harris's mocking smile as he said, 'Go back where you belong.' Never would Stacy give him that satisfaction.

'We're going to stay, Cajun, and what's more, we're going to enjoy ourselves. No more are we going to avoid Mr. Harris's ranch. If he doesn't like it, well then, that's just too bad,' asserted Stacy, rising to her feet. 'Tomorrow, though, I'd better go into town and post that letter before Carter sends a search party after us.'

The two started back for the cabin, Cajun trotting contentedly behind the heels of his mistress. Stacy's spirits rose as she walked. Her stride had a little spring in it and her face wore a satisfied expression. She was convinced that any future confrontation with Cord Harris would not find her coming out second best.

The next morning Stacy overslept, awakening at the persistence of the Shepherd's nuzzling. Hurriedly she had dressed and made coffee. She had hoped to get an early start into town. Just as quickly she fed the dog and gave the sorrel some oats and fresh hay before donning the shirt that matched her yellow slacks. Ordering Cajun to stay at the cabin, Stacy hopped into her black Jaguar and started down the trail to the main road.

She increased her speed, as she turned towards town. This time she was able to look a little more at the view around her. The tall stone mountains seemed to rise out of the prairie as they reached for the sky, their peaks changing into a dark grey contrasting the tans

45

and greens of the plains below. The panoramic view was breathtaking. An occasional greasewood tree dotted the horizon with an exclamation point.

As the car passed the bend in the road where Stacy had had her run-in with Cord Harris yesterday, its speed increased perceptibly. Stacy didn't want to be reminded of that episode and was glad that she could hurry by it. But her spirits were dampened by merely passing the place, causing her to ignore the scenery and concentrate on the road. It was difficult to escape the image of those dark, compelling eyes that had watched her so intently as she sat astride her horse the day before. Their sardonic gleam remained indelible on her memory along with the tanned, sculptured face and dark, almost black hair.

A little over a half hour went by before Stacy reached the town of McCloud. The streets were fairly quiet with only a few people walking from store to store. She parked her sports car in front of the post office. As she climbed out of the car she removed the letter from her purse before walking into the brick building. Nodding a good morning to the clerk in the mail room, Stacy dropped her letter in the outgoing mail slot. She started to leave and then hesitated. Turning around, she walked back to the counter in the mail room.

'Excuse me, is there any mail here for Stacy Adams?' she inquired.

'You're the young lady that rented Nolan's hunting lodge, aren't you?' the quiet voice drawled. 'Yes, you had a letter, but I gave it to Cord to drop off to you. You've met him, haven't you? He said he knew you and since he's your neighbour, it seemed natural.'

'You gave *him* my letter?' Stacy was astounded. 'He knew I would be coming into town.'

'Maybe it just slipped his mind,' offered the middle-aged man. 'He'll probably drop it over to the cabin today. People are pretty neighbourly around here.'

'In the future, please hold my mail here until I come personally to pick it up,' Stacy said, checking her rising temper. The clerk had obviously thought he was doing her a favour, so she really couldn't blame him.

'Yes, ma'am,' he replied, eyeing her quizzically.

With a quiet thank-you, Stacy turned away from the counter and walked out the door. Reaching the sidewalk, she stopped and hesitated for a minute. She decided that it would only be polite to stop in and talk to Mrs. Nolan and thank her for all the extra work she had gone to at the cabin.

As she walked into the grocery store, she noticed Molly talking to a young, red-haired woman with two spirited youngsters tugging at her skirt. When Mrs. Nolan recognized Stacy coming in, her face immediately broke into a smile that reached all the way to her eyes. The young woman beside her also turned to meet Stacy. Her smile held as much welcome as Molly Nolan's.

'Stacy, I was wondering how you were gettin' along,' the elder woman said, walking up to take both of Stacy's hands in her own. 'Cord said he met you on the road yesterday and you seemed to think you were doing all right.'

'Yes, I'm doing fine,' Stacy replied, biting her lip to keep from making a caustic comment about Cord Harris. 'And I love the cabin. Mr. Nolan told me about all the decorating you did to make it more feminine, and I want to thank you.'

'Well, don't thank just me, thank my daughter, too,' Molly said, indicating the redhead beside her. 'I'm glad you stopped in, because I was really lookin' forward to you two meetin'. Mary, this is Stacy Adams, as you must have guessed. And this is my daughter, Mary Buchanan.'

'I'm so pleased to meet you at last. Mother has talked of nothing else, but that "lovely young girl" living all alone in the cabin, and she didn't quite do you justice,' the young woman smiled, extending a hand to Stacy.

'Thank you,' Stacy replied. 'Your mother has really made me feel at home.'

'I think she'll always be the mother-hen type looking after her chicks regardless of whether they're hers or not,' teased Mary, smiling affectionately at the woman beside her. 'As you must have guessed, these two Indians here are mine. This is Jeff and this is Dougal.'

Stacy knelt down to shake hands with the two young boys.

"You're awful pretty,' Jeff said, scrutinizing the golden-brown hair that fell becomingly around the oval face smiling back at him. ' 'Most prettier than Mom.'

'Well, thank you,' Stacy laughed.

'You have conquered him,' Mary smiled, gazing at her oldest son with pride. 'But then he always had good taste. Takes after his father.'

'Naturally,' said Mary, 'and don't ever forget it!'

'That's Mom, always reminding me what a catch I made, as if I would forget,' Mary grinned. 'Are you in a hurry or anything? Why don't you come over to my house for coffee?'

'That would be wonderful,' said Stacy, warming to the friendliness of the attractive woman. 'My car's parked right out front and——'

'Good, we walked down here and now we can beg a ride back,' Mary said with a bewitching smile. 'We only live a few blocks away.'

'You two run along then,' said Molly Nolan, 'so I can get back to work. Take care of these two boys. And don't let them eat all that candy I gave them.'

Mary directed Stacy to her home, a beautiful ranch-type house with a large fenced yard. The boys brawled out of the car reluctantly, wishing the ride could have lasted longer.

'They really got a thrill out of riding in your car. They'll remember that for ages,' said Mary, opening the front door and waiting for Stacy to enter first.

'I enjoyed it, too,' Stacy answered as she followed the other girl into a big, spacious kitchen. 'As trite as it sounds, I love children.'

'Well, I'm not going to make that natural comeback of "wait until you have some of your own", because I love mine and wouldn't change them for the world,' Mary agreed, heating coffee for the two of them. 'Mothers that moan and groan about all the trouble their children make almost drive me up the walls.'

'I know what you mean, although I'm not too experienced on the subject,' Stacy said, sitting down at the table.

'Tell me, do you have someone waiting back home?'

'Sort of,' said Stacy, remembering Carter Mills and his recent proposal.

'Sort of? You mean, he hasn't popped the question and you've come out here to make him see how much he misses you?' Mary concluded as she joined Stacy at the table with the coffee. 'Cream or sugar?'

'No, black,' Stacy answered. 'He did propose before I left, but I'm not sure if I want to get married just yet.'

'Do you love him?'

'I suppose so. I've never dated anyone else but him. We just knew each other so well that——'

'I see what you mean,' Mary nodded. 'I suppose with

49

the loss of your father and all, you didn't want to make any rash decisions.'

'Partly,' Stacy sighed.

'Maybe being apart will help you decide how much you really do care for him,' suggested Mary, realizing that the girl beside her was confused. 'Fortunately, there never was any doubt for me as to how I felt about Bill. He's the doctor here. The minute he got into town and took over old Doc Gibbon's practice, I knew he was the man I wanted to marry. I was almost twenty-two by then and had dated my share of men.'

'I wonder if that's my problem. Travelling with my father on his various photography assignments the way I did, I was never in any one place long enough to meet people my age.' It was comforting to be able to confide in Mary, a comparative stranger. 'And when I got back to town I always had Carter to fall back on. I admit I did have a crush on one of the reporters Dad worked with,' Stacy chuckled.

'I guess everyone has those,' Mary laughed. 'I had it bad for Cord Harris. I used to chase him all over.'

'*Cord Harris?*'

'Yes. Every girl around here has fallen under his spell at one time or another. He used to be quite the playboy,' said Mary, a smile playing at the corners of her mouth.

'That woman-hater? I can't imagine him being polite to anyone!' commented Stacy.

'I assure you he's not a woman-hater. He's a little bitter after that dirty deal Lydia Marshall pulled on him. But it's only a matter of time before some girl breaks through that thin veneer of his, and then you'll see what I'm talking about. When he turns the charm on, nobody is immune,' Mary concluded with a shake of her titian hair.

'You're looking at one girl who is immune,' Stacy said vehemently. 'He is beyond doubt the most arrogant, despicable man I've ever had the misfortune to meet!'

'I see he's made a distinct impression on you.' Mary hid a smile with difficulty. 'I think you may have judged him a little too quickly. Ignoring his superb good looks and his great six-foot-four frame, you'll still find he has all the requirements of a good husband and father. And if that isn't enough, he owns the biggest ranch around and runs it with a profit.'

'That's all well and good, but I still pity the woman that ever marries him. He didn't hesitate to form a hasty opinion of me, and I don't intend to turn the other cheek.'

'Whew! The sparks must fly when you two get together,' Mary exclaimed, amused and puzzled. 'Funny, I thought you two would hit it off rather well.'

'Well, we don't,' Stacy said, hoping to close the subject. She couldn't bring herself to confide in this understanding girl about yesterday's episode. The humiliation was too fresh in her mind to talk about.

It was the middle of the afternoon before she bade the friendly family good-bye and promised to stop the next time she came to town.

In less than an hour, the young girl was back at her cabin being greeted by the wildly thumping tail of the Shepherd. Happily the two entered the cabin. While Stacy was preparing their supper, she noticed a note on the table. Walking over to pick it up, she saw an envelope underneath it. Quickly she read the note.

'So sorry I missed you,' it read. 'I took the liberty of bringing your mail.

C.H.'

'The nerve of that man!' Stacy said aloud, ripping the note into shreds and throwing it into the fireplace. ' "So sorry I missed you." Hmph!' she muttered, returning to the stove. 'Well, I'm not!'

After eating, she took her coffee out to the porch and read the letter from Carter in the waning light.

CHAPTER FOUR

THE late afternoon sun cast a long shadow of horse and rider picking their way through the rocky foothills. The red horse pranced a little as a lizard darted across their path, but responded to the quiet words from the rider on his back. From an arroyo on their left came the German Shepherd to rejoin his mistress.

Stacy called a hello to the dog and urged the horse into a canter on to the opening flatland. A smile rose on her lips as she turned to survey her backtrail with satisfaction. To her there could be nothing as beautiful as this untamed land. She was glad she had finally decided to trespass on the Circle H home range. The scenery was fantastic in its undisciplined beauty. Pulling the stallion up near some greasewood bushes, she dismounted to sit in their shade and gaze at the panoramic view before her.

After removing the flat gaucho hat, she dusted her white blouse off. They had been exploring since midmorning and even though she could feel the tiring of her muscles, she was still exhilarated by the wonderful country she had seen. She glanced at her watch and knew that when she remounted she would have to go directly back to the cabin in order to make it before sundown. After dark she might have trouble finding her way back.

Her thoughts turned to the letter she received yesterday from Carter. She knew he wouldn't be so eager for her to return if he were here beside her to enjoy all this scenery. And return she would have to. She couldn't cut herself away from the rest of the world indefinitely. Nature in all its harsh beauty had brought this realization to her today. She had decided during her ride that she would return in two or three weeks. This would be her vacation. She was sure that was the way her father would have wanted it. She'd get a job somewhere, maybe in a travel bureau. If not she would find something else.

But marriage? No, she wasn't ready for that, she thought as she shook her head. She cared too much for Carter to grab at the straw of escape he offered her. When they married, or rather when she married, Stacy knew she wanted to put her whole heart into it and the family that would come. She could only hope that Carter would understand that she wanted herself whole again before they made any life together.

Standing up, she faced the gentle breeze ruffling her long hair and smiled as she inhaled the fresh air. Life was good and there wasn't any sense in worrying about things that hadn't happened. Crossing over to the sorrel, she picked up the reins. Remounting, she whistled to the dog and turned her horse into the mountains from which they had come.

The horse broke into an eager trot, refreshed by the brief rest in the meadow. Stacy captured his spirit and eased her hold on the reins. The horse immediately moved into a rocking lope. As they reached the rock-strewn foothills, his gait slowed to a fast walk as he picked his way. Cajun followed not far behind. Stacy turned for one last look at the grassland she had left.

At that moment, with Stacy turned and off-balance in the saddle, a rattlesnake resting underneath a near-by bush sounded his warning. Before Stacy could turn around, Diablo was screaming, rearing high into the air. His terror was beyond restraint as he shook his h ad violently, protesting Stacy's instant tightening of the reins. Spinning in a half rear towards the flatland, the stallion unseated his light rider completely. As Stacy lost her grip and tumbled off, the horse bolted, taking his avenue of escape.

Unable to break her fall, Stacy landed heavily on her shoulders. Her neck snapped back at the impact, striking her head on a rock. Pain seared through her body. Valiantly she attempted to fight the unconsciousness that threatened her. She struggled up on one el-bow, catching a glimpse of Diablo streaking across the meadow with his tail high. Vaguely she recognized the Shepherd racing towards her before she succumbed to the promising relief of blackness.

Frowning, Stacy turned slightly to look where the voice had come from. With difficulty she forced her eyes to focus on the smiling face hovering above her.

'Where am I? My father, is he——' she started, her brown eyes glancing around the unfamiliar setting in panic. Then she closed her eyes and added, 'I remember now. I fell.'

'Don't try to talk,' admonished the doctor. 'You've had a bad fall, but you're going to be fine. I'm Dr. Buchanan, Mary's husband.'

Attempting a smile at the recognized name, Stacy tried to speak. 'Is Mary here?'

'No, you're at the Circle H. Cord Harris found you

and brought you to his ranch. You owe him a great debt.'

'No!' Stacy cried, feebly struggling to rise from the bed. 'I can't stay here, I can't!'

'Now listen, young lady,' the doctor said, gently restraining her movement. 'You need rest. The best place for you right now is in this bed.'

Pleadingly she looked into his face, her eyes clouding with tears as she desperately willed him to change his mind. His returning gaze was adamant. Involuntarily her eyes turned to the doorway that was now blocked by Cord. It was impossible to tell how long he had been there, his fierce gaze taking in both parties.

'Oh, why,' she sobbed helplessly, 'why did you have to be the one who found me?'

'I assure you I wasn't out looking for you,' was the caustic reply. 'I found your horse running loose and backtracked him.'

'That's enough talking,' interrupted Dr. Buchanan. 'It's time you rested.'

Not having the strength to fight either her unwanted host or the doctor's orders, Stacy turned her face from both of them and allowed the frustration and pain to sweep her away. The two men's eyes locked over the girl, the rancher's defiant and unflinching, the other's probing and questioning.

'I think we should leave her to rest in quiet,' the doctor suggested, gathering up his instruments.

It was late evening before Stacy woke again. She lay quietly in the bed and studied her surroundings with a little more interest. The bedroom was masculine with heavy Spanish furniture and bold, definite colours. She couldn't help wondering if this was the rancher's bedroom. It seemed stamped with the same austere personality that branded Cord Harris. Dark mahogany beams coursed the ceiling, accenting the white, textured paint. The coarse-grained effect was carried through in the curtains with their loose-weave tweed in reds and oranges that was repeated in the coverlet on her bed.

Stacy pushed herself into a sitting position in the bed, fighting off the wave of nausea that followed the movement. She was wearing a nightgown. The realization shocked her as she looked down at the yellow bodice. How and when had she changed? Who had helped her? Her face crimsoned at the thought of the muscular Texan. It was even her own nightgown. How had he come into possession of it? Unless, of course, he had sent someone after her things. But he wouldn't dare have the nerve to touch her!

'Well, I see you've returned to us. I thought you were going to sleep all through the night,' came a low voice from the doorway.

Stacy's eyes snapped up to face her unexpected visitor, her cheeks still blushing. 'What time is it?' Stacy stammered, unnerved at seeing the man who had been occupying her thoughts.

'After eight,' Cord replied, pulling up a chair beside her bed and gazing at her intently. His voice held no trace of the sarcasm she associated with him as he asked, 'How are you feeling?'

'Better,' she replied, unable to meet his penetrating eyes. 'I want to thank you for all you've done. I——'

'There's no need. I consider myself lucky that I spotted your horse. I hate to think how long you might have lain out there before you were found.' His low voice still carried that gentle tone that was so unfamiliar to her and did such strange things to her heart. 'Here, let me fix those pillows for you.'

Self-consciously Stacy allowed him to add another pillow behind her head. Aware of his nearness, she glanced up to his face, taking in the clear cut of his jaw and soft firmness of his mouth, but refusing to look above the high cheekbones at the dark, unfathomable eyes. She caught the scent of his cologne which she remembered so vividly from their encounter on the road. It was difficult to ignore the muscular chest and arms encased in the crisp white shirt. Stacy was sure he could hear the wild beating of her heart and cursed the way his physical presence could arouse her.

'Isn't that more comfortable?' said Cord, reseating himself in his chair. A smile was showing faintly on his mouth as if acknowledging the girl's embarrassment at his nearness. He couldn't fail to detect the flush growing in her cheeks as she sat silently with downcast eyes. 'Perhaps, Stacy, we should try to begin again,' he said, his voice changing to an impersonal tone at her continued absorption with a bow on her gown. 'We got off to a rather bad start. The doctor feels that it's best for you to stay here until you can get back on your feet. As it will only be a temporary situation, it will make it easier for both of us if we ignore our personal feelings.'

Surprised at his open acknowledgement of the unspoken antagonism between them, Stacy looked up into the two dark eyes regarding her so thoughtfully.

'Well, are we friends?'

Hesitantly Stacy placed her slim hand in the outstretched palm. It was engulfed in the large, tanned hand. She felt he held it a little longer than was necessary, yet the suddenness of his release upset her. His brows were now contracted in that old familiar frown and his mouth curled in a whimsical smile as he rose and looked down at her. Once again his size and air of superiority overwhelmed her.

57

'I imagine you're more interested in getting something to eat than listening to me. I'll send Maria in with some soup and tea,' the dark figure said, moving towards the end of the bed. 'Oh, by the way, your dog is outside and your horse is bedded down in one of our stud pens. I also took the liberty of bringing a few of your things here from the cabin. I hope you don't mind.'

'No,' Stacy answered, surprised at the meekness in her voice.

'Good,' he said, a twinkle now in his eyes. 'In case you were wondering, Maria "prepared" you for bed.'

Indignation rose in her as the tall rancher left the room. 'He's positively insufferable!' she thought. How could she have been taken in by that initial gentleness? Just imagining how he must have been laughing at her all the while he was sitting there angered her further. He was right about one thing—for the time being, she had to compromise until she was on her feet again. The throbbing in her head forced her thoughts to change to quieter things.

By the time the robust housekeeper, Maria, arrived with her food, Stacy's composure had returned, though she was sure her cheeks still retained some of their unnatural colour.

'Ah, the leetle one is feeling much better, no?' smiled the jovial Mexican, placing the tray with a steaming bowl of broth on Stacy's lap. 'The head, eet does not hurt so much?'

'Only a little. The soup smells good,' Stacy replied, inhaling the invigorating aroma of the hot broth. She was hungrier than she had thought. Thankfully Maria left the room and Stacy was allowed to eat at her leisure. She had just finished the last of the tea when the Mexican woman returned for the tray.

'That was very good, Maria,' Stacy smiled, handing the tray to the waiting hands.

'*Gracias*. I cook good. Meester Cord, he say my cooking the best anywhere in Texas.' The large woman giggled at the audacity of the claim.

'Well, perhaps he exaggerated a little, but it was very good,' Stacy laughed.

'You get some more sleep now,' Maria instructed, helping Stacy settle back under the covers. 'We have you up in no time. Doctor say for you to keep warm and rest, but thees bed so beeg you get lost in it. I tell Meester Cord, but he say eet all right. Pooh! You should have a man to keep you warm, not a beeg bed.'

Stacy could feel herself blushing at the woman's advice. She remembered again her impression that this was Cord's bedroom. She had to ask.

'*Si, si,*' the big woman laughed. 'You theenk maybe he sleep here tonight. No, he thought eet better he sleep in office.'

Maria continued her laughing, her belly rolling with the force of her mirth and her fatty underarms bouncing as she carried the tray out of the room. Stacy glanced apprehensively around before putting out the light. Although fearful that she would be unable to sleep, she dropped off almost immediately.

The morning sun was dancing its patterns on the braided rug beside Stacy's bed. Maria had already brought in her breakfast and had helped her clean up. Rather than attempting to brush the hair around her wound, Stacy had merely pulled it back and tied it with a bow to match the bedjacket that had been brought along with her other clothes. She felt much better as long as she ignored the dull pain in her head and the sniffles in her nose. She was just examining the unusual scrollwork in the bedroom door when it opened to admit the smiling face of Cord Harris.

'Good morning. Maria said you were up.' His low voice was cheerful with no trace of sarcasm. 'Do you feel like a visitor?'

'A visitor?' Stacy echoed, trying to think of who would be coming to see her. 'Yes.'

'Okay, feller, come on in,' said Cord, swinging the door wider to admit a cautious German Shepherd.

'Cajun!' Stacy exclaimed happily as the big dog recognized the figure in the bed and bounded to her, his tail wagging happily. With his front paws on the bed, he proceeded to give her a thorough washing with his big tongue. 'Stop it, you silly idiot!'

'I think he's rather pleased to see you. He refused to eat this morning and wouldn't move away from the front door, so I decided the best thing would be to let him see for himself that you were all right,' Cord explained, still standing in the doorway.

'I hope he wasn't too much of a bother,' Stacy said after she had managed to push the Shepherd off the bed and on to the floor where he sat gazing at his mistress with undisguised adoration. 'I'm afraid we're rather attached to each other.'

'I have some work to do around the ranch, so I'll leave the dog here for company. I've instructed Maria to bring you some books from the library. I know we don't have the elegant surroundings you've been accustomed to, but if there's anything else you would like, just ask and we'll see what we can arrange.'

'Thank you,' she replied, wishing she could think of something else to say. 'Everything's fine, really, and I'll try not to be any trouble to you.'

'You won't be—at least, not any more than I can handle,' he replied. The mocking smile returned to his face before Cord left, closing the door behind him.

'Have you ever been "handled" before?' Stacy asked the Shepherd, wondering why Cord had developed such a negative attitude towards her. 'I imagine he thinks he can "handle" anything that comes along!'

A few minutes later Maria arrived with some novels and magazines. Stacy noticed a couple of her favourite books and settled back to read. The day passed rather swiftly. With each knock on the door she half expected to see the rancher appear. When Maria returned for the supper tray that evening and Cord still hadn't come, Stacy decided that he wasn't going to come. Strangely enough, she felt disappointed. She tried to attribute it to her loneliness and desire for company regardless of how arrogant he might be.

CHAPTER FIVE

WITH a contented sigh, Stacy rested her head against the cushion and gave the Shepherd lying beside her an affectionate pat. Her soft brown curls lay carelessly around her neck, touching the edge of the simple orange and yellow shift with its V-neck and capped sleeves. Her tanned legs glistened all the way down to the Roman sandals she wore.

A subtle application of powder hid the slight redness around her straight nose that was the last reminder of the cold that had racked her body with chills and fever the past week. Her recovery had been swift, thanks to the quick action of Dr. Buchanan who had been summoned as soon as the course of her illness became apparent, and had given her medication.

Stacy was so engrossed in her outdoor surroundings that she failed to hear the measured steps entering the cobblestoned veranda until they were a few feet from her. Instantly she recognized the deliberate walk; hadn't she listened for it enough times outside her bedroom door this past week? It belonged to Cord Harris. Looking up, she met the full gaze of the rugged man's dark eyes. Her own travelled over the blue turtle-necked shirt accenting his broad shoulders and muscular arms, then down the trim waist and narrow hips, taking in the black slacks tapering over his dress boots.

So accustomed was she to seeing Cord in ranch wear, Stacy was surprised that he wore the dressy sports clothes with such ease. Most outdoor men she had met always looked uncomfortable in anything other than their everyday wear. She couldn't help noticing that there was no tell-tale sunburn where the hat brim ended nor where the sleeve of his shirt started. He obviously found time to make use of the pool.

Uncomfortably aware that she had been staring, Stacy blushed. A tall glass of iced liquid was held before her by a large, tanned hand. Timidly she accepted it, and her half-raised eyes caught the bemused smile on Cord's face. Though he had noticed Stacy's scrutinizing stare, Cord made no comment as he pulled up a rattan chair beside her.

'You're looking very well,' he said gently, his eyes flicking over her face. 'I hope the drink is satisfactory. I don't know if it's included in the doctor's orders, but it can't do any harm.'

'Thank you. It's fine,' Stacy replied, taking a sip out of the tall glass. Her senses were tingling with the nearness of her host as the smell of shampoo and shaving lotion wafted over to her in the evening breeze.

'I imagine it feels rather good to get outside after being shut in for so long.'

'Yes, it does. You have such a beautiful view. You must be exceptionally proud of your home,' said Stacy, a nervous lilt in her voice. She felt an unaccountable need to keep the conversation going.

'The antiqueness of the hacienda doesn't offend you?'

'Oh, no!' she exclaimed, her eyes widening. 'It's lovely. You must have done a lot of remodelling.'

'Yes, we did. The original hacienda enclosed this area here. It served as a fortress against attacks in the early days. When I decided to remodel it, I eliminated the south and west wings. Even now there's more room than a bachelor needs,' Cord informed her with a smile.

'But when you marry and have children, it will be perfect,' Stacy said as she looked at the whitewashed adobe walls.

'Undoubtedly.' There was a coldness and withdrawal in his tone and his attention was riveted on a distant mountain.

'What I meant was the size——' she stammered.

'I understand what you mean, Miss Adams,' returning his dark, expressionless eyes to her. 'But I don't anticipate that prospect being fulfilled in the near future.'

Obviously he was referring to his star-crossed romance with the girl Mary had spoken about. 'You never know,' Stacy replied a little more brightly than she felt. 'I'm sure there are a lot of girls who are very anxious to change your mind, Mr. Harris.'

'Are you one?' A raised eyebrow disappeared into the black hair curling over his forehead.

'I wasn't referring to myself,' she replied a trifle indignantly.

'It's very romantic-sounding to marry a man who owns a spread the size of this one, but reality is quite another thing,' he continued. 'This is a hard, demanding land even in these advanced times. The hours are long and the results are unpredictable at best. A wife can expect to be alone a great deal, and isolated. As far as entertainment is concerned, it's non-existent with the exception of an occasional social gathering. The same with the large department stores you're accustomed to. Major shopping requires a trip to San Antoine or El Paso. The rigours of this life are more than a city girl would want to cope with.'

'I wasn't applying for the position, Mr. Harris,' Stacy retorted, rising from the chaise with a reddened face.

'Cord,' he supplied, towering over her as he rose. Taking her arm, he steered her towards the pool, his eyes sparkling with amusement. 'Come over here. I want to show you something.'

'What is it?' Her impatience was marked by the sharpness in her voice.

'Really, Miss Adams,' Cord said in a mock scolding voice. 'I would have thought you'd learned by now how to take a little teasing!'

'I have met certain egotistical men who would be vain enough to believe that all women fall at their feet!'

'As I have met women who feel they're the answer to every man's prayer and he should succumb to their charms.' The two had reached the opposite side of the pool and stood facing each other defiantly, his hand still upon her arm. The air between them crackled with the unspoken challenge. His voice was low as he

64

turned to face the horizon. 'Continuing this subject would accomplish nothing. We both have our own views.'

'Precisely,' Stacy said crisply. 'Now if you'll show me whatever it is you wanted me to see, I'll return to my room.'

'You wouldn't be interested.'

'What was it?' Stacy asked, slightly curious despite her annoyance with the arrogant man.

'Only an old family cemetery. I'm sure some ancient gravestones wouldn't interest your sophisticated tastes,' Cord replied sarcastically, his back now turned to her.

'I would like to see it.'

'It's not necessary,' he answered, as if this was an attempt at an apology on Stacy's part.

'Mr. Harris, the last thing I would do is go to patronize you. You said earlier that we should bury the hatchet and be friends. Obviously your wounded ego can't comprehend anything but undying loyalty. Now I would like to see "your" cemetery. If you don't want to accompany me, tell me where it is and I'll go by myself.'

The biting tone of her voice turned Cord towards her, his cool eyes examining her face as if assuring himself of her genuine interest.

'It's only a little way from here, but it's uphill. I wouldn't want you to overdo it your first time out. Perhaps we should postpone it.' At the angry denial forming on Stacy's lips, Cord went on, 'But if you're sure you want to go, I'll go with you.'

'I'm sure.'

'Very well.'

He started to take her arm again, but Stacy shrugged him off and began walking in the direction he had indicated. Cord followed a step or two behind as they made their way up the knoll behind the house. The incline was slight, but in Stacy's weakened condition she found herself out of breath when they reached the top. She managed to ignore the sardonic gleam in Cord's eyes and pushed on towards the wrought iron enclosure ahead.

The assorted crosses and gravestones were dwarfed by a large monument in the centre. Years had weathered most of them, but Stacy noticed that the area was well kept. The grillework, which should have rusted from age, still had a certain freshness in its black exterior and the ground had been seeded with grass, its green blanket lovingly covering the graves in a spring shroud. Cord opened the gate and Stacy walked inside.

The two walked silently on the trodden path around the dozen headstones before coming to a stop near the centre. Most of the dates were in the late 1800s and early 1900s. Four of the smaller crosses marked children's graves. One stone was recent, dated eight years ago and bore the words 'Stephen Harris— Father'.

'Is that your father's grave?' Stacy asked quietly, the word "father" bringing a melancholy to her voice as the freshness of her own loss washed over her.

'Yes.'

'I didn't notice your mother's. Is she buried here?'

A shadow passed over his face as Cord replied, 'She's buried back East with her family.' There was a briskness in his voice and a hardness in his eyes. 'She couldn't stand the ranch and its demands on her and my father. A few years after I was born she went back to her family.'

'She left you?' Stacy asked, pity in her heart for the now dead man and his abandoned son.

'Father gave her no choice,' Cord said, his steel black eyes on her face, rejecting the sympathy he saw. 'I doubt if you'd understand. This is a hard land. You must take what is yours and then fight to keep it. My mother was a pampered child used to being waited on, so the future that was offered meant nothing to her. She wanted the luxuries she was accustomed to and her demands never stopped, not on my father's attention or his money. There wasn't enough of either for her.'

'And the ranch came first,' Stacy murmured astutely.

'Do you see this marker here?' Cord asked, turning to the centre monument. 'Elena Teresa Harris, my grandmother. She was a Spanish aristocrat who fell in love with my grandfather, who was a struggling rancher at that time with a lot of dreams. She was a real woman. He had nothing to offer her but an old adobe three-room house, a few head of cattle and a lot of land that was dry most of the time. But it didn't matter to her.'

There was no denying the respect and admiration in his voice as he spoke. Momentarily he stepped forward and opened the gate for Stacy, following her out. Engrossed in their conversation, she accepted his hand on her arm as they walked to the edge of the knoll looking down on the ranchyard below. With his other hand, Cord pointed towards the western mountains, purpled in the twilight.

'The Mescalero Apaches used those mountains as a stronghold and raided settler and small ranchers at will. And the "Comanche War Trail" is not far from here either. At the turn of the century the Indian menace had ended and this western region was populated by cattlemen seeking these rich pastures where grass was so abundant. Most of the settlers ran more cattle than the land could support—overgrazed it. That's why there's so much desert land out here today.'

'Can't it be reseeded? Left alone to grow back?' There was concern in Stacy's upturned face.

'It's too late for most reclamation. Either the wind carries the seed away, or the rain doesn't come when it's needed, or it washes the seed away before it gets a chance to deepen its roots. Ignorance and greed do more damage to the future than they do to the present,' Cord answered grimly. 'But my father and grandfather realized this. In more than one way, I have them to thank for what I have today.'

'You must be very proud of them,' Stacy said with a smile. 'A lot of things have changed since your grandfather's time.'

'He was a cattleman, tried and true. He'd turn over in his grave if he saw sheep grazing on his land,' Cord chuckled.

'Sheep?' Astonishment was written on Stacy's face. 'You raise sheep?'

'Yes, I have a few hundred head of registered stock on the higher pastures.'

'You don't run them with the cattle?'

'Sometimes, usually in the summer when we move the cattle to the foothills. We also have some Angora goats, but they're in the experimental stages as far as our ranch is concerned. Quite a number of ranchers have had good success with them. And there's our quarter horses. We have two exceptional studs and several young breeding prospects. I've doubled the number of brood mares in the home herd. We have an auction on the grounds every spring, selling some of the yearlings and two-year-olds that we aren't going to keep or older brood mares we want to replace with new blood.'

'I didn't realize you had so many individual enterprises,' Stacy mused, awed by the size of the ranch's operation. 'I suppose there are oil wells, too.'

'No civilized Texas ranch would be complete without them,' Cord laughed quietly at the dazed expression on his companion's face. 'We have four on the east boundary. Only two are still in operation. Most all of the ranch property is outside of the oil-producing region.'

'I'm beginning to understand what the expression "cattle baron" means,' Stacy commented, looking up at the bronze face.

'Don't let the magnitude of all of it lull you into thinking it's an easy life,' he warned her. 'As diversified as the ranch has grown, it's only increased the work load and the difficulty of control.'

Stacy grimaced at his words. It was hard to imagine this powerful man not in control. He was so sure of what he wanted that nothing would dare stand in his way.

'Looks like Dr. Buchanan's car driving in,' Cord went on, watching a station wagon pull up behind the house below. 'We'd better go down. Marie will probably have dinner ready shortly, anyway.'

Nodding her agreement, Stacy followed him down the slope. By the time they reached the veranda, the smiling face of the young doctor was there to greet them. To Stacy's pleasant surprise, his wife Mary had accompanied him. The happy red-haired woman walked forward, arms outstretched to the younger girl.

'You look marvellous!' Mary exclaimed, clasping Stacy's hands warmly in hers. 'Tell me, Stacy, how have you two been getting along?' she teased in a low voice. 'I don't see any battle scars.'

'Cord and I have buried the hatchet, haven't we?'

Stacy replied with a throaty laugh. Glancing at the tall figure standing beside the doctor, she continued, 'We found some common ground that we both agree upon.'

Only the rancher understood the oblique reference to their earlier dialogue about their opinions of each other. Coolly she met his dark eyes, keeping the smile off her lips with difficulty. But in Mary's matchmaking mind, a totally different conclusion was reached.

'Well, this is news,' Bill Buchanan remarked. 'The last time I was here, Stacy, you couldn't wait to leave.' With a grin on his boyish face, he added to Cord, 'Maybe my patient's suffering a relapse.'

'I think she's just recognizing some of the attractions that can be found here,' Cord replied, quirking his mouth into a smile. 'With a girl as pretty as Stacy, I'll have to act as a guide myself to keep the young men from falling under her spell.'

Stacy caught the emphasis on her name, realizing he had noticed she had used his Christian name for the first time. Deliberately she met his mocking gaze and taunting words.

Stacy couldn't explain, even to herself, why she had referred to the angry words they had had before. She had enjoyed the easy companionship on the hill and the informative talk. Why had she taunted him? Did she feel safer with his mocking words and sarcastic smile? Pointedly she turned the conversation to Mary's two children. Several times she felt Cord's eyes searching her face, but she deliberately avoided looking at him.

'I'm afraid we're rather poor hosts, Cord,' she murmured, trying to cover the confusion he was causing by standing so close to her. Unaccountably, her hand drifted on his arm. 'We didn't offer the doctor and Mary something to drink.'

There was a darting look of surprise in Cord's eyes as he looked at the upturned face, but it was quickly suppressed by a smile to his guests. Guiltily she dropped her hand.

'I'll have Maria bring us something. Anything special you'd like, Bill, Mary?'

'No,' Bill laughed. 'Anything tall and cool will do.'

Cord left them for a moment to arrange for the refreshments. During that time Mary and her husband seated themselves in two of the garden chairs while Stacy settled on the cushioned settee. A few minutes later Cord returned followed by the plump Mexican woman carrying a tray laden with drinks and hors d'oeuvres. To Stacy's chagrin, Cord sat on the settee with her. Her annoyance escaped the other couple's attention amidst the confusion of accepting the refreshments Maria offered, but the one-sided smile on Cord's lips indicated that he had noticed her dismay.

To Stacy's relief, the conversation remained on a light vein. Several times she was uncomfortably aware of the dark brown eyes studying her and the magnetic closeness of the outstretched arm on the back of the couch. Mary, with her naturally lively personality, monopolized most of the conversation with anecdotes of the children, but gradually the subject turned to Stacy and her accident.

'When Bill told me that day about your fall, I practically insisted on bringing you into town with us,' Mary chattered. 'But he assured me it was better to leave you here where you would have ample opportunity to rest.'

'Actually what I said was "peace and quiet",' inserted the doctor with a smile. 'That's something hard to come by in our house.'

'He's always complaining about the boys,' explained

71

Mary, 'but he loves them as much as I do. Anyway, I can see how right he was. You look the picture of health. Of course, with this kind of scenery who would want to stay in bed?'

There was a twinkle in Mary's eyes as she gave Cord a sideways glance. Hastily Stacy spoke up, not wanting the innuendo to go any further.

'This is a beautiful ranch,' she rushed. 'The whole land around here is fascinating. It reminds you what little time has passed since it was a frontier.'

'Texas history is fascinating,' agreed the blue-eyed doctor.

'Were you at the cemetery when we came?' Mary directed at Cord. Without waiting for his affirmative nod, she continued, 'I wish you could have met his grandmother, Stacy. She was a wonderful old woman. You never thought of her as old, though. She was much too vital and active. I was only nine or ten when she died, but I remember her so well.'

'Cord told me a little about her,' Stacy said.

'She was remarkable. Somewhere amongst all her Spanish ancestry she inherited a pioneer spirit that was indefatigable,' Mary went on. 'But there was a certain way about her—the way she carried her head or looked deep inside you—that reminded you of her blue blood. My mother always said Doña Elena was the only one able to handle Cord.' In a conspiratorial aside to Stacy, she added, 'He was really a terror as a child—fantastic temper!'

Cord chuckled at Mary's words. 'You forgot to mention Grandmother's temper. I've always thought she cared so much for me because I inherited her temper.' In a mockingly tender tone, he added for Stacy's benefit, 'Thank heaven, I've learned to control it.'

'I'm afraid, Cord, there've been a few times when

72

you've caused us to doubt your words,' Bill Buchanan smiled with a dubious shake of his head. 'Don't get me wrong, Stacy, I'm sure the right woman would be able to deal with him, but I would hate to be on the receiving end of his temper when it does go out of control.'

Embarrassed by the sly matchmaking of the married couple and the recollection of the controlled display he had shown that day on the road, Stacy murmured a vague response. Thankfully, she was interrupted by Maria announcing that dinner was ready.

'You will be joining us, won't you?' Cord asked. Mary began to make an excuse, but Cord interjected, 'I'm not taking no for an answer. It's too seldom we have social visits and we won't let you go away so soon, will we, Stacy?'

He extended a hand to her which she was unable to refuse without being obvious. Distracted by his touch, Stacy half heard the lighthearted banter and acceptance by the pair. She felt herself being ushered into the dining room behind them, the tall shoulder of the rancher brushing against her. Her muscles tensed as she stifled a desire to pull violently away from him.

She had baited him at first about their earlier quarrel and became a little personal, acting as hostess when she herself was only a guest. Playing the little charade had amused Stacy at first as she had enjoyed seeing the surprised look in Cord's eyes. But now she had the distinct feeling that he was laughing at her. Somehow he had succeeded in turning the tables on her, making her the brunt of the joke. And she wasn't enjoying it at all.

As if he had read her mind, Cord whispered to her as he seated her at the table, 'You should have checked the rules.'

Stacy's brown eyes looked apprehensively into his,

but she couldn't find any words to answer him. His expression as he seated himself opposite her at the head of the table was pleasant, but his eyes hardened speculatively as he watched her flushed cheeks turn away to respond to a question from Mary. Twice during the meal Stacy was forced to look away from the probing glance of the aquiline face. The dinner seemed to last so long that she was sure it would never end. She was so tense she felt she was sitting on a lighted powder-keg that would explode at any moment. But when Maria served the coffee and dessert the conversation was still on safe topics. A tide of relief washed over her at the end in sight.

'Hey, come back!' Mary teased, waving a hand in front of Stacy. 'Didn't you hear what I said?'

'I'm sorry, Mary, I'm afraid I was daydreaming.'

'I was wondering if your accident had changed your plans, about staying?'

'No, not really,' Stacy replied, avoiding Cord's interested look. 'I'll be staying a couple more weeks before going back.'

'I'm afraid our country is a little too hard on her,' Cord interposed with a smile. 'After all, Mary, we were raised here and are used to it, but Stacy is from the East. I imagine it's a little tame and boring around here.'

'That's not true at all,' Stacy retorted impatiently.

'It's just that there's no future here for you, isn't that it?' A sarcastic smile played on Cord's mouth.

'Yes—I mean no,' stammered Stacy, recognizing that she was under a subtle attack.

'Now, Cord——' Mary began.

'Surely you realize that the newness of the adventure has probably worn off for her,' he interrupted. 'After all, how many mountains do you have to see before

74

you've seen them all? A lot of people have come West with grand ideas, only to run back when the inconveniences and isolation have become too much for them.'

'I don't mind all that,' Stacy denied. 'I love this country.'

'You know, Mary, it takes stamina to carve out a future in this land.' Cord was deliberately ignoring Stacy and addressing his remarks to the redhead on his right. His voice was low and vindictive. 'Luxuries become vastly important when you're suddenly denied them after having them all your life.'

'He's comparing me with his mother!' Stacy thought indignantly. 'You don't know what you're talking about,' she said, crumpling her napkin on the table.

'Of course. How stupid of me not to realize that appearances are deceiving,' the mocking tone in his voice and a sarcastic curl on his upper lip. 'I should have recognized that behind the high-fashion clothes, the expensive sports car and the blooded horse there beats the heart of a country girl, unspoiled by a life that's catered to her whims.'

The room was filled with tension as the two glared across the table at each other. Stacy longed to lash out at him, but she knew she would only be playing into his hands. She sensed the discomfort of the other two at the table. Somehow she managed a feeble laugh.

'It seems you have me figured out.' A weak smile on her flushed cheeks. 'I'm just a simple country girl.'

A flicker of admiration crossed the tanned face, replaced quickly by a derisive gleam.

' "Simple" is a particularly appropriate adjective, as it denotes showing little sense,' Cord replied. 'You showed a remarkable lack of it when you journeyed unescorted out here where you knew no one, and proceeded to live alone in a remote cabin, unprotected from possible molesters, and went out riding alone on a horse you couldn't control to places you didn't know. By a stroke of luck you're not lying dead out there now.'

'I don't think that your guests are interested in your opinions of me and my behaviour,' Stacy replied, pushing her chair away from the table.

In the living room, Mary caught up with her.

'What's up with you two?' she asked.

'We just don't get along,' Stacy answered, her hands clutched tightly together. She glanced nervously over her shoulder into the other room.

'You seemed so friendly when we first came that, to be honest, I'd hoped you two had made a match of it,' Mary went on.

'That's impossible!' Stacy exclaimed, disgust and anger in her voice. 'We manage to carry on a civil conversation once in a while, but it always seems to end with us at each other's throats. It's useless to even pretend that we can stand each other. He's so cynical and self-centred that he insists everyone kneel at his feet, and he's not finding me so subservient.'

Immediately upon uttering her words, Stacy felt Cord's presence in the room. Defiantly she turned to face the glowering eyes. The tall man with his broad shoulders seemed to fill the room, diminishing everything near him.

'Our guests are leaving.' The dark figure finally spoke. 'Are you going to the door with them?'

Stacy turned without answering Cord and walked with Mary as she collected her purse and started towards the front door. Stacy's back prickled ominously, aware of the rancher walking directly behind her. Before reaching the front patio, Stacy murmured an apology to the girl beside her, speaking in a low voice.

'I'm sorry you were dragged into the middle of our fight, Mary. I so enjoyed your coming out here.'

'Don't you worry about it,' Mary admonished. 'It happens to the best of us. You just hurry up and get better.'

'I second that,' Bill added, putting his hand on Stacy's shoulders. 'Professionally speaking, get yourself another couple of days' rest and limit your activities. After that you can do as you want.'

Looking up at the pleasant face of the doctor, Stacy gave him a timorous smile. Her pleasure at the kindness of her new friends was overshadowed by the dark man who was standing so close to her that her whole being screamed its knowledge. With cheery good-byes, the couple walked down to their car. A little forlornly, Stacy watched as the car disappeared down the winding lane. Resolutely she turned to face Cord and his scornful eyes, only to find him gone. Glancing quickly around, she saw his familiar form striding towards the stables. Puzzled and relieved at the same time, she walked into the house.

CHAPTER SIX

For the past two days, Stacy had taken special pains to avoid Cord Harris. Her success was achieved with the co-operation of the rancher, who apparently did not want her company either. Digging the toe of her boot into the sandy soil, Stacy looked around the grounds hesitantly. The time had come to talk to him and she wasn't looking forward to it at all. She had fully regained her strength and wanted to make arrangements to return to the cabin. The last of her packing had been completed after lunch, which left her with the unpleasant task of finding Cord. The big German Shepherd padded contentedly along at her side as she wandered past the open doorway of the office. A glance inside verified the inner feeling that he wasn't there. With an impatient sigh Stacy continued to the stables.

'He's probably out on the range somewhere,' she thought grimly, gazing out beyond the buildings.

At the corrals she noticed a horse and rider rounding one of the barns at a gallop. Not recognizing the man, Stacy waited. Her curiosity was aroused by his haste. Her ears caught the shouting of voices not far from the stables and she turned to see the reason for the commotion, but the buildings blocked her view. The rider had just reined his horse to a stop by the corral gate and dismounted.

'What's wrong?' she asked the cowboy.

'S'cuse me, ma'am, but I got to call the doctor,' the man murmured, starting to hurry past her.

'What happened? Who got hurt?' Stacy cried, a horrifying picture already forming of Cord lying unconscious on the ground.

'That red devil of a stallion slipped out of the stud pen when Chris went in,' he answered, hurrying towards the open office door with Stacy right behind him. 'The young fool climbed on his horse and tried to rope him. The horse went berserk and attacked him. Luckily the Boss and us was headed in from off the range and saw what happened. Don't know how bad the kid's hurt—can't get near him.'

'Diablo!' Stacy gasped, staring at the man reaching for the phone to the office.

'The Boss is mad enough to kill that horse,' muttered the cowboy into the phone, not directing the sentence to Stacy.

As she heard the man reach the doctor, Stacy rushed out of the office towards the standing horse. She jumped on the buckskin and turned him towards the distant sound of voices. Her thoughts were barely coherent as she shouted to the Shepherd to follow and kicked the already winded horse into a gallop. She just knew she had to get there.

'Kill Diablo!' The words rang like a death knell in her ears. Confused, she whipped the horse with the reins as he bounded around the buildings and headed towards the mounted figures beyond. As she drew up by the two mounted horsemen, she saw a rider trapped under his fallen horse with her red stallion between him and the two riders. A rope was flying free from Diablo's neck as he eluded the ropes of the other two riders. His neck and withers were white with foam as he continued to lash out with his wicked hooves.

'What the hell are you doing here?' shouted Cord Harris as he sighted Stacy dismounting her horse. His face was contorted in anger as he swung his big bay around to face her. 'Get back to the house where you belong!'

'He's my horse!' shouted Stacy, turning away towards the stallion who was lunging, teeth bared, at the other mounted rider.

'You crazy female,' roared the rancher, reining his horse over beside her, 'can't you see that damn stud is loco?'

It was then that Stacy noticed the bullwhip in the angry man's hand, the end dragging in the dust raised by the bay's dancing hooves. Fire flashed from her eyes as she raised her head to meet his dark eyes.

'What do you propose to do? Whip him into submission?'

'If I have to, yes. That boy over there is hurt!'

'Get out of my way!' Stacy demanded. Pushing his horse away from her, she walked to face the red stallion.

A shrill whistle rang from Diablo as he pawed the ground and shook his flaxen mane at the solitary figure in front of him. Rearing, he flashed his black hooves through the air, his ears snaked back.

'Diablo!' Stacy commanded, attempting to pierce the frenzied mind of the stallion. 'Diablo, settle down!'

His ears remained flat against his head as he lashed out with his back feet at the Shepherd worrying him from behind. Stacy could see the fallen horse attempting to rise, only to fall back on its side. As the stallion started to charge at her, she called to him once again, her voice raising in authority. Stacy thought she saw his ears flicker up as he swept towards her. When he was just about on her, she stepped aside and he thundered by. Spinning around, he faced her, tossing his blazed head. Out of the corner of her eye, Stacy saw the two mounted riders moving. One was headed for the injured rider and Cord was coming towards the stallion, the whip rolled on the saddlehorn and a rope flicking the air in readiness.

'Diablo,' her voice changed to a caressing whisper, 'easy, boy, settle down. It's all right, baby. Come here. Come on!'

But the excitement and the almost forgotten memory of the scar on his neck was too much. The red horse couldn't curb the demon driving him. His delicate head bobbed up and down, the foam flicking off his neck. He recognized the girl in front of him, but he was filled with a new sense of hate and strength. Out of the corner of his eyes he caught the movement of horse and rider coming up behind him and danced around to face them. Stepping forward Stacy called to him. This time he spun swiftly around and raced towards her, his teeth bared and his head low. When Stacy attempted to jump out of his way, the stallion veered into her, jostling her to the ground with his big shoulder.

Breathless but unhurt, she raised herself up to see Cord streaking after the horse. He yelled at the other horseman and both ropes encircled the red sorrel at the same time. Screaming his anger, the horse attempted to charge the furthest rider, only to be brought up short by the rope dallied around Cord's saddlehorn.

'We got him, Boss! We got him!' yelled the other rider triumphantly, as the horse struggled futilely between the two ropes. It only took him a few minutes to realize he couldn't hope to win. Swiftly the two riders led him to the gate of the stud pen from which he had just escaped.

Dusting herself off, Stacy saw the third rider who had been sent to call the doctor kneeling beside the fallen horse and rider. Hurriedly she made her way over to them, arriving the same time as Cord. His expression was grim as he knelt beside the pain-racked form of the young cowboy.

'Take it easy, Chris,' Cord instructed. 'We'll have you out of there in no time. Doc's on his way.'

'My leg's broken,' groaned the young rider, gritting his teeth with pain. 'Get me out from under this damned horse!'

'Shortly, how bad's that horse's leg?' demanded Cord, directing his words to the dusty figure trying to quiet the downed gelding. The only answer was a negative shake of the head.

Without a word, Cord rose and walked over to his bay horse and extracted his rifle from the scabbard. Stacy stood numbly watching the action, unable to move or react. The loud report of the gun as it silenced the life of the injured horse deafened her. Overcome by shock and horror, she did not see the doctor arrive or the boy being carried away on a stretcher; the only thing she could see was the inert form of the dead horse. The tears glazing her eyes seemed frozen, too. At last her vision was blocked by Cord's dusty, sweaty form. Stiffly she raised her tear-filled eyes to his blurred face.

'Why?' she whispered, forcing the words through the lump in her throat.

'When Chris roped your horse the sorrel charged, knocking them down, breaking Chris's leg and his horse's, too. The doc says he's going to be all right, six weeks or so off the leg and on crutches for a month or more.'

'No,' Stacy mumbled, barely coherent. 'The horse! Why did you have to kill him? It wasn't his fault,' she sobbed. It was her first experience with what seemed to her brutality and she couldn't keep her eyes from straying to the dead horse.

'The horse?' exploded Cord. 'Do you realize that I could have lost a man? A human being! And all you're worried about is a horse!'

His anger pierced her shock and she turned to his face again and read the distaste and disgust that filled it. He didn't understand. She was upset about the rider, but she couldn't reconcile herself to the cold-blooded killing of the horse.

'But he's going to be all right, don't you understand? He'll be back, but the horse is dead and you killed him! As if it was nothing!' Her voice was shrill with shock and near-hysteria.

'Nothing? Do you realize that I'm now without a horse and a rider? Do you think it's going to be easy to replace a man at this time of the year?' he roared, grabbing her arm in a vicelike grip. 'I have you to thank for that, you and that horse of yours!'

'Oh, sure, it's all my fault,' she cried sarcastically. 'Well, don't worry. I'll pay for the hospital bills and any inconvenience this caused you.'

'You're damned right you will!' Cord replied. His voice lowered threateningly. 'But your money won't buy your way out of this one. You're going to take Chris's place. For once in your life, you're going to see what it's like to work to pay a debt.'

'What are you talking about?' Stacy asked, her body now trembling with anger.

'You've gained a lot of sympathy with that poor orphan act of yours around here. I bet it really broke your heart when your father died and left you all that money,' he replied, scorn and contempt deep in his voice.

His words cut like a knife into her heart as the horrible accusation left Stacy speechless. Unconsciously she felt the contact of her hand against his cheek. Her palm was stinging as the deepening fire in his eyes once again focused on her.

'So that's the way the little cat plays,' he murmured through clenched teeth. 'Today you got away with it, but I wouldn't try it again if I were you. You start to work tomorrow,' he stated. 'And wear something practical, like jeans. We don't hold any fashion shows out on the range.'

Her feet were rooted to the ground and the angry

tears in her eyes trickled down her cheeks as she watched Cord stalk away. Her hands were clenched into tight fists as she tried to find the words to scream after him. But her mouth refused to open and the words never came out. She stood there shaking with uncontrolled anger that gradually gave way to gasping sobs. Cord Harris had already mounted his horse and ridden off in the direction of the ranch house before Stacy moved from her position. Slowly she made her way in the same direction, her mind jumbled with thoughts of hatred for the rancher and compassion for the injured boy and the dead horse.

By the time Stacy reached the yards, the dust from the ranch car was halfway down the road. Silently she made her way to the hacienda, oblivious to her actual surroundings. Once inside the house and in her bedroom, Stacy sat on the bed and looked at the possessions she had earlier collected to leave.

With one hand she wiped the angry tears away from her eyes as she sat going over again their conversation. It was wrong to be concerned for the horse as opposed to a human being, but it had been the shock of the horse's death. Perhaps she was even wrong to accuse Cord of brutally killing the horse without a thought if he could be saved or not. But Stacy could find no excuse for his outrageous attack against her about her father's death. Besides, she had never told him that she was orphaned, though she had told the Nolans, but no one, certainly, knew about the money she had inherited! The anger in her heart faded away and was replaced by the crushing feeling of despair. How could she ever hope to convince him that this wasn't true? But why should she try? The confusion of her thoughts drove her to her feet and she paced the room. Resentment of Cord Harris boiled inside her.

Just exactly how was he going to make her stay against her will? He certainly couldn't force her to work. And besides, just exactly what did she know about ranching? Stacy stopped in front of the mirror, an idea forming in her mind. He couldn't stop her leaving because he wasn't even here. She glanced quickly at her watch and just as quickly outside. More time had gone by than she realized. The sun was already down and Cord must have been gone for at least two hours. If she intended to leave before he returned, she didn't have much time. Quickly she began gathering her belongings and setting them outside her room.

Naturally, he would accuse her of running away and refusing to face his challenge, but let him think what he liked. Unfortunately she had been forced to accept his hospitality when she was ill, but there was no need to stay any longer. It was enough that she had offered to pay the hospital bill for the boy and reimburse Cord for the horse. If financially she was unable to pay him, that would be the time to try to arrange some way to work the problem out. Even she had to admit that she was responsible for her horse.

Stacy had just slipped her fringed jacket on and picked up her purse and started out of the bedroom when she heard the big oak door close. Numbly she stood beside her luggage and stared at the tall form standing at the bottom of the stairs. Cord's features were hidden in the shadows, but Stacy could well imagine the dark brows gathered together and the clean, hard set of his jaw, and most of all the grim line of his mouth. Her eyes were wide and darkening with apprehension as she felt the trembling course through her body. Neither spoke as the tension grew.

'I take it you're planning on going somewhere?' came the low baritone voice.

'What if I do?' Stacy retorted defiantly, lifting her chin in challenge.

'Then I would suggest you forget it,' was the cool reply as Cord stepped out of the shadows. There were new lines on his face that Stacy hadn't noticed before, but there was no mistaking the hard quality in his voice. He cast one further glance at the luggage and the still figure above him. 'You might as well unpack.'

'You don't actually believe you can keep me a prisoner here against my will?' Stacy exploded, in anger.

He gave her one brief glance before replying. 'You're in my debt and it's up to me to set the terms of payment.'

The hopelessness of fighting this man raced through Stacy and her shoulders slumped slightly, acknowledging defeat. The fire went out in her eyes and was replaced with despair and confusion. Struggling, she attempted to take one last stand. 'I will not stay in that room one more night!'

A glint of amusement showed in his eyes before he turned his face away from her.

'As you like. There's a guestroom down the hall. Use it,' he paused briefly. 'In case you're interested, the boy's going to be in the hospital for a few weeks and inactive for a couple of months.'

Stacy felt the heat rising in her cheeks at her inconsideration for not asking about the injured rider's condition. Why did he always manage to make her seem so heartless? Frustrated, she gathered up her cases and stalked into the hallway, stopping at the first doorway on her left.

She was too upset to take in the surroundings of the room. Her anger was too close to the surface to allow her to dwell on anything but Cord's dark eyes and sculptured face. His cool indifference irritated her. All she had done was make a fool of herself and increase his belief that she was spoiled and selfish. Stacy knew she could expect no mercy at his hands. He expected her to take the rider's place regardless of her sex.

'Very well, Mr. Harris,' she whispered to herself. 'I can take anything you can dish out. No quarter asked.'

The sun had barely touched the sky the following morning when there was a loud knock at Stacy's door. Sleepily she raised herself up on one elbow and looked out the window and then over to the clock on the dresser. It took her a minute before she remembered the previous day's events.

'Yes?'

'It's time to get up,' came Cord's voice from the hall. 'That is if you want coffee and some breakfast before work.'

He didn't wait for a reply, but strode away from the door. Determinedly, Stacy clambered out of the bed. It took her only a few minutes to dress in her Levi's and shirt and to tie her hair back at the nape of her neck. A little smile played on her soft lips as she looked at the image reflected in the mirror. If Mr. Harris thought that blue jeans and a plain blouse were going to make her look less of a woman then he was wrong. She couldn't keep the pleasure out of her eyes as she surveyed her gentle curves. She checked to make sure her riding gloves were in the pocket of her suede jacket, picked up her hat and walked down the stairs to the dining room.

Unfortunately Cord wasn't there. Stacy queried Maria, who replied that Mr. Harris had already taken his meal and was out giving instructions to the men. Maria was plainly confused by the turn of events and kept casting puzzled glances at the young girl. When

Stacy finished her toast and coffee, Maria said that Stacy was to meet the Boss out in the yard.

Gratefully Stacy realized that most of the men had already gone. It would have been embarrassing to be subjected to the forbidding rancher's orders in the presence of his men. As it was, she recognized his tall form still talking to two men. His back was to her, so he didn't see her approach, but Stacy was sure he knew she was coming.

The two men standing with him attempted to ignore the approaching girl. The taller of the two was only a few years older than Stacy and obviously embarrassed by the situation. He kept his head down, his hat preventing Stacy from seeing the expression on his face. The other man was considerably older and wizened. The constant sun on his face had made his skin so leathery that Stacy was unable to judge his age. When she approached the group the older one met her gaze openly, compassion and sympathy etched in the eyes that squinted in the morning sun. It was a comfort to recognize an ally here.

'It's about time you got here, Adams,' Cord said crisply, turning his aquiline features towards her. 'I want you to go with Hank and Jim today to gather the stock cattle in the winter range,' he ordered, casting only a cursory glance at the petite figure beside him. 'Any other questions, Hank?'

The older man shook his head negatively.

'Okay, mount up.'

Stacy started to follow the two men as they walked to the horses standing saddled on the other side of the corral, but was called back by Cord. Turning to face the imposing figure, she took her gloves out of her jacket pocket and began putting them on her hands, hoping to stave off the nervousness she felt facing him.

88

'Yes,' she said, looking boldly into his face, her voice matching the crisp tone he had used earlier. She was unable to read his dark expression.

For a minute he didn't answer, then he said, 'Hank will show you all that needs to be done.'

'All right,' she replied, disliking the searching eyes that seemed to probe deep inside her. 'Anything else?'

'No. Good luck.' His tone was indifferent and conflicting with his words.

Briskly Stacy turned from him and walked to where the two mounted riders waited. The one named Hank handed her the reins of a short-coupled bay pony. Silently she mounted and turned her horse to follow the other two.

Shortly after leaving the ranchyard, the younger of the two men rode ahead, leaving the wizened old cowboy alone with Stacy. Normally she would have been enjoying the early morning ride, but today's circumstances made her conscious of the humiliating position she was in. Pride forbade her to look at the silent, hunched figure beside her. For a time the two horses moved along at their slow, shuffling trot, until the rider beside her pulled his horse into a walk and Stacy's mount automatically matched the pace.

'Miss Adams,' came the questioning, rough voice, 'now it ain't none of my business and you can tell me to shut my mouth, but if we're going to be riding the range together, it gets mighty lonely if all you can talk to is yore hoss. Now, it ain't in me to question the Boss's orders, but me nor none of the boys hold you responsible for what happened to the kid the other day. It's gonna be a long day in the saddle, specially for a dude like you, but it shore does make the day go faster if there's a bit of jawin' goin' on.'

Stacy had the distinct impression that this was the

longest statement the man had ever made, and she smiled at his thoughtfulness. He was trying to put her at ease in his own clumsy way and himself as well.

'Thank you, Hank. I appreciate it more than you know.'

'Well, I been working on this spread ever since the Boss was in knee-britches, and I seen some strange things. But I gotta admit this is the first time we've ever had us a lady wrangler. An' the Boss says you gotta pull your own weight,' he said, shaking his head in confusion.

'I intend to, too,' Stacy replied, a grim look of determination on her face. 'I don't know anything about ranching or cows, but I can learn. At least I can ride and am in fair shape.'

'Well, now, miss, I reckon you can ride all right, but you gotta relax a little more. Ya ain't in no hoss show, so you don't have to worry 'bout how you look,' Hank said with a slight smile. 'An' I'd watch what you call cows. Safe thing is to call 'em cattle.'

'I stand corrected,' she laughed. 'Tell me, Hank, what exactly are we doing today?'

'We're gonna be rattlin' the brush for bunch-quitters mostly an' gettin' the herd ready for movin' to the summer pasture. Most of the men trucked their horses to the far end of the pasture an'll be workin' towards us with the main herd.'

'Trucked their horses?' Stacy asked quizzically, her brown eyes examining the weathered face of the cowboy.

'Yep. It's a modern West you'll find. Rather than spendin' a lot of time ridin' to where the herd is, now they jus' load the the horses up in trucks or trailers and haul 'em as close as they can.'

'It's a miracle they don't use jeeps to round them

up,' Stacy exclaimed half to herself, in amazement.

'A few years ago when we was really tryin' to gather all the scrub bulls an' strays, the Boss ordered a helicopter to search 'em out. Things have changed,' Hank muttered. 'Reckon we ought to catch up with Jim?'

The brisk morning air was beginning to warm with the rising sun. Already the morning dew was rapidly vanishing from the undergrowth wherever the sun's rays probed through the shade. The distant mountainous hills were cloaked in a golden haze that cast its shimmering glow upon the grassland stretched out below it. The morning air was bereft of any breeze and the stillness was broken only by the shuffling trot of the three cow-ponies and the occasional call of the quail. The three riders travelled several miles before arriving at the first barbed wire fence. They rode along the fence until they arrived at a gate. Stacy and Hank waited astride their horses while Jim manoeuvred his horse into position to unhook the gate and open it for the other two. After they had passed through, the young cowboy followed, closing the gate behind him.

'This is where we start to work, miss,' the wizened cowboy said, indicating the land spread out before them.

'But I don't see any cattle?' said Stacy, looking at the vacant pasture.

'That's the general idea. If they was right out in plain sight it wouldn't be quite so much work. But they seem to know every ravine and bush on the spread and that's where they plan to stay.'

'But I thought that you raised domestic cattle, a Hereford cross of some sort?' she queried, plainly puzzled.

'We do, but they been left alone. They're just about

as skittish of humans as the old longhorns that used to graze this land. Only difference between the two is these ain't half as ornery as them,' Hank replied, squinting his eyes to look over the land. 'We usually split up a bit here, but you stick close to me for a while, miss.'

The three riders loped off; the younger cowboy moved fifty yards to their left and they all began scouring the brush. It was hot dusty work for horse and rider, and it wasn't long before Stacy removed her jacket and tied it on the back of the saddle. Between the heat of the sun and the constant exercise, Stacy's bay began perspiring, too. They scared up a couple of head of cattle, as they worked their way along. Stacy began to respect the game horse she was riding. By mid-morning they had about fifteen head of cattle driving in front of them. Hank instructed the young girl to keep them going while he and Jim added other strays with them.

At first she thought he was giving her an easier job until she began breathing in the dust that the cattle were kicking up. She wasn't even able to relax on the horse. Every time she allowed her attention to wander from the herd that was the precise time that one of the animals decided to make another break for the open bush. The little bay instinctively gave chase and cut it back into the herd. Quite a few times Stacy was positive that the horse was going to spin around and send her flying in the other direction. Her legs were so weary from gripping his sides and her body so covered with dust and grime and sweat that she was sure that she wouldn't make it through the rest of the morning let alone the whole day. Each time one of the cowboys added another steer to the herd, Stacy could hardly stop from sighing outwardly. She had learned for every steer in the herd her horse had to cover twice their distance.

Her mouth was dry and gritty, but she was afraid to sip out of her canteen for fear that one of the herd would decide to leave. The girl was happy to see Hank ride up alongside, but trying to smile a hello was an effort. He didn't look at her directly, but Stacy could still recognize a ghost of a smile on his face.

'Mighty dirty work, ridin' drag on a bunch of scrubs,' he murmured in the air. 'We're comin' up on the water tank where we'll meet up with the chuck wagon for lunch. Reckon maybe you could do with a rest, huh?'

'I don't mind admitting that I could, Hank,' Stacy replied, feeling her lips crack as she spoke. Giving the little bay an affectionate pat on the neck, she added, 'I think he deserves one too.'

'The remuda will be there. His work is done for the day,' the cowboy answered.

'Oh, look!' cried Stacy, turning her attention to the left. 'Isn't that Jim coming?—and it looks like he's got a little baby calf across his saddle.'

The younger cowboy joined them with a new white-faced calf lying crosswise on his saddle with the mother following alongside, lowing soothingly to her youngster.

'He's darling!' Stacy exclaimed. 'How old is he?'

'Just a couple of days,' Jim replied, the shyness still evident in his failure to look directly at Stacy, but proud of her interest in his find. 'I found them out in the brush. The calf wasn't able to keep up, so I thought I'd give him a ride to the calf wagon.'

'Calf wagon? What's that?' Stacy asked, her attention diverted from the snow-white face.

'There's usually a bunch of these latecomers that are

93

too little to keep up with the herd, so we have a trailer we put 'em in until we reach the night's holdin' ground and then we mammy 'em up,' Hank replied, amused at Stacy's concern for the calf. 'Take the little critter on in, Jim, we'll be there shortly.'

'Isn't that what you call a dogey, a baby calf?' Stacy asked watching as Jim rode on ahead.

'A dogey is really a calf without a momma, but a lot o' people call all calves dogies,' Hank answered.

'The cattle have settled down a lot. It must be your being here. Before, every five minutes one was heading in a different direction,' Stacy commented, enjoying the conversation with the knowledgeable cowboy.

'Nope, it's not me. They smell water. We just happen to be going the same direction as them.'

The cattle and two riders topped a small rise in the ground and came upon a high plateau covered with tall stands of pampas grass and creosote bushes. Ahead Stacy could see the large water tank and windmill. Beyond that was a station wagon and several pick-ups and trailers. A look of astonishment crossed her dust-stained face.

'That's the chuck wagon?'

A dry chuckle escaped the old cowboy's throat. 'I told ya the old West was gone. They bring the food from the ranch house and trailer the remuda to the noon stop,' the old man smiled. 'You go on and ride ahead. These cattle ain't goin' nowhere 'cept to that tank. Rest while you can. We're gonna be hittin' the saddle for another long afternoon.'

Gratefully, Stacy reined her little bay out around the herd and set him at a lope for the waiting vehicles. She rode over to where a cowboy waited by the trailers. There were already several riders over by the station wagon; some were eating and some were just getting their food. Behind the trailers Stacy noticed a couple of Mexicans cooling off some cow-ponies with replacements picketed along the trailers. Slowly she dismounted. Her bones and muscles were so sore that she stood for a minute to adjust to the solid ground beneath her feet. Now that she was on the ground, she wasn't so sure that she could walk. She took a few careful steps in the general direction of the wagon and realized that she was going to navigate all right under her own power, so she joined the men at the station wagon where they were dishing out food from the rear.

The good-natured grumbling and banter that had been going on when Stacy rode up had stopped, and Stacy became uneasy. She had been so comfortable with the old cowboy, and so tired and hungry from the skimpy breakfast, that she neglected to remember her awkward position. With a red face and a trembling hand she accepted the dish of stew and beans with a thick slice of bread alongside from one of the cooks and a steaming mug of coffee from another. Nervously she turned around to search for a shaded place to have her meal. All eyes were on her as she turned; some looked away abruptly while others eyed her boldly.

'Ma'am,' came a hesitant voice from her right. Stacy turned and with relief recognized the young rider, Jim. 'If you like, you can join me. Not many shaded places left.'

'Thank you, Jim,' she said, looking for the first time into the hazel eyes of the young cowboy. 'I guess I did look a little lost.'

'Yes, you mustn't mind the men. They aren't used to seeing women around camp,' he replied, removing his hat to run his fingers through his bleached brown hair. There was a boyishness about his face that deceived his true age which was in the middle twenties.

In between bites of food, Stacy asked, 'Have you worked here long?'

'Off and on all my life. Got out of the service a couple years ago and went to college, but I work here in the summers for tuition money,' he replied, a look of seriousness crossing his face.

'What are you studying?'

'Forestry, conservation,' was the quiet answer.

'Are you planning to be a park ranger?' Stacy inquired.

'Hopefully. Mr. Harris has suggested coming back to the ranch, but I think I'd rather not. Initially I was going to be a vet., but I discovered that I was more interested in the agricultural and ecological side,' he answered, enjoying the interest Stacy was taking in him.

'I wouldn't let Mr. Harris's wishes interfere with what I wanted to do,' Stacy said, a trace of bitterness in her voice as she stabbed at a piece of beef in the stew.

'No, of course not,' came the low, mocking reply.

Stacy jerked her head up and practically choked on the piece of meat as she stared into the tanned face of the rancher. Jim scrambled to his feet in embarrassment.

'We were just discussing my college plans, sir,' he stated, his jaw clenched tight, defending Stacy in his own way from the sardonic smile of his employer.

Swiftly Stacy got to her feet to prevent any further remarks on her behalf. It was humiliating enough to have to look up to Cord, but to be seated at his feet was too much. Cord Harris shifted his gaze from the young cowhand to the hatless girl before him. Boldly she met his gaze, conscious once again of her dust-covered clothes and face.

'Perhaps you would like to go check on your horses

for Miss Adams, Connors,' Cord suggested with a definite tone of dismissal.

The cowboy cast a wavering glance at the girl at his side. Stacy smiled at him with a great deal more confidence than she felt. Her pulse was racing at an unsettling pace. Reluctantly Jim Connors left the two standing alone beside the trailer.

'You seem to have gained yourself an admirer.'

'Don't be ridiculous! He was only being polite. He obviously has been taught some manners—which is more than I can say for some people,' Stacy said scathingly.

'I see you've managed to survive the morning in fair shape.' Cord ignored her insult and leaned against the side of the trailer to light a cigarette. Unconsciously he held the match until it was cool, all the while his gaze travelling over the dirty face of the girl.

'Yes. I managed quite well. Surprised?'

'No. I imagine you could do anything you set your mind to,' he replied. 'I only wonder if you have the staying power.'

'Hey, Boss, is that the filly you picked up at the sale last week?' Hank walked up beside them, his attention fixed on a chestnut sorrel at the far end of the trailer. The horse didn't like being tied up and pawed the ground impatiently while pulling at the reins. 'Shore is a nice-looking thing.'

Cord's eyes never left Stacy's face. 'Yes, she is.'

Stacy could feel herself begin to blush, but she couldn't break away from the compelling eyes.

'Do ya' think she's gonna be able to settle down to ranch life?' Hank asked, and then addressed his next remark to Stacy, not noticing that she was paying little attention to him. 'She was raced a few times and she's used to a lot of fuss and bother. Spoilt, you might say.'

A mocking smile crossed Cord's lips as he watched the discomfiture registering on Stacy's face. 'It's hard to tell, Hank.'

'Shore seems awful fractious. It'll take a lot of patience to change this one's way of thinkin',' the old cowboy went on with a shake of his head.

'It will that,' Cord said with a throaty laugh. 'It will that. Well, mustn't detain you two any longer from your work. I'll see you later.'

With no more than a brief nod to Stacy and a friendly slap on the back to the cowhand, Cord strode over to where the young horse stood tethered, the secretly amused expression still on his face. Untying the reins, he swung his tall frame easily into the saddle as the spirited horse danced beneath him. He didn't even glance in their direction as he reined the sorrel over towards a group of riders talking over their last cup of coffee. Stacy couldn't hear what was said, but gathered it was an order to mount up, because shortly after they dispersed and walked over to where their ponies were tied.

Out of the corner of her eye, she saw Jim walking up leading two horses. He handed her the reins to a big Roman-nosed buckskin. Stacy could tell that Jim was embarrassed about leaving her in Cord's clutches, but at this moment the tanned face was still plainly visible in her mind and the delicious, throaty laugh was still echoing in her ears. Silently they mounted and rode over to join the grizzled cowhand, Hank, and get at the afternoon's work.

CHAPTER SEVEN

STACY had thought the morning long and arduous, but by six o'clock that evening she knew the true meaning of bone-weary. She yearned to give a cry of joy when she sighted the windmill that indicated the night's holding ground for the cattle.

Her failure to try to shirk her work off on to them had gained her both Jim and Hank's respect. Several times they would have taken over for her, but she hadn't let them. It would have been easy for her to trade on her womanhood, and they would have allowed it, in spite of their employer's order.

Hank suggested that she ride on ahead and get a cup of coffee for each of them, but she declined, saying with a tired attempt at a laugh that she was going to need help getting off her horse. At the moment it seemed almost too true to be funny. A short time later they hazed their small herd in with the main one settling down for the night about a hundred yards from the camp.

A sense of peace cloaked the riders as they rode back into the strange western camp of motorized vehicles where the odour of petrol and oil mixed with the smell of sweaty horses, cattle, and humans. Good-naturedly Stacy accepted the helping hand of the younger cowboy as she dismounted. She felt no self-consciousness as she limped her way to the station wagon and the promising aroma of coffee. Hank had arrived before the other two and was talking to the riders who had gathered around the lowered tailgate.

'Hank,' Stacy groaned, looking into the grey eyes, a

smile of mock pain on her face, 'I think you're looking at the very first bow-legged lady wrangler. I'll never walk straight again as long as I live, let alone be able to sit down!'

There was a considerable amount of sympathizing laughter from the group and, more important, acceptance. Accompanied by a goodly amount of jesting and joking, Stacy was presented with a steaming cup of the cook's java. After inhaling the steam rising from the cup, she emitted an audible sigh of appreciation.

'Cook, you are a master chef, but tell me, where is the bath water?' she exclaimed, and met with another round of laughter. 'Do you boys go through this every day?'

'Twice on Sunday,' one of them replied, and laughed at the expression of mock disbelief on Stacy's face.

'Spare me the details and help me find a way to sit down!'

Several of the riders stepped forward, including Jim Connors, and with exaggerated care lowered her to the ground. Despite her aches and pains, Stacy was beginning to enjoy herself, and so were the men. There had seldom been a woman in their midst and definitely none that had joined in making fun of herself and her situation. With a sparkle in her eyes, she started to make another comment to the men, only to notice that they had grown very quiet and were looking beyond her. Still in a jovial mood, she turned her radiant smile to include the object of their attention. Cord Harris's frame had cast its shadow over the group. His expression was a study of amused interest in the girl and the surrounding riders. Stacy couldn't say why or how she had the nerve to say what came next.

'Oh, Patrón, please allow this lowly peon to remain

seated in thy great presence, for I vow I couldn't rise if you commanded me.'

There was a chilling stillness as the men waited for their boss to answer. Stacy was horrified at her words, but it was too late to retract them. She held her breath along with the men. The low chuckle that finally came relaxed everyone and most of all the seated Stacy.

'Charlie, give me a cup of that brew of yours while I sit down beside this señorita,' Cord directed with a grin to the cook.

Someone had started a campfire, and Stacy fixed her attention on it rather than the disconcerting man beside her, trying to ignore the delicious chill that had quaked her body at his pleasant laugh. The sun was beginning to set now, casting its coloured shadows on the countryside, while the two sipped their coffee in silence. The cook brought them a plate of beefsteak and beans and refilled their coffee.

'Well, what do you think of the cattle drive?' Cord asked as they began eating their meal. 'Is it what you expected it to be?'

'No,' Stacy replied with a smile, 'not meant as a complaint, but it's a lot harder work than I thou ht.'

'So far you've come through with flying colours,' he said.

'Meaning you don't think I'll last.'

'Meaning I have no opinion except that you've done very well.' There was a mocking glint in his eyes as he went on, 'You really should do something about that temper of yours. You're a little too quick to take offence.'

'Perhaps I've had cause,' Stacy replied, her gaze still occupied by the flickering campfire flames.

'Touché,' Cord smiled, his eyes observing the still face. 'I imagine you're pretty tired after today's work.

The remuda hands will be heading back to the ranch house shortly. You can catch a ride with them, or wait a little longer and I'll give you a ride back.'

'Is everyone going back?' Stacy was astounded. 'You mean you just leave the cattle unattended to stray all over?'

'No,' Cord chuckled, 'most of the men will be staying and taking their turns at riding herd. They've brought along their bedrolls,' he added, indicating places where some of the men had already made them up.

'Then why am I going back to the ranch?'

'Because you didn't come prepared for staying overnight and because it wouldn't be permissible for a woman to spend the night out here on a trail drive,' Cord replied a little curtly. 'Plus you've only been out of a sickbed a few days. It would be foolish to overdo it.'

'Oh, but I'm just one of the boys, remember?' Stacy mocked, her brown eyes flashing bright sparks, magnified by the burning embers.

'During the day,' he qualified in his crisp tone.

'I'm staying the night here.' Stacy's voice was low and determined.

'You will be returning with me.'

'Then you'll have to carry me forcibly from here, and that would make quite a scene. But then you don't mind scenes, do you?'

'You're forgetting that you have no place to sleep,' Cord stated. 'Didn't you learn from your last experience what can happen staying out in the cold at night?'

'I'm quite sure I'll be able to make some sort of arrangement to borrow a blanket or something from someone.'

102

'Or perhaps share a bedroll?' was the sarcastic reply. 'I'm sure you'd have plenty of offers.'

'You dirty-minded beast!' Stacy exclaimed, forgetting the tired muscles in her body and bounding to her feet. The fury mounted in her face as she waited for Cord to join her. 'I don't know what kind of women you're familiar with, but let me assure you that I don't fit in that category!' Her voice raised as she struggled to keep control of herself. 'I don't have to listen to that kind of talk from any man!'

Cord grabbed hold of her arm, preventing her from running away from him. Trembling, Stacy stopped, neither attempting to pull away from his vice-like grip nor turning to face his cold dark eyes.

'Are you hoping one of your knights will come to your rescue?' he asked in a mocking whisper that she just barely heard.

Unable to reply, she stood immobile. Finally she heard a sigh leave his lips at the same time he released her arm.

'I believe an apology is in order. Therefore I apologize for the insinuations made and will make accommodation for you to spend the night here,' Cord said quietly.

Still Stacy did not turn to face him. There were hot tears of humiliation and hurt in her eyes as she felt his hands touch her shoulders and slowly turn her around to face him. With surprising gentleness his large hand cupped her chin and raised it up so that he could see her face. His own expression was hidden by the shadow of his Stetson hat.

'I guess we're both a little tired and on edge,' came the familiar deep voice. 'Get a good night's rest.'

Cord turned quietly and left. She was conscious of a feeling of emptiness as the chill of night stole over her shoulders and face where a moment ago his hands had been. The anger had vanished, leaving Stacy staring off into the dark after him. Uncertain, she turned back to the flickering campfire and the quiet figures of the ranch hands.

Jim Connors walked up to her from behind one of the trailers carrying a bedroll and a blanket. His bright, questioning hazel eyes searched her face, but Stacy accepted the bedding with only a quiet thank-you and walked over to the other side of the fire. Dully she watched some of the hands loading horses into vans and start pulling out. Involuntarily she searched the darkened forms for Cord and strained to catch the quiet conversation for the sound of his voice, but with no success.

She slipped under the covers of her bedroll and stared up into the dark blue sky overhead, plagued by a variety of emotions—hurt, anger, humiliation, resentment, but most of all a wonder and mystification towards this unpredictable Cord Harris. At last the tired muscles claimed her attention and ignorant of the hard ground and chilling air she drifted off to sleep.

She was sure she had just barely fallen asleep when a hand began gently shaking her shoulder. Her eyes fluttered open to a starlit sky. Stacy had difficulty focusing on the figure beside her in the absence of light. At first she thought it was Cord, but then she recognized the smaller build of Jim Connors.

'It's time to get up.'

'It's dark yet,' she muttered, sleep heavy in her voice.

'It's four o'clock,' the young cowboy answered lightly. 'We rise early around here. Breakfast is almost ready. Better get washed up.'

A moment later he was gone. Painfully Stacy rolled out of her bed, all of her muscles crying out for her not to move. It was all she could do to stand up. Stiffly she walked over to a basin of water warmed by the re-kindled fire. Gratefully she splashed the water on her face, enjoying the clean sensation it gave her skin. Awake now, she glanced around the camp with interest.

Everywhere there was activity. Horses and riders were walking along the outside of the camp and other riders were mumbling sleepily over their coffee and flapjacks. Over to the east, the sky was beginning to lighten with the coming dawn.

While she was eating the enormous breakfast Jim had brought her, Stacy saw the remuda trucks approaching with a load of fresh horses for the day's work. Since Jim had already finished his breakfast he offered to get her a mount for the morning. A few minutes later he returned leading a big, rangy sorrel and a smaller-built pinto. Quickly Stacy finished off the last of her pancakes and carried the plate and mug over to the station wagon. Several of the riders had already left when she returned to the waiting cowboy. Hank had joined him, mounted on his horse.

'Ready for another day, miss?' he asked, a smile spreading over his tanned face. Watching her slip her hat on, he added, 'Now a real cowboy puts his hat on as soon as he gets up.'

'I'm still learning,' she laughed in return, taking the pinto's reins from Jim. 'What's the agenda this morning?'

'Gotta sweep the east side of the main herd for strays,' he replied, swinging his pony in that direction.

A groan passed Stacy's lips as she mounted her horse. It was a mixture of dismay at the orders and a rebellion of her sore muscles at returning to the saddle.

'Is Mr. Harris joining the drive today?' she asked.

'Oh, he stayed the night last night and took one of the watches,' replied the older cowboy. 'Imagine he's headin' the herd up now.'

'Oh,' Stacy murmured. The idea that Cord had spent the night in the camp was oddly disquieting to her.

'It's a gorgeous morning,' she exclaimed as her pony danced beside Jim's mount as if in emphasis of her words. The sun was climbing the sky now, chasing away the last vestiges of the night's shadows.

'It's spring,' the young cowboy replied, capturing the exuberance of the attractive girl at his side.

'And it's a beautiful country to be in, in spring!' she laughed. 'It makes you feel great just to be alive!'

'You really like it here—in Texas, I mean?'

'I love it,' Stacy answered, not noting his qualifying words. 'There's room here. I mean, you feel free. No one's crowding you. It's hard to describe.'

'I know,' Jim replied, his eyes studying her face. 'Let's ride over this way. I'd like to show you something.'

'What is it?'

'You'll see,' he said, looking ahead as they altered their course to the left. 'What brought you here to Texas?'

For a minute Stacy didn't answer, but there was something about the young man with his close-cropped brown hair that made her want to confide in him.

'My father was killed in a plane crash about a month and a half ago,' she answered quietly. 'We were very close. You see, my mother died a few months after I was born, so all there ever was was my father and me.'

Jim studied the girl quietly with his hazel eyes, but didn't interrupt her.

'He was a freelance photographer, quite famous in his field. From almost the time I could walk he took me with him on his assignments. I was never in one place long enough to make any real friends. Oh, there were a few that you always got reacquainted with when you returned somewhere,' Stacy added, her thoughts turning to Carter Mills, 'but it really all boiled down to each other. Dad had chartered a plane to fly us back to Washington after a trip into Tennessee. Over the mountains we developed engine trouble and crashed.'

There was a silence for a time while Stacy fought to control the lump in her throat. Staring in front of her, she began to speak again. 'Cajun, my German Shepherd, was along. I was knocked unconscious, but somehow he managed to pull me out of the plane and shortly afterwards it burst into flames. My father was still inside.'

'Your father was Joshua Adams,' said Jim.

'Yes,' she answered, a whispered hoarseness creeping into her voice. 'Afterwards I was confused. A lot of Dad's friends and colleagues offered to help, but I didn't really know what they could do.' A stilted laugh came from her lips. 'He always loved the West. I guess I came out here for two reasons, to be close to him and to find what I wanted out of life.'

'You've been here before?'

'Not here specifically, but Dad had assignments in El Paso several times and various other places in Arizona and New Mexico,' Stacy answered, then added with a laugh, 'I really didn't expect to spend my time chasing cattle!'

Understanding that she was trying to shake off the

sadness that talking about her father had raised, Jim Connors joined in with her laugh.

'No, I don't imagine you did. Hank and I were along with the Boss when he found you that morning on the range.'

'You were?'

'The Boss was fit to be tied when he found your horse,' Jim stated, smiling over at the girl. 'He was the first one to spot your dog and reach you. None of us had ever seen him in such a state before. He was snapping orders around so fast and wouldn't let anyone else near you but him.'

'He was probably afraid I'd sue him for allowing that snake to be on his property,' Stacy laughed, ignoring the inquisitive glance.

'You two don't get along very well,' Jim commented.

'It's not my fault. I think he just hates women in general,' she replied.

'No, I don't believe that,' the cowboy said with a dubious shake of his head. 'After his engagement to Lydia, I don't believe he's taken women at face value any more. He's forgotten the word trust.'

'Whatever his problem is, it's not mine.'

'The place I wanted to show you is right over here,' Jim said, turning his pony abruptly to the right towards a small hill. 'I was in a lecture class where your father was a guest speaker. I think you'll appreciate this.'

The two riders topped a small rise to view a meadow covered with a sea of blue flowers. They paused briefly on the hill as Stacy gazed awestruck at the beauty of the multiple blossoms waving brightly in the morning breeze. Mother Nature had covered the hill in a luxurious blanket of deep blue. In the distance they could hear the songs of birds bringing the earth alive on that hill.

'It's beautiful, Jim. What are they?' Stacy exclaimed at last.

'Bluebonnets.'

'Such a beautiful blue, almost purple.' Her gaze remained on the flowers. 'They put the sky to shame.'

'Shall we ride down?' he asked.

Stacy didn't answer, but touched the pinto's flank with her heel. Single file the pair rode down the hill to the meadow, stopping in the midst of the indigo profusion. Jim dismounted before Stacy and helped her off her pony. His hand remained on her elbow as they walked companionably amongst the flowers. Stacy couldn't resist picking a small bouquet and inhaling the sweet fragrance.

'I'm so glad you brought me here,' Stacy said, turning to face the young cowboy. She only had to raise her eyes a few inches to look into the light hazel ones.

The hand that had been on her elbow slipped up to her shoulder, and the cowboy's other hand moved to rest on the opposite side. The bouquet held in Stacy's hands was the only thing separating them when they both heard the sound of an approaching horse. Simultaneously they turned to face the hoofbeats. It only took Stacy an instant to recognize the rider sitting so straight in the saddle and the blood began pounding in her heart. Cord Harris reined his horse down the hill towards the couple, stopping just short of them.

'Am I interrupting something?' came the implying tone. Not giving either one a chance to answer, he rested an arm on the saddle-horn and said, 'Then let's get back to work and save the flowers for off-duty hours.'

Both Stacy and Jim mounted their ground-hitched

horses with a certain amount of chagrin, fully conscious of the accusing dark eyes. Once on their way again, the rancher nudged his horse between the pair as if separating two naughty children. Stacy's lips set in a grim line, resentful of the childish way Cord was treating them. He was unmindful of her displeasure. After they had left the meadow of bluebonnets, Cord turned his head slightly towards the quiet cowboy riding on his left.

'I want you to ride back to the main herd and help Jenkins on the point, Connors. I'll accompany Miss Adams back to where Hank is holding some strays,' ordered Cord in a tone that defied a negative answer.

The young cowboy reined his pony abruptly away from Stacy and his employer, dug his spurs into the horse's flank and was away at a gallop. Angrily Stacy turned on the forbidding form still beside her.

'You had no right to reprimand him. It was as much my fault as it was his.'

'I'm glad you see it that way. It's just what I was thinking too,' Cord replied, an amused smile on his lips, but flashing fires in his eyes. 'However, if it's any of your business, I was looking for him to tell him just that before I found him with you.'

Stacy was more than a little taken back. She had naturally assumed that Cord was disciplining her companion because of Jim's interest in her. The reddening of embarrassment flowed in her cheeks.

'But that doesn't mean I approve of you bewitching my men to such an extent that they forget to do their job.'

'I don't know what you're talking about,' Stacy muttered.

'You surely don't expect me to believe you were looking for strays on foot in that field?' he questioned.

'No, I don't!' answered Stacy exasperatedly.

'Then there really isn't anything more to be said, is there?'

'Yes, there is!' Stacy exclaimed. 'You don't have the right to tell me who I may or may not make friends with.'

'I have a great deal to say about it,' matching the angry tone in Stacy's voice. 'You are in my employ and as such, your actions become my responsibility. If I feel it's necessary, I'll dictate who you may associate with and who you may not.'

'Are you telling me I'm to leave Jim alone?'

'I'm telling you that you will not flatter my men and seduce them into having any romantic notions towards you. Is that plain enough?' Cord flashed.

'Perfectly!' she retorted, and kicked her pinto into a canter.

The two silent riders hadn't travelled very far from the meadow when they came in sight of the wizened cowboy driving a half dozen steers. With a wave of his hand towards Hank, Cord wheeled his horse away from the pinto and headed back across the range as Stacy fell in beside the wrangler.

Shortly before noon the small band joined up with the main herd. Stacy searched the riders around the main herd for some sign of Jim, but only caught a glimpse of Cord, which deterred her from looking more closely. She wasn't in the mood for another run in with him. Quietly she followed the wizened Hank to the encampment where they ate lunch and changed horses. Hot and tired, Stacy sat silently astride her horse in the noonday sun and waited for the veteran to join her. He ambled over to the ground-hitched pony beside Stacy and mounted.

'We'll be stayin' with the herd this afternoon,' he

stated. 'The two of us will be ridin' the right flank.'

Several times that afternoon Stacy caught sight of Jim, but only once did he acknowledge her presence with a wave. Stacy felt guilty for possibly getting the young cowboy into trouble; she only hoped that Jim wouldn't hold it against her. Of course he couldn't very well rush over when he saw her—after all, he was working. Twice she found herself looking around for some sign of Cord Harris, but if he was taking part in the afternoon drive, he escaped Stacy's eyes. Instead of feeling relieved that his watchful eyes were not on her, she felt empty.

At four o'clock the herd arrived at a stand of cotton-wood trees that marked the course of a rushing stream. This was the night's encampment. They drove the cattle across the shallow water, bedding them down on the opposite side. As Stacy followed Hank back over, she looked wistfully at the swift-running water. What an opportunity to wash some of the grit and grime off!

All the hands had gathered around the cook wagon where the coffee was fresh and hot. Stacy and Hank dismounted at the remuda trailers and joined the others. By tomorrow morning the herd would reach the summer pasture and the drive would be over until fall. Stacy stood quietly and sipped her coffee while listening to the boasting and grumbling of the veteran cowhands. Supper would be dished up shortly and she wanted to go down to the stream before then. She finished the last of her coffee and handed the cup to the cook. None of the group paid any attention to her as she walked away towards the cottonwood trees.

Stacy strolled leisurely, following the river upstream. Five hundred yards from camp where the stream widened as it made a turn, she stopped. This

112

was the perfect place to bathe, far enough away from camp to ensure privacy and far enough upstream for the water not to be muddied by the cattle crossing. Even an obliging tree had a lowhanging branch on which she could hang her clothes. Happily she swept the brown hat off her head and pulled out the rubber band holding her hair. Free from the confinement, the long chestnut hair fell caressingly around her shoulders as she sat down by the edge of the water to remove her dusty boots. Her toes wiggled happily in the coarse sand as their owner gazed blissfully at the beckoning water, glistening brightly with captured rays from the sun. Stacy hopped to her feet and made one last glance around her bathing hole to make sure there were no uninvited two-legged visitors, before shedding her blouse and jeans.

Clad only in her undergarments, she waded into the water. A small shudder ran through her at the unexpected coolness of the stream. She hummed merrily as she rubbed away the dirt and grime of the drive. Carried away by her enjoyment, Stacy failed to hear the sound of hooves muffled by the sand. A horse and rider came to a halt beside the overhanging cottonwood where Stacy had hung her clothes.

Still humming her happy tune, Stacy entered the shallower water and began wading towards the bank. Glancing at the tree, she stopped in the now waist-deep water, stunned by the sudden appearance of the horse and rider. Her surprise was quickly replaced by a self-consciousness of her scanty attire. Swiftly she lowered herself into the water.

'You could have had the decency to let me know you were there, Mr. Harris!' she exclaimed, her face red with shame as she addressed Cord's mocking face.

'I missed you at camp and came out looking for you,'

113

the deep voice replied, ignoring her angry criticism.

'Well, now you've found me, so kindly leave so I can get dressed.' Her embarrassment replaced by indignation.

'I'll wait for you over there,' Cord said, smiling, as he indicated a group of trees where his view of her would be obstructed. Amusement was all too visible on his face as he reined his horse around and left.

Hurriedly Stacy clambered up on the bank, chagrin and resentment hampering her. Trying to dress quickly, she struggled to pull the clothes on over her wet body. The sleeves of her blouse clung to her wet arms and with fumbling fingers she managed to get it buttoned and tucked into her Levi's. The boots slipped on easily even over the damp socks. She removed her hat from the tree and began running towards the place where Cord waited.

Cord stood silent beside his horse observing her approach. The haste with which she dressed and rushed to meet him had flushed her cheeks and her brown eyes were bright with tension and embarrassment. Stacy stopped a few feet in front of Cord and hesitated. Her eyes searched his face, desperately trying to read his inscrutable expression.

'Come on,' he said, 'I'll walk you back to camp.'

A little breathless, she fell into step beside him as he led his horse in that direction. The saturnine face never once turned towards her as they walked in silence. The strain was too much for Stacy. With her free hand she ran her fingers through her damp hair nervously.

'I was hot and dusty from the drive.' A hint of defiance was in her voice.

'The water certainly looked inviting,' Cord commented, refusing to take the bait of the unvoiced challenge she had made. 'To be honest, I was tempted to

114

join you.' He searched her face, his eyes travelling from the damp tendrils of her hair around her forehead down her straight nose and coming to a halt at her moist parted lips.

Stacy knew they were very close to camp now. In her side vision she could make out the moving forms of the cowhands. She knew she should feel self-conscious at the possible observance of her and Cord, but she was only aware of the broad shoulders and the strong tanned face of the man beside her. He must have read the confusion and bewilderment in her gaze as she tried to fathom this change in his attitude towards her, for he abruptly released her arm and began their course once again for camp.

'I've never known a woman yet who could turn down a chance to freshen up,' Cord teased. For some reason that she could not or would not acknowledge, Stacy felt safer back on their old grounds of mocking banter.

'How can I properly seduce a man if I go around smelling like a cow?' she returned, a new lift in her walk and swing to her head.

'You have a very good point,' Cord agreed as they walked into the camp area. 'Go grab yourself a bite to eat, little one. I'll see you later.'

Stacy felt his hand touch her shoulder lightly as he moved away from her towards the horse vans. The warmth of his touch radiated as she visualized the imprint of his hand on her shoulder. Abstractedly she walked over to the group of men, conscious that her whole attention was focused on the retreating figure. Throughout the meal, she involuntarily watched for his approach. When he failed to come she was depressed. Usually she dreaded his presence, and here she was looking forward to it. What manner of man was

115

he that he could make her want to be with him and hate him at the same time?

The cottonwood trees surrounding the camp hastened the darkening purple of the setting sun. Shadows had begun casting their black forms through the camp. The flickering fires seemed to grow increasingly brighter. From the other side of the flame she recognized the figure of her riding companion of the morning. Jim seemed to be looking for someone as he stood studying the various clusters of hands. Then he spotted Stacy and made his way around the campfire to where she was sitting apart from the others.

'Hi,' the serious hazel eyes smiled. 'Been looking for you.'

'Work hard today?' Stacy asked.

'Not too. I'm sorry I had to leave you in the lurch like that today,' Jim said, squatting down beside her.

'We didn't come to blows if that's what worried you,' Stacy laughed. 'I didn't mean to get you into trouble, Jim.'

'Seriously, Stacy, I like you. You know that, don't you?' Jim asked quietly. When she failed to reply, he added, 'Are you engaged or anything?'

'No.' Stacy avoided the turned head beside her. She should have felt pleased by his affection, but she found herself regretting the turn the conversation had taken. 'I like you, too, Jim. You're a very good friend.'

'That's the way I feel too,' he replied. 'I hope I'll be able to see a lot more of you.'

'I hope so, too,' Stacy said. 'I've never had too many friends.'

'Stacy,' affectionately, a calloused hand raised itself and the fingers caressed her smooth cheek, 'you're quite a girl. I bet you could turn a man down and make him feel happy about it!'

CHAPTER EIGHT

'CONNORS!' snapped a voice a few feet away from the couple.

Both Stacy and Jim sprang guiltily apart at the biting tone as Cord stepped out of the shadows. Part of his face was still hidden by the darkness, but there was no doubting the leashed fury in the set of his jaws and the furrow in his brow. His dark eyes narrowed menacingly as he stared at the young cowboy.

'You have a unique talent for turning up when you're not expected,' Stacy accused, not liking his dictatorial manner.

'Obviously,' was the reply. Cord's penetrating gaze flickered briefly to Stacy and returned to Jim.

'Well?' he demanded.

'I have nothing to say, sir,' Jim answered, his chin jutting out as he met the censorious eyes.

Stacy could feel the resentment burning inside her. The way that Cord was humiliating Jim in front of her was unforgivable! His pride was being stripped away right in front of her eyes. How much did Cord think Jim could take? And why should it concern him that she had been talking to the cowboy?

Jim regarded Stacy silently. Finally he bade her good night and walked away. Furious at the tyrannical rancher, Stacy turned to face him, her brown eyes flashing as she trembled from the anger building up inside her.

'Just who do you think you are, Mr. Harris?' she cried. 'Do you get some kind of big thrill humiliating a man in front of a woman? Or do you just like everyone to know that you're Mr. Big Shot around here?'

'I don't see where it's any concern of yours what my reasons are,' said Cord, his voice still fierce with controlled emotion.

'That's a remark typical of you,' Stacy said bitterly. 'You consider yourself a law unto yourself, responsible to no one. Well, you're nothing! Do you hear me, nothing! Why, Jim is more of a man than you could ever hope to be. And furthermore, if you think you've succeeded in lowering him in my eyes, you're sadly mistaken. Before, I only considered him to be a friend, but now I can see that, compared to you, he's the only man on earth for me.'

'You admit, after all, that it is a man you want,' Cord retorted, a muscle in his jaw twitching in his own mounting anger. 'I seriously doubt if you would know a man if you saw one.'

'I know that whatever it is I'm standing in front of now, it's not a man!' she snapped, fully aware that she was pushing Cord too far, but beyond the point of caring. She enjoyed degrading this paragon before her.

The slender thread that had held his temper in check snapped as his face grew black with fury. Roughly he grabbed Stacy's arms, drawing her so close to him that she could see the throbbing veins on the side of his jaw. The iron grip of his fingers dug deep into her shoulders as she struggled uselessly against his muscular chest. He was much too strong for her. As one large hand moved, sweeping around her waist, the other grabbed her long brown hair, twisting her head back until she was forced to look into his face. Crushed against his chest, she stared tremulously into the now coal-black eyes.

'By God,' Cord said hoarsely, 'I'll not have you throwing yourself at my men. If it's an affair you're after, well, I'll take care of that right here and now!'

Slowly his face lowered down to hers as if enjoying the apprehension Stacy felt as she realized he was going to kiss her. Valiantly she tried to struggle again, but he restrained her easily. His arm tightened around her as if he meant to crush out every ounce of resistance. As his mouth pressed cruelly against hers, Stacy felt a fire of passion sear through her body. The fierceness of his kiss, meant to punish, hurt, and humiliate, stifled any effort she might have made to respond as the bristle of his whiskers scraped her skin. But the whirlpool of his nearness kept spinning in her mind and the throbbing of her heart must have echoed into his ears as it did in her own. When Stacy felt he would never let her go, Cord stepped away. The suddenness of his release jolted her off balance and she fell to the ground. Stunned, she lay there staring up at the towering figure.

'Never back a man up in a corner,' Cord said, the coldness back in his eyes. 'I told you once before to learn the rules before you played the game.'

'I despise you!' Stacy gasped, rising to her feet and flinging herself at him.

He caught her wrists easily and stared emotionless at the teardrops running down her cheeks. She kicked and scratched at him, but the attempts were warded off easily until she was finally exhausted by her efforts.

'You've beaten me,' she finally murmured, fighting the lump in her throat. 'You can always force me to do what you want, but you can never make me feel anything but disgust for you.'

There was no sign of self-reproach in his eyes as Cord looked at Stacy. As he lowered her imprisoned hands and released them, he stood silently searching her face for what Stacy didn't know.

'I know,' Cord finally sighed. 'I know. Come on, we'd better join the others.'

'Is that all you've got to say?' Stacy asked in a small voice, slightly astounded. 'No apologies? If that's the way you treat your women, I can see why you got jilted.'

Cord's face turned to stone at her words and his dark eyes bored deep inside her. Uncomfortably aware that she had trespassed on to something that was none of her affair, the numb Stacy stood there, tear-streaked and proud.

'I don't intend to apologize for my actions. I don't know what you heard about Lydia and me, but whatever it was, it's none of your business,' the cold, hard voice replied. 'Consider what happened tonight a lesson you should have learned long ago. You're not an unattractive girl. You're lucky that I haven't fallen under your spell or the outcome of tonight could have been quite different. Fortunately, I know you for what you are, and the cheap tricks your kind use to satisfy your egotistical craving for attention and admiration.' The sarcasm seeped through his words. 'The subject is closed.'

Stacy couldn't speak. She looked into his face, repelled by the disgust mirrored there. Bewildered, she offered no resistance when Cord took her arm and guided her back towards the campfire. Several times she stumbled on the uneven ground, but he never hesitated in his stride. Nor did he even glance her way; only the hand on her arm verified that he acknowledged her existence.

When they reached the campfire, he released her and walked on into the circle without her. Grateful to be away from him, Stacy slipped over to her bedroll, praying no one would speak to her or see her tear-

120

rimmed eyes in the glowing firelight. Hiccupping silent sobs, she crawled into her covers. Cursing him for his unwarranted opinion of her, she snuggled inside the blanket for comfort, but her body and mind retained the memory of the strength and warmth of his arms and the brutality and fire in his kiss. Vainly she rubbed her lips with the back of her hand, but the memory was indelibly marked. Sleep crept up silently on her exhausted body.

The morning sun shone brightly down on Stacy astride the little bay horse she had ridden the first day. She could take no interest in the surrounding country as she rode along the flank of the herd. Listlessly she sat on the pony and let her gaze blur in the multitude of cattle.

Last night in her dreams she had relived Cord's embrace, but this time it was filled with passion and desire. She had returned Cord's kiss with equal fervour. The dream was almost more disquieting than the actual kiss. Afterwards she had clung to him, driven by a desperation that he would reject her. She felt she had somehow betrayed herself in that dream. She hated Cord Harris and everything he stood for. The shame and guilt she felt for the imagined kiss far exceeded the humiliation the actual kiss had filled her with the night before.

The pounding of approaching hooves aroused her from her thoughts. Looking up, Stacy recognized Jim Connors astride the galloping horse. He waved and rode by to pull up beside Hank. They exchanged a few words between them, causing an embarrassing flush to flood Stacy's cheeks as she wondered if they were discussing her. If it had been one of the other days, she would have dropped back to join them, but she was afraid to face them today for fear they could read in her face the events of the night before. A few minutes later Hank rode up beside her.

'We'll be reachin' the pasture in the hour,' said Hank. 'The Boss told Jim this morning that as soon as we got to the summer pasture you were to go back to the ranch house.'

'Why? Did he say?' Stacy asked, dreading the prospect of meeting Cord Harris again.

'Nope. One of the hands will be there with a pick-up and you'll ride back with him. And the Boss wants you to go to his office as soon as you get there,' Hank replied, the same searching look in his eyes. 'You had another go-round with the Boss last night, didn't ya'?'

Stacy started to deny it, but knew she couldn't fool the sharp-eyed cowhand and nodded affirmatively.

'You two do rub each other's fur the wrong way,' he smiled with a shake of his head. 'Jim said the Boss come up on you two last night.'

'I suppose he jumped all over Jim this morning?' Stacy remarked bitterly.

'Jim figured he would, but he didn't say a word about it, in fact he even put Jim in charge of one of the brandin' crews,' the veteran smiled, watching Stacy's face closely for her reaction.

'He did?' The amazement was written on her face. 'Probably his way of apologizing,' she reasoned to herself.

'I imagine you're thinkin' me to be an ole gossip, but are you sweet on Jim or somethin'?'

'No,' said Stacy, a hint of a smile appearing on her face. 'We're friends. He knew my father, or met him at a lecture.'

'Good,' the old cowboy grinned with a satisfied gleam in his eyes.

'Good. Why?' Curious at his unusual remark.

'Ain't his type. You need somebody stronger to hold you in check. Fire and fire always makes a bigger flame.'

'I didn't know you mixed matchmaking with philosophy, Hank,' she laughed. 'Tell me, do you have someone in mind?'

'I do, but I ain't tellin'. You'll know soon enough,' Hank answered mysteriously. Kicking his horse, he added over the din, 'Better get back to work.'

Laughing, Stacy joined him, the gloom of the morning fading in the wake of the sagacious cowboy. When the last steer had been chased through, Hank motioned towards a waiting pick-up, indicating that that was the one Stacy would be taking back to the ranch house.

She rode over to the remuda trailer and dismounted. Dodging the milling horses and riders, she made her way to the truck. The driver opened the door for her and motioned her inside. Stacy exchanged a few pleasantries with him, but the growing anticipation of meeting Cord after last night's episode gradually silenced her. Her imagination had all sorts of reasons for his wanting to talk with her. If she was lucky he might want to put an end to the bargain they had made.

Driving into the yard, Stacy noticed an unfamiliar gold-coloured Cadillac parked in front of the hacienda. Even though she wasn't familiar with all the vehicles of the surrounding neighbours, she was sure she had never seen any car like that before. A curious sense of foreboding filled her as the pick-up pulled up beside the house gates to let her out.

Tired and filled with dread, Stacy walked with her bedroll and hat in one hand and suede jacket in the other. As she opened the door she wished she had a

123

chance to clean up and change before meeting the formidable Cord Harris, but knew that he expected her as soon as she arrived. Resentment flared briefly within her, as she recognized that he wanted her at a disadvantage. How could she appear cool and in control if she looked like a dirty urchin?

Stepping inside the cool interior of the entry way, she became aware of voices in the den. Uncertainly she stopped before the closed door and tried to recognize them, but the thick oak door muffled the sounds. 'Maybe he's busy and doesn't want to see me now,' she thought. No, she might as well get it over with. Resigned, she placed the items in her hands on the bench outside the room, gave a few brisk brushes at the dust on her jeans and blouse, smoothed her long hair back to where it was caught at the neck, squared her shoulders, and knocked at the door.

'Come in,' came the muffled reply.

With more confidence than she felt, Stacy opened the heavy door and walked into the room. Cord stood directly in front of her beside his desk. There was a nonchalance and ease in his carriage that intensified her nervousness.

'Come on in,, Miss Adams,' Cord instructed with a slightly imperious wave of his hand. His mocking eyes flicked over her dishevelled appearance and he added, 'I see you've just got here.'

'I understood you wanted to see me right away,' Stacy said defensively, looking the tall figure in the eye. 'If you're busy I can come back later.'

'No, that won't be necessary,' he said. His gaze left her to travel casually to the tall-backed chair in front of the desk. 'You don't mind waiting a few minutes, do you?'

For the first time Stacy's eyes searched the room for

the second voice she had heard outside. So intent on meeting Cord was she that she had momentarily forgotten her curiosity about the owner of the Cadillac outside. A movement in the chair captured her attention. The over-sized leather chair with its back to Stacy had hidden its occupant from her view. Now she saw the slender, stockinged legs, the high heels and the polished nails of a feminine hand. As the graceful figure rose from the chair, Stacy felt the quiver of a premonition flow through her. The woman was strikingly beautiful. Her hair was jet black and drawn back into a chignon, emphasizing her high cheekbones and creamy skin. Her eyes, as they turned to survey Stacy, were as black as her hair and sparkled with a subdued fire. She was several inches taller than Stacy and managed to give the impression that she was looking down that graceful nose at her. The dark eyes glowed with pleasure as the woman looked at the bedraggled appearance of the other girl.

'You are going to introduce us, aren't you, Cord dear?' the strange woman asked in a clear, melodic voice.

'Of course,' he replied, his eyes never straying from Stacy's blushing face. 'Lydia, I'd like you to meet Miss Stacy Adams. She's been helping me around the ranch here, as you can tell. Miss Adams, this is Lydia Marshall, a very old friend of mine.'

Murmuring an incoherent hello, Stacy nodded. Lydia—that was the woman Cord had been engaged to! Conscious of the significance of the two being together, she flashed a questioning look at Cord. His face maintained the same mocking expression that she had become so familiar with these past weeks. The gleam in his eyes that she had previously attributed to his satisfaction at her untidy appearance held something more. Maybe they were back together again, but what of Lydia's husband? A thousand questions raced through Stacy's mind as she tried to concentrate on the conversation between the two, but the only thing that remained implanted in her mind after Lydia left the room was the silky voice of the dark-haired woman.

Stacy stared at the closed oak door trying desperately to shake the chilling dread that grew within her.

'I said would you like to sit down, Adams,' the deep voice repeated in a slightly louder tone.

'Of course—I'm sorry,' Stacy mumbled, further embarrassed by her inattention. She walked over and sat in one of the straight-backed chairs beside the desk. Cord had already seated himself behind his desk and was shuffling through a few papers.

'She's a very beautiful woman. Did her husband come with her?' Stacy blurted out before she realized it.

'No,' Cord replied, a whisper of a smile in his eyes and a smug satisfaction on his lips. 'It seems Mrs. Marshall is getting a divorce.'

'Oh,' Stacy managed in a very small voice. Why did it upset her that the two were obviously getting back together?

'Now to get at the reason I called you in here,' he started briskly. 'It's quite clear that our previous arrangement is not going to work, at least not the way I planned.'

'I'm still willing to write you a cheque for any of the damages that I've caused,' she volunteered, sitting nervously on the edge of her chair. 'I quite understand that you wish to be rid of me now, and I assure you the feeling is mutual.'

'I'm afraid you misunderstand,' he said, raising one eyebrow. 'I still believe you should work your debt out. What's obvious is that you can't take the place of one of the men, or even half of one. Therefore I propose that you handle something more in a feminine line.'

'I don't quite understand what you're getting at?'

'As I mentioned to you once before, each spring I have an auction where I sell some of my registered quarter horse stock, Texas-style. That means a barbecue and a party.' Cord's eyes were sparkling as he watched the dawning comprehension on Stacy's face. 'I'm sure with your country club background you'll be able to organize this year's activity, which will leave me free to take care of the ranch.'

'How many people will be here?' Stacy asked, ignoring the veiled sarcasm in his last statement. 'When is it going to be?'

'Before the day's over, I imagine several hundred people will have been here at one time or another. The date is set for June the ninth, almost four weeks away,' he answered, studying her face thoughtfully. 'Now, if you think it's too much for you——?'

'Not at all,' Stacy said defensively. 'But I must admit I'm curious why you didn't ask Mrs. Marshall to act as hostess and co-ordinator for you.'

'It's really none of your business, the reasons for my decision to use you, but I've already said that I wanted you to work your way out, and this seemed the only alternative.' His voice had grown cold at her presumptuous statement. 'And Mrs. Marshall is going through a difficult adjustment and shouldn't be expected to supervise the preparations for a gathering of this size with the emotional pressure she's presently under. Besides, it wouldn't exactly be proper for Lydia to do so at this time. Of course, I doubt if you would realize that.'

'I didn't know that other people's opinions bothered you,' she retorted, stung by the masterly way he was protecting his former fiancée.

'It depends a great deal on the people involved,' Cord's icy voice replied. 'There are some people whose reputation I wouldn't want damaged, and there are some people who aren't going to be around long enough to worry about.'

'If you're making some subtle reference to me, I would prefer that you speak your mind,' Stacy said angrily. 'You've acquired some ridiculous idea that I go around flirting with every man I meet. At least I don't go accosting guests staying in my home!'

'I thought you'd have better sense than to bring that up,' Cord snapped in a dangerously low voice. The muscle in his jaw twitched its familiar warning sign again. 'Last night is better forgotten. Most women would have had enough pride not to have brought it up again.'

'I don't happen to be most women!' Stacy retorted, rising agitatedly from her seat to stand with her hands clasped tightly on the back of the chair. 'Evidently you expect me to forget it with a snap of my fingers.'

'Frankly, I don't care whether you forget it or not,' Cord said, looking up at the slim figure. 'Unless, of course, you want a repeat performance.'

'That's the last thing I would ever want from you!' Guilt burned across her face as she remembered her response to his kiss in her dream.

'Very well,' he said, closing the subject and turning his attention to a sheaf of papers in front of him. 'Here are some of the arrangements already made for the sale which you should make yourself familiar with. You may use this den as the centre of your activities. I won't be disturbing you since I take care of most of my paper work in the office. Quite likely there'll be a few details you will want to go over with me. You can contact me at that time. I believe that's all.'

His cold tone of dismissal froze the angry words in Stacy's throat. She stood by the chair for a moment, but he didn't raise his eyes from the stack of papers. Briskly she turned on her heel and strode out of the room, giving the heavy oak door an added impetus as it closed. Gathering her belongings in the foyer, she stalked up the stairs to her room, where she flung her bundle down on the floor and stared at her glowering reflection in the dresser mirror.

An hour later, as Stacy was walking out of the bathroom after showering and changing her clothes, she met Cord in the hallway.

'I neglected to give you the keys to your car,' Cord said briskly, his cool, dark eyes taking in the freshness of her appearance. 'You'll be needing transportation, so I had one of my men bring it over from the cabin. It's in the garage.'

'How thoughtful of you,' Stacy replied sarcastically.

'I also had a typewrter installed in the den,' he added, his eyes narrowing at her tone. 'I believe that should take care of the things you'll need.'

'I'm quite sure everything is satisfactory,' she said, starting to brush past the handsome figure. But his muscular arm shot out and blocked her passage. Stacy's flashing eyes looked up at the darkening face.

'You can wipe that expression off your face,' Cord stated threateningly. 'A good thrashing would do wonders for a spoiled brat like you.'

'Violence is your solution to everything, isn't it?' she answered, not flinching under his penetrating gaze. 'Now, get out of my way and let me by.'

Shaking inwardly, she pushed his arm out of her way and walked briskly down the stairs. At the bottom of the steps stood the dark beauty of Lydia Marshall, her black eyes icy cold as she watched Stacy walk past her. The ice vanished as Cord made his way down the steps behind Stacy.

'There you are!' Lydia said in her saccharine voice. 'I was beginning to wonder if you'd forgotten me. I fixed us a drink. I hope I've remembered how you like them.'

Lydia's voice fluttered after Stacy like a flaunting red cape, but she didn't wait around to hear Cord's reply. Hurrying blindly into the den, Stacy leaned against the closed door and waited for the trembling in her knees and the pounding of her heart to return to normal. Why did she let Cord arouse her this way? He never acted the same way towards her twice. One time he was teasing and friendly as he was when he had found her at the river, and the next time he was violent and abusive, as when he had kissed her so brutally. And today he was the Don, condescending and dictatorial, making sure she knew where her place was. As far as Stacy was concerned Cord deserved the icy Latin beauty of Lydia Marshall with her sickening, ingratiating airs. Oh, how Stacy wished for the steadiness of Carter Mills. She was growing extremely weary of being a barometer of Cord's emotions.

Discouraged and weary from the last three days of riding, she crossed over behind the desk and sat dejectedly in the chair and studied the stack of papers in front of her. The image of the tanned hands shuffling through them crossed her mind. Absently she shifted through them, her attention straying at first until the magnitude of the party with all its details began to sink in.

Horror-stricken, she sat in the big swivel chair and went through the papers once more. If he hadn't been so antagonistic she would have explained that she had never given even a dinner party for more than twelve people in her life. What was she going to do now? The memory of his derisive, mocking smile flitted in front of her as she saw herself trying to explain to him.

'Oh, how he'd like that,' Stacy thought. 'It would really please him to see me fall flat on my face. Well, that's not going to happen. I'll have to work a lot harder than I thought, but if I'm lucky, he'll never see the few mistakes I'll make.'

With renewed confidence she tackled the stack of papers again and began to sort a plan out in her mind.

CHAPTER NINE

THE red sorrel tossed his flaxen mane in the air and snorted his displeasure at the firm hand curbing his pace.

'Easy, Diablo,' Stacy quieted him, but he continued to pull at the bit.

Maybe a good gallop would release some of her tension, Stacy thought. The row she had had with Cord earlier that afternoon had taken its toll on her patience. Two weeks had passed since he had put her in charge of the sale festivities. the co-ordination of all the various activities was a full-time job and exceedingly trying for someone who had never done it before, despite the assistance from the wives of the permanent hands. Stacy had been pleased with the job she had done thus far. She also had the feeling that Cord was satisfied with her work, too. Not that it really mattered what his opinion was, she told herself. But this afternoon when she was going over some of the correspondence with him regarding the preparation of the auction itself, Cord had asked her for the printer's proof of the sales catalogue. Stacy knew nothing about it and confessed her ignorance of it to him.

She could still see the thundering expression on his face when he heard her words. She burned at the memory of his scathing remarks. If only she had been able to explain to him her inexperience in arranging such affairs, but the humiliation had burned too deep to allow any room for further scorn. The man was so callous that he couldn't possibly possess anything that even remotely resembled a heart.

Cord had been gone almost every day since the initial meeting when he had turned the preparations over to her. Sometimes during the day he took time to confer with her, but their conversations were limited strictly to the auction. Stacy didn't know if the ranch work was pressing or if he was merely avoiding spending any time with her. Lydia breezed in several times looking for him, occasionally condescending to consult Stacy for Cord's whereabouts, conveying the impression that he was helping her with the technicalities of her divorce. Usually she found him somewhere, since Stacy often saw them from her window, Cord's head bent low to catch some confiding remark the raven-haired woman made, her arm resting possessively on his. Stacy normally turned guiltily from the window, blushing as if she had been caught in the act of eavesdropping on an intimate conversation. Other times she watched until they were out of sight before returning to her work with an odd sense of depression about her.

She was positive that Cord's continued absence in the evenings was caused by Lydia. Strangely enough Stacy found herself either missing him or dreading his arrival, and she refused to let herself delve into the reasons for her contradictory emotions.

Several evenings Jim Connors had joined her on the veranda, and they had chatted away, discovering many interests in common. Stacy enjoyed the easy companionship of the young cowboy with his ready laughter and undemanding company. It was a vast difference from her tempestuous relationship with Cord Harris. With Jim she felt comfortable and at ease, not worrying about each little word she said and how he was going to interpret it. The friendly relaxed atmosphere that surrounded her when she was with Jim reminded her of the way she had relied on Carter Mills.

Carter. He seemed eons away. Had it only been such a short time ago that she had been with him? His last letter had been chatty and full of interesting tidbits of various mutual acquaintances, but it also held an underlying current of concern that Stacy couldn't ignore. She knew he was waiting for an answer from her, one that she couldn't give. She had difficulty even recalling what Carter looked like; all she could summon up was a blurred image of short, sandy hair and shining blue eyes so unclear that it could have been Jim she was picturing rather than Carter. Maybe the resemblance between the two was the reason she was so drawn to Jim. Stacy really couldn't say. But she had no desire to think on it. She probably would have been better off if she had never come out here, but then she never would have fallen in love with this wild, rugged country. Even in her present circumstances, Stacy enjoyed the closeness of the demanding landscape. Gone was the overcrowdedness, the smog, and the endless blare of traffic; in its place was endless space, fresh air, and the muffled calls of God's creatures.

With a glance at the sinking sun, Stacy remounted the rested horse and turned him towards the ranch house. Her wandering thoughts were brought up short by the knowledge that she had to return before the sun was too far down.

All too quickly they reached the stables. Stacy dismounted and led the docile sorrel through the fence gate to the stable area. Humming contentedly, she didn't hear the approach of the wizened Hank.

'You shore are mighty cheerful,' Hank crackled behind her.

The sudden voice startled her. 'Hank! You shouldn't do that!' she admonished with a shaky laugh. 'You practically scared me out of my boots!'

'You looked so happy and contented that it seemed a pure shame to spoil such a pretty picture,' he grinned.

'I thought only the Irish had kissed the Blarney Stone. Seems you people out here must have one of your own,' she teased, a sparkle lighting up her brown eyes.

'Pshaw! Ain't nothin' fancy about tellin' a pretty girl she's pretty when all she had to do is look in the mirror an' see,' Hank replied with a grunt.

Warmed by the affection of the gnarled man beside her and the caressing rays of the firey-bright sun, Stacy had a tremendous urge to spread her arms and envelop the great wild, rugged land that had captured her so completely. Instead she raised her face to the gentle breeze and inhaled the fragrant perfumes it carried.

'I love this land!' she exclaimed, ending in a regretful sigh. 'I'm going to hate leaving all this behind.'

'I thought you didn't like it here?' Hank commented, turning his head away to hide the twinkle in his eye.

'I've never seen anything like it. At times it's so harsh and desolate, but the beauty is still there. Oh, no, Hank, I don't like it, I love it!'

'Humph! If you're so fond of this place, why leave it? Why don't you just move to some part of the country around here?'

'It wouldn't be the same,' Stacy replied with a gentle shake of her chestnut hair.

'What's so special about this place, anyway?'

'It's a hundred different things. The sun wouldn't set quite the same. The hills wouldn't be the same colour,' she explained hesitantly.

'The sun sets the same anywhere,' Hank snorted. Then he turned to her rapturous face, not even trying to hide the gleam in his eyes and added, 'What about the Boss?'

'What do you mean?' Stacy queried, stiffening at the reference to the enigmatical Cord Harris.

'Ain't he a part of all this?'

'Of course not! He's——'

'He's the only reason why you're wantin' to stay here at all,' Hank grinned, hurrying on before Stacy could voice the protest forming on her lips. 'Quit kiddin' yoreself that you're only here to work out the trouble yore horse caused.'

'He won't let me go,' Stacy cried.

'You won't let yoreself go,' Hank answered. 'Face it, girl, the only hold he has on you is your heart. You love him. I've known it for a long time.'

'No,' Stacy said weakly as the gruff words sank in.

'Reckon it's about time the cat was let out of the bag. If you got any guts at all, you'll admit it to yourself.'

135

Stacy stood speechless after the retreating figure. In love with Cord Harris? Impossible! Why, he was the most arrogant, rude, hateful person she had ever known. She hated him! Memories raced through her mind—the racing of her pulse when he entered a room, the torment and pain of his mocking smile, the burning of her skin at his touch. Stacy groaned, remembering the black hair with its wayward lock that fell on to the tanned forehead and the dark, flashing eyes that so many times threatened to consume her with their fire, and the finely chiselled cheekbones with their shadow of a beard, his mouth that had bruised and battered her with his kiss when all the time she had been seeking it, waiting for it.

Impatiently the stallion turned and whickered to the slim, freckled figure. Numbly she led him to his corral. stumbling several times, unable to focus on anything but the vivid picture of Cord etched in her mind. She loved him! This torment that possessed her when he was near was the desire to love which was antagonized into hate by his rejection. As she turned the sorrel loose in his paddock, Stacy allowed the realization to wash over her. How could she have been so blind not to have recognized it before? A bubble of elation filled her as she raced to the hacienda. A flush filled her cheeks; a glow lit her brown eyes; and a smile spread across her face with the warming knowledge of her discovery. Stacy Adams loved Cord Harris, her heart chanted. She wanted to scream it to the world. Breathlessly she threw open the heavy oak door and rushed into the silent hall.

The emptiness stopped her. He wasn't here. He had left with Lydia this afternoon after Stacy had quarrelled with him. The desolation swept over her. How could she have forgotten Lydia with her raven hair

136

and porcelain skin? The divorcee with her dark beauty had returned to Cord, returned to accept the love he had once laid at her feet. It was she he cared for, not Stacy. The excitement of her new-found love had allowed Stacy to forget one vital thing—Cord despised her, despised everything she stood for!

'Get hold of yourself, Stacy Adams,' she scolded, wrinkling the golden freckles on her nose at the self-pity that wanted to swallow her. 'Your father didn't raise a quitter. Cord thinks you're a feckless girl without an ounce of sense to your name and concern for no one but yourself. You've got to show him before it's too late that he's wrong. At least you can fight for him. You can give that raven-haired witch a run for her money!'

With grim determination Stacy swept aside the waves of melancholy. First things first and the first was washing the dust off from her ride and after that she would dress for dinner. Tonight she'd wear her backless jersey culotte dress with the bold turquoise and emerald design. She had brought it along on a whim, but now she would put it to use.

A spark of combat gleamed in Stacy's brown eyes as she undressed swiftly and stepped under the biting spray of the shower. 'Cord,' she let the name roll lovingly from her lips. It had the sound of a man, the tensile strength of a whip cracking overhead. The rugged land of Texas had bred a man to match and conquer its harsh terrain. Remembering the strength of his hands, the steel of his arms and the solidness of his broad shoulders, she felt a quiver of passion course through her. If only she could look into his dark eyes and see a desire and a love for her there, how perfect her world would be.

By the time she had stepped out of the shower, she

had recaptured the earlier enchantment of her new emotion. With a youthful resiliency she had bounded back with a sureness based on faith rather than common sense. Briskly she rubbed the rough terry towel over her body. Singing happily to herself, she returned to the bedroom where she proceeded to dress with a great deal more care than she had ever bothered with before.

Finished, she stood before the large dresser mirror inspecting her reflection with a critical eye. The brilliant blues and greens of her dress offset the light golden tan of her arms and the sun-bleached highlights in her hair. With a final glance at the satin shoes peeping under the floor-length skirt, she winked a compliment to her reflection and left the room.

With a regalness of carriage that denied the flutterings in her heart, Stacy descended the stairs. The plump Mexican housekeeper was setting the table in the dining room. The confidence in Stacy's face took a little dive when she saw only one place setting. She almost asked Maria when Cord was expected home, but pride wouldn't let her concede the possibility that he wouldn't be returning early. Her inquiries on previous evenings had always been met with a negative answer and she couldn't bear to hear one tonight.

'The señorita looks lovely tonight,' Maria bubbled with her usual wide smile. 'You have a date with Jeem, maybe, no?'

'No,' Stacy smiled as she tried to steel herself against the trembling in her body.

Quietly she seated herself at the empty table and tried to eat the attractive dishes placed before her. But the anticipation that consumed her didn't leave any room for food even though she tried valiantly to show an interest in the fruit salads and cold meats that

Maria had prepared so painstakingly for her. Finally, after picking away at a pineapple confection for several minutes and not tasting a bit of it, Stacy pushed herself away from the table. It was no use. The tension and apprehension of waiting had stolen her appetite. She was just too excited to eat. Nervously she rose from her chair and began pacing by the table.

'Do you not feel well, señorita?' the Mexican woman asked, standing in the doorway of the dining room.

'It was really a very good meal, Maria. I just don't have any appetite,' Stacy apologized, not wishing to hurt her feelings.

Maria seemed to accept Stacy's explanation and began clearing away the dishes. Stacy watched for a minute, trying to gather the courage to ask Maria if she knew where Cord was.

'You perhaps would like your coffee out on the patio?'

'Yes, that would be nice,' Stacy murmured absently. Quietly she started to walk from the room, then stopped and in a nonchalant voice asked, 'Do you expect Mr. Harris home early this evening?'

'Oh, no. He went to a cattlemen's dinner. He usually very late,' was the reply before Maria bustled off to the kitchen.

Dejectedly Stacy walked through the living room to the large glass doors that led on to the veranda. The hope had washed out of her eyes as she slid the doors open and stood on the cobblestone floor outside.

The loneliness seemed to seep into her bones, quelling all the hope and confidence she had summoned. Restlessly, Stacy walked farther out and leaned heavily against a pillar supporting the balcony above. She struggled desperately to fight the dejection and listlessness that was surrounding her. The pool shimmered darkly in the dim light, a hint of ominousness in its depths. She gazed in the direction of the family cemetery on the gentle knoll above the house, hidden from direct view by the adobe walls. Silently she whispered a prayer to Doña Elena, Cord's grandmother. If she understood how much Stacy loved this country and her grandson, perhaps the ghost of this Spanish woman would intervene on her behalf. But no, that only happened in dreams. Wishing Cord by her side could not make it so.

Absently Stacy heard the sound of steps on the patio. Assuming it to be Maria with her coffee, she remained leaning against the pillar, not wishing the Mexican woman to see the tears that threatened to roll down her cheeks.

'Just put the coffee on the table, Maria. I'll serve myself in a minute,' Stacy's voice was uncommonly low, her throat choked by the emotion she couldn't control.

'The coffee's already here. You don't mind if I help myself before it gets cold, do you?' came the reply.

'Cord,' she whispered faintly. For a moment, she was afraid her legs wouldn't hold her. In that brief moment he rushed to her side.

'Stacy, are you all right?' His hands seized her shoulders roughly.

'Yes, yes, I'm fine. You startled me,' Stacy eplied shakily, refusing to look into the probing dark eyes for fear they would see the naked love she felt.

'For a minute there I thought you were going to faint. You were as pale as a ghost. Are you sure you feel all right?' The concern still in his voice as his tanned hands remained on her arms.

His nearness overwhelmed her. She was so conscious of the rich black cloth of his suit, the brilliant whiteness of his shirt, and his face just inches from hers, that she couldn't look up. She couldn't let him see what he was doing to her. Her eyes concentrated on his left hand, the strong fingers, the dark, curling hairs peeping out from the cuff of his shirt.

'You're hurting me!' Her voice came out weakly as her body threatened to sway against the massive chest that presented itself so invitingly.

'I'm sorry,' Cord said, moving abruptly away from her, a briskness returning to his voice. Stacy glanced up, but his eyes were hidden in the night's shadows and she was unable to determine his reaction. Did he consider her a silly city girl afraid of the dark? 'I didn't realize I was holding you so tightly,' he finished.

Firmly Stacy got hold of herself. She mustn't act like a coltish schoolgirl. After all, this was what she wanted, a chance to be alone with him. The trouble was her tongue was twisted up with the love in her heart. How much easier it would be just to tell him she loved him. Casually she walked up to the edge of the veranda to join him.

'Care for a cigarette?'

'Yes, thank you,' Stacy replied, watching the masculine hands holding the cigarette case as they removed another filter-tipped cigarette and lit it for her. The sudden flare of the lighter illuminated the rough features of Cord's face, outlining the lines of tiredness etched around his mouth.

'Maria didn't expect you back till much later. She said you were at a cattlemen's dinner. Have you eaten?' she asked, trying to keep too much concern from showing in her voice.

'Yes,' he replied noncommittally.

'Are those type of things usually over this early?' Stacy asked, desperately trying to keep the conversa-

141

tion going, hoping he wouldn't notice her nervousness.

'No, it was still going on when I left.' His reply was abrupt and gave Stacy the impression that he didn't feel like talking.

'I imagine you're rather tired. Perhaps you'd rather I left so you could relax?' she suggested, willing the pain to leave her heart.

'You're extremely solicitous tonight,' Cord replied, an eyebrow raised quizzically in her direction. 'Yes, I am rather tired, but no, you don't need to leave. If you want to make yourself useful you can pour me a cup of coffee.'

Without replying Stacy walked over to the table. As she stood bathed in the light from the living room, Cord's low voice carried to her, 'You look very becoming in that frock you're wearing.'

'Thank you,' she murmured, trying to still the trembling that ceased her hand.

'Were you expecting company tonight?' His voice had changed from an indifferent tone to the familiar mocking one.

'No,' Stacy said too swiftly, trying to cover the embarrassment that his observation had caused. If only he knew that the only person she expected was him! 'I just felt like slipping into something different.'

Cord walked over into the light near Stacy. She handed him his coffee, her own dark eyes flicking up to meet his as she did so.

'I was hoping you'd be up,' Cord said briskly, moving out of the light where she couldn't study his expression.

'Oh,' Stacy cursed inwardly at the breathlessness in her voice.

'I wanted to apologize for this afternoon. You're doing an excellent job on the barbecue and I was un-

142

reasonably harsh.' He seemed to hesitate as if waiting for a reply, but no words came from her lips. 'No harm has been done, and the fault was mainly mine for not advising you about the catalogue.'

'No,' Stacy rushed, 'I should have realized that——'

'Whoa!' Cord laughed. His warm deep mirth thrilled her. 'Let's close the conversation before we start a mutual admiration society.'

'But that's just what I want to do,' Stacy thought as she joined the laughter. She felt rather than saw the tension ease out of him as he turned and flicked his cigarette off into the dark. She watched the arc of the glowing embers as it sailed through the air to be lost in the shrubbery. Her long fingers stubbed her own cigarette out in an available ash tray. Cord had moved over to the pillar where Stacy had been standing when he had arrived. She wandered a few feet to the other side of him, her own cup of coffee held caressingly in both hands, enjoying the feel of its warmth to her palms.

'Oh, the stars are out!' she exclaimed as she looked into the velvet sky at the brilliant array.

'Now you've seen stars before,' the mocking voice said.

'Yes, but you see, when I was looking out here earlier, there were only one or two dim stars and now there's hundreds,' Stacy explained, radiant with her enthusiasm. 'It seemed so lonely with no moon and just a couple of stars, but now it's magnificent.'

'Tell me something, Stacy,' he said, leaning lazily against the pillar, his dark gaze surveying the lithe form beside him, 'are you really what you seem? One time you're a dewy-eyed girl enraptured with a flower or a moon or something, another time you're a hot-tempered Irish colleen fighting me tooth and nail, then you're a cool, sophisticated debutante acting out

143

a part like earlier tonight in your fine satin gown. Which one is the real you?'

'Will the real Miss Stacy Adams please stand up?' she laughed, not wanting to face the serious eyes. But when he failed to join in with her joke, Stacy added as truthfully as she could, 'I suppose I'm all those things.'

Her eyes tried to read his expression, but his face was in the shadows. He stood quietly for a time until the silence became too much for Stacy and she nervously walked over and placed her cup near the coffee urn.

'Stacy?' There was a hesitation in Cord's use of her name that she couldn't identify.

'Yes?'

'Would you come here a minute?' If only she knew what made his voice seem so different, almost unsure. 'I'd like to ask you something, if you don't mind.'

Stacy's heart beat wildly as she moved beside the tall figure leaning negligently against the white column. He didn't turn to look at her, but continued to gaze out into the night.

'How can a man go about asking a woman who has had all the material things she's ever wanted and whose beauty ensures her all the attention she could ever desire to share her life with him?' Cord's voice had a briskness of controlled emotion that wrenched at Stacy's heart.

With difficulty she suppressed a strangling gasp. 'Oh, dear God,' she thought, 'he's asking me about Lydia.'

'What can I offer her? A life in a country that she must dislike? A monotonous existence?' he went on derisively. 'Just exactly who does the giving and who does the taking in that kind of a situation?'

'I—I would think offering her your love would be enough,' Stacy stammered, pain racking her body in

144

silent sobs, her mind reeling and tormented with doubts.

His dark head twisted sharply to scrutinize her face which she had turned to look out into the night so that the grief that was filling her eyes would be hidden.

'Would that be enough for you?' his low voice asked, but he didn't wait for a reply. 'And just how would you let your man know?'

'It would be enough for me if the right man asked,' Stacy answered, a calmness settling over her heart, knowing his love would be all she would ever ask. She turned to face him, and a serenity radiated from her face as she added, 'And if he loved me, he'd know.'

A dark hand reached out and imprisoned her wrist, pulling her over beside him. Her breath came in rapid gasps as the dark, fiery eyes bore into hers.

'If he was unsure, how would you go about telling him, Stacy?' Cord's voice vibrated near her hair. She felt his left hand slip behind her waist, coming to rest on the bareness of her back, its contact searing through her body. His right hand released her wrist and travelled up to her white throat to caress the side of her neck just below her ear. She knew she had only to lift her head slightly to his face, but she couldn't. Very gently, his thumb slid under her chin, forcing her head up. Stacy's eyes didn't travel any farther than his mouth that was slowly descending upon her own.

At the first touch of his lips upon hers, she stiffened, not wanting to give in to their gentle demands. But soon, as Cord's ardour continued, she succumbed rapturously—begging, then demanding, the passion coursing her body at the answering hunger in his embrace. Who would have dreamed that Cord would kiss her in this way? Lydia, yes, but Stacy? Lydia! With a start Stacy came to her senses. Cord wasn't kissing her, not with this much passion. He was pretending she was

Lydia! Briskly she broke from his arms, standing terrified in front of him, ashamed of what he must surely guess. His face was at first soft as he looked down at her until the panic-stricken expression on her face registered. Immediately Cord's eyes blazed with fire as he turned abruptly away, his immense chest rising and falling at a rapid rate.

'We seem to have got carried away by our conversation,' he said roughly, removing a cigarette from his case and lighting it.' 'Our thoughts were obviously far apart.'

With an audible sigh of relief, Stacy realized he was mistaking her submission and acceptance of his kiss as a pretence that for her, he too was someone else.

'Luckily we both know what we feel towards one another, so there isn't any need to feel embarrassed,' he added, refusing to look at the unmoving girl beside him.

'No, thank goodness,' Stacy replied with a shaky laugh. 'It could have proved very awkward otherwise.'

She moved a step away from him, her body still trembling uncontrollably from his kiss, the initial magic of his lips destroyed by the knowledge that she was only a substitute for Lydia Marshall.

'I imagine it's getting rather late,' Cord said quietly. 'I suppose we ought to be turning in.'

'I am rather tired,' Stacy replied, grasping the straw he offered. 'I'll see you in the morning.'

With as much poise as she could muster, she walked out of the veranda into the living room. Cord followed a few paces behind, but as he entered the living room the phone rang. At the bottom of the stairs, Stacy heard him answer it.

'Harris Ranch, Cord speaking.—Yes, Lydia, I left the meeting a bit earlier than I'd planned. I intended

146

to call you but——' Stacy didn't wait to hear more.

With a cry, Stacy rushed up the stairs. She couldn't bear to hear him talking to Lydia. It was going to be difficult enough to face him tomorrow without increasing her pain tonight.

CHAPTER TEN

THREE days had passed since that fateful evening with Cord. There were faint circles around Stacy's brown eyes and a slight drawnness in the full mouth, indicating the sleepless nights and tension-filled days. Cord had repeatedly ignored her, no longer checking with her every day as he had done before. In fact, twice when Stacy had been out walking and had seen him in the distance, he had changed direction to take himself out of her path. A crushing sense of defeat had closed in on her as she realized that he couldn't even stand to see her.

Abruptly, Stacy rose from the desk, refusing to let the melancholy within her interfere with her work. The sale was only a week away and there was a great deal still to be done. She was grateful that her time would be so occupied with the auction that she wouldn't be able to dwell on her own problems.

There was a light rap at the door to which Stacy called out for whoever was there to 'come in'. The oak door to the den swung wide to admit the vivacious form of Lydia Marshall.

'I'm not interrupting you, am I? Because if you're very busy, I'll just stay a minute.' An effusive quality in her low voice caused Stacy to cringe inwardly.

'No, not at all,' Stacy replied quietly, taken aback at the unexpected arrival. 'What can I help you with?'

'Nothing really. I just thought you might have time for some coffee and a little chat.'

'Certainly,' Stacy agreed, wondering what in heaven's name they were going to talk about. 'Just a minute and I'll ask Maria to bring some coffee. Would you care for a roll or anything?'

'I hope you don't mind, but I already asked her to bring some on the chance that you would be free,' came the quick reply, followed by a throaty laugh that grated the back of Stacy's neck.

'How thoughtful of you,' Stacy answered with a smile that didn't quite reach her eyes. Seating herself in the chair behind the desk, she continued, 'It's seldom that I have the time to take a coffee break. It will be a pleasant change.'

'I thought as much,' said Lydia, rising from her chair as the plump Mexican woman entered the room carrying the coffee service. 'I'll take that, Maria. I didn't order any sweet rolls. Did you want any, Stacy? I have to watch my figure, so I decline.' At the negative nod of Stacy's head, Lydia dismissed the rotund woman with a curt 'thank you'.

The proprietorial air that Lydia had adopted irked Stacy, and with difficulty she managed to accept the cup of steaming coffee offered her.

'Oh, before I forget,' Lydia exclaimed, reaching down beside her chair for her purse, 'I was by the printer's, and I remembered Cord mentioning something about needing the proof for the catalogue so I picked it up. I hope you don't mind. He mentioned how hard you were working, and I thought I'd save you a trip into town.'

'Thank you,' Stacy said coolly, accepting the pamphlet. 'Unfortunately I still have to go into town for some other things. I'm sure Mr. Harris will appreciate it, though.'

'Well, I knew how upset he was over it,' the smiling Lydia went on. 'I hope he didn't get too difficult. I know what a temper he sometimes has.'

The familiarity oozed out of Lydia's red lips, no doubt making sure that Stacy fully understood just exactly how friendly Lydia was with Cord. An anger slowly began to burn within her.

'Naturally, he was upset,' Stacy said firmly, 'as I was, but everything's under control now. It was merely a lack of communication.'

'I'm glad to hear it.' An icy glare was in Lydia's black eyes. 'I offered to help with some of the work, but Cord assured me that, at this time, it wouldn't look right. Besides, he thought you were doing an adequate job.'

Stacy's cheeks flamed at the emphasis of the word 'adequate'. The sickening knowledge that she had been casually discussed during one of their conversations lay heavy within her. The solicitous tone of Lydia's words coated the coldness that was enveloping her heart with a bittersweet veneer.

'Mr. Harris indicated that your present—er—circumstances wouldn't allow you to take too active an interest in the actual arrangements of the affair,' Stacy murmured quietly, wondering where she found the voice to speak at all.

Lydia's dark eyes narrowed as she smiled and said, 'Then Cord did explain a little of the problems we face.' With a disconcerted sigh, she went on, 'It's common knowledge how we've always felt for each other, despite my foolishness that got me into this mess. I wonder now how I could have been so naïve as to trade in all this for a sun that shines the same on the Riviera as it does here. I assure you, Stacy, it's a crushing blow to discover that to your husband you're no more than another possession to be dressed and displayed like a masterpiece by Renoir. If I hadn't known that Cord had promised that he'd always be here, I don't know how I would have made it this far. I guess it's knowing that my future is secure once again in Cord's hands. And it's just a matter of time and it all will be made official.'

Stacy didn't know if she could take much more of this conversation. She didn't want to know all their 'wonderful' plans. It was all she could do to contain herself and not jump up and pace the floor in desperation. Why was Lydia discussing this with her at all? Aloud Stacy managed to say something about how wonderful it was that everything was working out for them.

'Yes, it is,' Lydia replied, but her eyes were studying the flustered Stacy coldly. 'I'm so glad you see it that way. As attractive as Cord is, a lot of girls in your place would have developed a crush on him.'

'Mr. Harris and I rarely discuss anything but business,' Stacy answered numbly, trying to keep the emotion out of her voice. 'It would require a great deal of imagination to read more into his attentions towards me than actually exists.'

'You do understand I would dislike seeing you hurt accidentally when it could be so easily avoided. I know Cord feels a certain responsibility for you, and I wouldn't want to see you interpret it wrongly,' Lydia smiled smugly as she rose to place her coffee cup near the silver service. 'Well, I really mustn't keep you any more. I know you have a lot to do, and if I can help you in any way, please call me.'

'Of course,' Stacy replied, the smile on her lips stifling the pain in her chest, knowing that Lydia was the last person she would look to for assistance, and had the distinct impression that Lydia knew it.

Glumly she stared at the catalogue proof in front of her. Mechanically she leafed through the pages, her mind racing back to Lydia's words. 'Cord feels a certain responsibility for you, and I wouldn't want you to interpret it wrongly.' If only she could! If only she could read more into his actions than what they were. Responsibility? He had always acted as if she was a liability. It was a miracle he considered her at all.

Arousing herself from her thoughts, Stacy began rummaging through the drawers of the big oak desk looking for the copy of the proof supplied to the printer. She finally found it in one of the lower drawers and began the task of proof-reading the long list of quarter horses complete with their registration numbers, sires, and dams. It was tedious, but at least it required her full concentration and the floating image of the rugged Cord couldn't distract her. Flipping one of the pages over, Stacy straightened with a start. Mixed in among the papers was a piece of stationery with the letterhead of 'Lindsey, Pierce & Mills, Attorneys at Law'. The words fairly leaped off the page at her. Shocked, she glanced at the signature at the bottom of the letter. 'Carter Mills, Sr.'! What was a letter from Mr. Mills doing in Cord's desk? Drawn by the unexpectedness of the familiar letterhead and signature, Stacy began reading.

It was addressed to Mr. Cord Harris, Circle H Ranch, McCloud, Texas, and started out 'Dear Mr. Harris':

Miss Stacy Adams, the daughter of a client, has

151

rented a cabin located on your property. In writing this letter, I am stepping out of my sphere of authority. I would like to impose on you by asking that you keep a close watch over her.

The recent death of her father, a close personal friend, has left Miss Adams without any living relatives. Her father left her a very substantial income so that she is financially secure for the rest of her life. Unfortunately she has been very pampered in the past. Despite my protestations she has insisted on this self-imposed exile to recover from her grief. A stubborn and strong-willed young woman, her cosmopolitan raising has not prepared her for the rigours of western Texas, nor the dangers a young woman alone may face.

She has refused to discuss the length of her stay, insisting that it is indefinite. I would appreciate it, if it is at all possible, Mr. Harris, if you could persuade her to return. If she will not, I ask you to accept responsibility for her. I have enclosed a cheque which I hope will cover any inconvenience caused. I remain

Sincerely yours,
Carter Mills, Sr.

'No!' Stacy whispered, staring at the scrawled signature at the bottom of the page. The red-tinged eyes that had shed tears so readily before were as dry as her lips as the horrible truth began to dawn on her. The letter explained so many things. Why Cord had been so hostile the first day they met, advising her that she should return to the refuge of the city life she was accustomed to. Why he had felt so responsible when she had taken that fall off Diablo and insisted that she stay at his ranch to recover. And when she was well, the episode with Diablo had conveniently given him an excuse to keep her here. It was also the reason he was so concerned about one of his hands taking advantage of her. It was all so clear now. He had undertaken the job of guardian when she came and that was all she meant to him.

Lydia's words washed over her again, 'Cord feels responsible for you'. 'Oh, God,' Stacy thought, 'he must have told her, too.' Her humiliation grew clearer and clearer. How he must wish she was gone! Shamed and hurt, Stacy rose from her chair and stumbled around the desk, groping for some release from her misery. No tears fell on the drawn, pinched face as she made her way out the front door. The hurt went too deep to be salved by the shedding of a few tears. Waves of nausea swept over her as she stared numbly at the buildings and surrounding hillsides. A hesitant breeze fingered the tendrils of her chestnut hair as she stood immobile on the concrete walk.

A plump brown hand touched Stacy's arm. 'Are you okay?' came the concerned voice of the housekeeper.

Slowly Stacy turned and managed a weak smile before she replied, 'Yes, I'm fine, Maria. I just needed a breath of fresh air, that's all.'

'You don't look so good,' the Mexican woman shook her head as she followed Stacy into the house. 'Maybe you should take a little siesta?'

'I'll be all right,' Stacy returned a little impatiently. More quietly she added, 'I'm fine, really. It was just a bit stuffy in there.'

Pride and a sense of fatalism squared Stacy's shoulders as she went back inside, opened the door of the den, and entered. An unnatural calm had settled over her that walled the pain apart from her consciousness. If she could maintain this stoical control of her emo-

153

tions, she would be able to face the long week that lay ahead of her. At her first opportunity, she would announce to Cord that she would be returning East as soon as the auction was over. That would release him from any false sense of responsibility that he felt and remove her from his life for ever. Bleakly she replaced the lawyer's letter in the lower drawer and began mechanically rechecking the catalogue.

That evening Stacy was on her way down the stairs when she saw Cord talking with Maria in the foyer. The starchy freshness of his blue shirt and the sharp crease of his darker blue trousers indicated his plans to be gone that night. Still possessed by the stupor that had engulfed her earlier, she walked up to him. Poised, she stood waiting until his conversation with Maria was finished.

'Did you want to speak to me?' Cord's voice resounded harshly in her ears.

'Yes, if you can spare the time,' Stacy returned just as crisply, ignoring the uncontrollable racing of her heart. His dark eyes rested inquiringly on her pale, drawn face.

'What is it you wanted?'

'I merely wanted to let you know that as soon as this auction affair is over, I'll be returning home,' Stacy answered quietly but firmly.

An eyebrow raised sharply as his brown eyes hardened speculatively. 'This is rather sudden, isn't it?' he said, and without waiting for her reply, added, 'I take it you're not asking my permission.'

'No.'

'I see,' Cord snapped. The sharp coldness sent an involuntary shiver through the haggard Stacy. 'I didn't expect you'd last this long.'

The morning sun was high over the mountains before Stacy wakened the next day. She had cried herself to sleep the night before, but with sleep had come the endurance to face tomorrow. Mechanically she removed her dress, crumpled from being slept in, showered, dressed, and went downstairs for breakfast. As she gazed out the window of the dining room, the distant hills beckoned her. It was the week-end and there wasn't much Stacy could do for the auction. She decided to spend the day riding the hills. She wasn't up to another confrontation with Cord and this would be by far the easiest way to avoid him. With instructions to Maria to fix her a cold lunch, she hurried upstairs to change into her riding skirt and boots.

A few minutes later she was walking out of the front door, her hat swinging from one hand, her lunch in the other. There was no lightness in her step, but her stride was firm. Reaching the stables, she walked to the paddock where the sorrel was held. Diablo danced forward to meet her and nibbled playfully at her arm as she put on his halter.

She waved a greeting to Hank riding by the stables. Thankfully he was busy and didn't stop to chat. His eyes were far too sharp and she didn't want to be put through another ordeal. The niggling sense of defeat was too painful a reminder without talking about it.

Diablo was full of fire, prancing and side-stepping in defiance of his rider's efforts to hold him at a walk. Four people walked around the corner of the stable. Stacy's attention was concentrated on holding the spirited sorrel and guiding him to the pasture gate. She managed a cursory glance in their direction. Two ranch hands were walking in front of Cord Harris and Lydia. A stifled oath came from Cord as he pushed past the hands and ran towards the mounted rider.

The sudden movement towards Diablo startled the sorrel, spooking him into a half rear as he tried to turn in the direction of the approaching figure.

Before Stacy could utter a protest, Cord was by her side, grabbing her by the waist and pulling her off the horse while the other hand had a tight hold on the reins of the panicking stallion. Setting her roughly on the ground, he ordered one of the hands to hold the horse.

'What in the hell were you doing on that horse?' he blazed.

'I was going for a ride, if it's any of your business!' Stacy retorted, her own temper rising at the undignified treatment she had just received.

'You're damn right it's my business!' Cord raged, grabbing her wrist and twisting it to force her closer to him. 'Isn't one fall enough for you, or would you rather get killed the next time?'

'That was an accident. It would have happened no matter what horse I was riding,' her own eyes flashed in anger. 'I own that horse. He's mine, and you have no right——'

'I have every right in the world as long as I'm responsible for what happens to you while you're on this ranch,' Cord interrupted coldly, releasing her wrist with a scornful sweep of his hand. 'And as long as you're on this ranch, you're not going near that devil.'

'Thank heavens, I won't be here long!' Stacy returned sharply. Her anger was reaching a point where the powerful, intimidating man did not awe her. 'And you'd better think of a way to keep me away from that horse, because he's mine and I intend to ride him any time I please!'

In the background Stacy could see the contemptuous eyes of Lydia Marshall mocking her childish display. But her irritation with Cord's dictatorial manner and his overworked sense of responsibility ignored the malice that glinted through the black eyes. Approaching the small group from the hacienda was a tall man dressed in a blue sport outfit. There was something familiar about his walk, but Stacy's attention was directed back by Cord's voice.

'I'll lock you in the house if I have to, but you're not riding that horse. There's plenty of other mounts available if you want to ride,' Cord answered, his voice lowering in an attempt to curb his anger.

'No, thank you,' Stacy said sarcastically, turning sharply on her heel to walk in the direction of the dancing stallion.

The raised voices and angry tones had incensed the hot-blooded horse and his flashing white feet drummed the ground in a staccato rhythm. A rolling white eye glanced back to catch a flicker of movement. Pulling at the lead rope held by the ranch hand, Diablo reared slightly and just as swiftly came down and lashed out with his back feet at the unidentified person behind him. But just as quickly, Cord reacted, pulling Stacy away from the menacing hooves.

Holding her back and shoulders tightly against his broad chest, he muttered in her ear, 'You are the most stubborn woman I've ever known!'

The sudden and unexpected physical contact with Cord swept Stacy's breath away. She felt her knees trembling and her heart racing away with his nearness. She could only hope he would attribute it to the close call she had with the spirited horse. She was too weak to step away from him, cherishing the strength of his arms and the mild aroma of cologne from his freshly shaved face. Cord turned her around, keeping his hands firmly on her shoulders. His expression was

157

grave as he unhurriedly surveyed the pallor in her face.

'I've never met anyone in my life who needed a good spanking more than you,' he growled, releasing her and turning to the waiting group.

'Hear, hear!' came the laughing agreement of the stranger standing beside Lydia.

The happy baritone voice broke through the mist of tears that had taken possession of Stacy's brown eyes. Of course! She should have recognized him. With a broken sob, she rushed past Cord to the waiting stranger.

'Carter, Carter! I'm so glad to see you,' she cried, throwing herself in the young man's arms. Her voice was slightly muffled as she pressed her head against Carter's chest, but her unexpected greeting had brought Cord up short.

'Hey there, honey,' said Carter, surprised at the affectionate welcome he was receiving. Instinctively, his hand reached up to stroke the top of her head. 'If I'd known I'd be welcomed like this, I would have come a long time ago!'

Brushing away the tears that had trickled down her cheeks, Stacy stepped away and looked up into the gentle blue eyes. The suddenness of Carter's appearance combined with the unsettling contact with Cord had robbed her of her control. She realized that Carter had misinterpreted her welcome, but she was too relieved at having someone she could depend on here. His presence represented a refuge from the storm of emotions that was buffeting her around to the point of exhaustion.

'I take it you two know each other,' Lydia commented dryly, breaking the silence that had settled over the small group.

Embarrassed by her emotional greeting, Stacy

blushed slightly before turning to introduce Carter. She stammered an introduction to Lydia, overlooking an arched eyebrow and smug smile on the woman's face. Lydia offered a smooth manicured hand to Carter and one of her intense gazes while Cord stepped forward to complete the circle. His dark eyes were icy cold as Stacy started to introduce Carter to him, but Carter interposed before she could begin.

'Mr. Harris, I'm glad to meet you,' said Carter, grasping Cord's right hand firmly. 'I never thought I'd see the day that anyone would be able to refuse to let Stacy ride that horse and make it stick. I want to thank you for myself and my father for looking after her so well.'

'I won't mislead you by saying that it was an easy job. Miss Adams is a very strong-willed girl,' Cord answered dryly. 'Will you be staying long?'

'Only as long as it takes me to convince Stacy to come back with me,' Carter smiled, glancing tenderly down at the chestnut head beside him, 'hopefully, as my fiancée.'

CHAPTER ELEVEN

STACY had been covertly watching Cord's face, protected mentally by the young man standing beside her, but at Carter's statement Cord's eyes flashed their fire upon her.

'Isn't it wonderful, Cord?' Lydia gushed, her malicious eyes flicking over Stacy briefly before she smiled up at Cord and took his arm. 'What a romantic conclusion for a reunion! It's really just perfect, isn't it?'

'Yes, it is,' Cord agreed, but his voice sounded husky as if he was struggling to control his temper.

No one seemed interested in Stacy's answer to the public proposal, not that she would have offered one if she had been asked. But it grated her that everyone was taking an affirmative answer as a matter of course.

'Carter, I'm in charge of the annual sale of registered quarter horses that Mr. Harris has every year. It's this coming Saturday. Will you be able to stay until then?' Stacy asked, anxious to change the subject.

'Oh, Stacy, you don't have to let a little thing like that stop you,' Lydia inserted quickly before Carter could answer. 'I'm sure it would be perfectly all right if I stepped in for you. After all, it would be an emergency of sorts.'

The last sentence was directed more or less at Cord. Stacy had the distinct impression that Lydia was only too anxious to get her out of the way and the sooner the better. It was all Stacy could do to keep a sigh of relief from escaping her lips when she heard Cord's reply.

'It's too late to make any replacements. The sale is too close and it would mean unnecessary confusion. I don't believe it's all that vital that Miss Adams return immediately,' Cord answered, his cold eyes turning on Carter as if daring him to disagree.

'No, of course not,' Carter added hurriedly. 'As a matter of fact, Dad gave me a week to persuade you to come back with me. We'll just call it a little vacation.' The young lawyer exchanged a conspiratorial smile with Stacy before turning back to Cord. 'Is there a hotel in town where I could stay? I'd like to get settled in.'

'There's no need to stay in town,' Lydia began.

160

'No, you can stay here,' Cord interrupted, silencing the polite protest Carter had started to make with a wave of his hand. 'There's plenty of room at the hacienda. If you'll excuse us, I have some work to do, and I believe you mentioned that you had a luncheon engagement, didn't you, Lydia?'

With a firm hand on Lydia's elbow, Cord manoeuvred her away from the standing couple. Silence descended over Carter and Stacy as he surveyed her quietly.

'You never did answer my question. It wasn't exactly a question, though, was it?' the soft voice asked. 'Don't answer it now either. I'll ask it again later when the setting is a little more romantic. Right now you can direct me to my room and tell me all the "tall Texas tales" you've learned.'

With a nervous laugh, Stacy joined hands with Carter before moving towards the hacienda. Eagerly she related the happenings since her arrival, many of them taking on a humorous aspect on their recounting. Entering the adobe building, she ushered him to one of the spare rooms down the hall from hers, after suggesting that he meet her at the pool in half an hour.

Stacy was floating lazily on her back in the pool when Carter surfaced from his dive beside her. The pair swam round for an hour before pulling themselves up on the side, happy and exhausted.

Stacy studied Carter's lithe, tanned body through lowered lashes. His light, almost blond hair was still wet from the swim and his smooth, unlined face seemed unusually young when she compared it to the rugged, sculptured features of Cord. Soberly Stacy realized Carter wasn't as indomitable as he had seemed before, but she had fallen easily into their old comradeship, unable to let him know the change that had

161

taken place in her, the difference in her thinking.

'I know about the letter your father sent to Mr. Harris before I came out here,' Stacy said quietly, and noticed that Carter had the grace to redden.

'You understand that Dad was concerned about you,' Carter commented, squinting his blue eyes at the sun. 'As it turned out, we can be glad he did. I didn't know anything about it until after you were hurt.' Turning to study Stacy, he asked, 'What made you stay here—this auction?'

With as little detail as possible, Stacy explained the incident with Diablo, glossing over as much as she could Cord's antagonistic attitude towards her. Mischievous amusement spread over Carter's face when she finished, taking an impish delight at the implied humiliation.

'Imagine you out there chasing cows! That's too much!' he chuckled.

'Well, it wasn't too funny at the time,' Stacy retorted, unable to keep from bristling at his teasing. 'You don't exactly have a choice when Mr. Harris issues an ultimatum.'

'I rather got that impression this afternoon,' Carter said, sobering slightly, but a devilish gleam remaining in his blue eyes. 'I don't think patience is one of his virtues.'

'Hardly,' Stacy replied grimly. 'And he certainly doesn't have any patience where I'm concerned. I still think it was beastly of your father to write that letter, especially without telling me. When I remember some of the terrible things I said and did because I thought Cord was nothing but an arrogant tyrant who enjoyed ordering people about——'

'You mean he doesn't?'

'No. That is——' she stammered, struggling to find

162

the right words to explain her change of attitude without giving her true feelings away.

'Never mind,' Carter laughed, rising to his feet. 'I don't care what he is or does. He managed to keep you off that horse and in one piece until I could collect you. For all I care he could be Billy the Kid. Now, I'm going to change before this Texas sun of yours turns me into a lobster.'

The following night, as Stacy dressed for dinner, she dreaded the evening to come. She had hoped with Carter here that she would be able to put Cord in the back of her mind, but Cord had very successfully squashed that. Since her brief conversation with Carter alone the previous afternoon, Cord had been around constantly. If he didn't actually take part in their conversations, he was in an adjoining room. Either way his presence thwarted any attempts for privacy that Stacy and Carter might have made.

Carter had jumped at the dinner invitation when Stacy passed it on to him. His enthusiasm coupled with her earlier agreement left no way for her to back out. The anguish Cord's nearness would surely cause made her wonder if she derived some sort of bizarre pleasure from her torment. Each day that went by brought her closer to the time she would leave for good, thereby turning each glimpse of the virile man into a cherished memory to last the eternity she would be alone.

Willowy and delicate, like something out of a misty dream, Stacy descended the stairs to where Carter Mills and Cord Harris waited in their white dinner jackets. Carter didn't speak, but the admiration in his blue eyes sparkled a compliment that was more eloquent than words. Hesitantly Stacy looked into Cord's face for an affirmation of Carter's approval, but the dark eyes were masked and his opinion unrevealed, while the agitated twitching of the jaw muscle marred the still, stone-like quality of his brown face. Regretting that she had sought his praise, Stacy turned back to her escort.

'Are we ready?' she asked.

'And willing,' smiled Carter, possessively clasping his other hand over the delicate one on his arm.

A sleek and shiny brown Continental was parked in the drive. Stacy slid into the back seat behind the driver and waited nervously for Carter to walk around the car to join her. Apprehensively she glanced into the rear-view mirror to meet Cord's dark, enigmatical eyes that quickly looked away. The fair lawyer climbed in beside Stacy while Cord started the motor and manoeuvred the luxury car out of the drive. The conversation was sketchy during the journey to Lydia's, with Stacy too conscious of the dark head in front of her to do anything but pretend an interest in the scenery racing by.

'You're very quiet tonight,' commented Carter after they had parked and Cord had gone into the house to collect Lydia. 'Is something wrong?'

'No, of course not,' Stacy returned, a grateful smile on her face for the concern in Carter's eyes. How could she explain that the proximity of the driver upset her? 'I enjoy looking at the land, especially when the sunset is so close. It gives everything a mysterious peace.'

'That's my girl,' Carter muttered with a mocking shake of his head. 'Here she sits beside a man who's travelled halfway across the country to see her and she's admiring the scenery.'

'Oh, Carter, you know I'm glad you're here,' Stacy laughed, fully aware of the comfort his presence was to her.

'But I wonder if you're glad because it's me or because it's an old friend.' A sadly, serious expression was in his blue eyes as he gazed at her astutely.

Stacy's protest was arrested by the approach of a white-jacketed Cord with Lydia clutching his arm. There was a satisfied smile on his face as he gazed down at the chic woman. Stacy's heart experienced a painful tug as her brown eyes flashed a jealous green. Lydia's raven black hair fell loosely about her creamy white neck, accenting the sensuous décolleté of her lilac satin gown hanging precariously by two slim rhinestone straps.

As pleasantries were exchanged, Lydia glanced at Stacy's ring hand and then looked at Carter petulantly. 'I thought we were going to have something to celebrate tonight. Or did you forget to bring a ring along to make the announcement official?'

Carter managed a joking, noncommittal reply which escaped Stacy, whose attention was caught and held by Cord's intense gaze in the mirror. She felt the colour rising in her cheeks at the inquisitive and derisive expression in his deep brown eyes. Unwilling to take part in the conversation between Lydia and Carter, Stacy again forced her attention outside the glass windows. She managed to keep the jealousy and bitter pain from showing itself for Cord's mocking eyes to see.

Arriving at their destination, Stacy became enchanted with the rambling two-storey building nestled in a sylvan setting of pine trees and lush greenery. As the foursome entered the restaurant area, the host greeted Cord by his first name and ushered the group personally to a secluded table.

Carter held out the chair on Cord's left for Stacy, his hand lingering briefly on the filmy silk covering her

165

shoulder. The reassurance of his touch quieted the nervous tremor in her heart. With a still hand, she raised her champagne glass with the others as Carter made a toast.

'To Texas.'

'And the happy reunion of those who've been separated,' Lydia added, her gaze taking in Cord's profile possessively before turning to include the other couple.

Stacy was relieved when the dinner was served and over. At least in the lounge the entertainment would force conversation to the minimum. Leaving the table, Stacy and Carter followed the other couple into the lounge. Stacy's eyes were riveted on Cord's dark hair curling above the collar of his white dinner jacket. As if conscious of her inspection, he turned, gazing mysteriously for a moment into her startled brown eyes before speaking.

'I hope you won't be too disappointed in the band. The group is mainly Mexican in extraction, so you'll find the music has a Latin-Western flavour rather than the beat you're accustomed to.'

Inwardly Stacy flinched at the subtle undertone of censure that laced Cord's words. His opinion of her was so low already that it seemed useless to protest this statement. Without replying she and Carter followed them to a table. As soon as the cocktail waitress had taken their order, Carter asked Stacy to dance. She quickly obliged, happy to leave the disconcerting company of Cord and Lydia. Three guitars played the strains of an old ballad to the gentle tempo of drums. As she matched the familiar pattern of Carter's steps, a spray of confidence returned to Stacy.

'What's the matter with you tonight?' Carter asked suddenly, his blue eyes examining her face intensely. 'I have the feeling you're afraid or hiding something.'

166

Startled by his unexpected frankness, Stacy missed a step. A numbness seized her throat as hundreds of protests flashed through her mind, but before she summoned one, Carter went on.

'I don't think I want you to answer me. I think you'd lie or maybe not tell me the whole truth.' His tone was extremely serious. 'It would hurt too much either way. Stacy, if you ever want to tell me what's wrong, I'll be here no matter what.'

'Carter, I——'. Stacy began, tears of misery welling in her brown eyes.

'Sssh! We won't talk any more. Maybe later when we're alone, but not now,' he whispered in her hair, and drew her closer into the comfort of his arms.

When the last strains of the ballad faded away, the group struck up a bouncier tune and the young couple remained on the floor. The knowledge of Carter's affection gave Stacy a crutch to cling to and the ability to return to the table with a more sincere smile on her face. Despite the invisible support of Carter, the evening dragged. The mocking tone and twisted smile of Cord whenever he addressed her made Stacy nervous and the triumphant glitter in Lydia's eyes fanned the ache that throbbed so close to the surface. The envious lump in her throat swelled whenever she watched Cord dancing with the sultry black-haired woman. Towards the end of the evening, Carter asked Lydia to dance, leaving Stacy alone with Cord.

'They dance well together,' Stacy commented with an attempt at nonchalance as she watched Carter and Lydia fall into step. Cord gleamed back at her, an unamused smile that flickered briefly with an emotion that Stacy couldn't quite recognize.

'Jealous?' the low baritone voice spoke. 'Lydia is a very beautiful woman.'

'No, of course not,' Stacy returned, but there was a tremulous catch in her voice as she spoke. She was jealous of Lydia, but not for the reason Cord was thinking.

'Shall we dance?' Cord asked softly as he rose and stepped behind her chair.

Naturally she would refuse. Why punish herself further by being held in his arms when he desired another? What could it possibly accomplish but more heartache? But not a word of protest had passed her lips as she found herself in his arms on the dance floor. There was no retreat now and the glow that radiated unconsciously from her upturned face laughed at the recrimination of her conscience. The firm hand on the small of her back was strangely exciting and the tender brown eyes that looked down upon her made her heart race with uncontrollable happiness. At this moment it didn't matter whether he was dancing with her out of pity or courtesy. Her hand tightened imperceptibly in Cord's and with a gentle smile in his eyes he drew her closer to his broad chest until her brown head nestled against his shoulder. Ignorant of the melody of the song the band was playing, the conversation of the dancers around them, oblivious to anything but the thrilling nearness of Cord, Stacy danced in silence, capturing the sensation of the rhythmic sway of his hips, the gentle pressure of his body against hers, the firm clasp of his hand and the caress of his breath on her hair.

The dance over, as if by previous arrangement, Cord immediately suggested calling it an evening. Torn apart by the emotions that threatened to surface from his nearness and the hopelessness of her love, Stacy quickly agreed.

168

The ride home had been a silent one. Looking back on it two days later, Stacy tried to analyse the reason. Carter had been unusually quiet. In the past they had often spent hours without talking, but this time there was an uneasiness about him, as if he was grappling with a problem he didn't know how to handle. And Cord had answered Lydia's sentences so abruptly that even she fell to silence. It had been a relief when the Continental had finally turned into the ranch drive and Stacy had escaped to the sanctity of her room.

Carter had been his old self the next morning, laughing and joking as before. After volunteering to help Stacy with the auction arrangements, he had pitched in with a familiar gusto, running errands into town, checking with Hank regarding the yearlings, and taking some of the more time-consuming tasks off Stacy's hands. Cord had reverted to his old habit of unexplained absences. The past two days he had practically avoided Stacy and Carter, joining them only once for dinner Monday evening and leaving immediately afterwards. He had not mentioned where he was going, but later that evening Stacy had seen a light burning late at the ranch office. Lydia hadn't been over either, which surprised Stacy as the divorcee had almost become a fixture at the ranch since her return.

Removing the paper from the carriage of the typewriter, Stacy forced her thoughts to return to the business at hand. Her morning had been consumed with last-minute requests for circulars of the auction. This one was finally the last. Slipping the information into an envelope and stamping it, she placed it with a stack of similar letters that awaited Carter's return from the stables. If she was lucky she would have time for a cup of coffee and a cigarette before she had to meet the wives of the ranch hands to go over various details they would be responsible for during the barbecue.

Leaving the den, Stacy walked towards the kitchen to help herself to some coffee. But Maria appeared in the archway between the dining room and living room carrying a small tray with a steaming cup of coffee and a sweet roll on it.

'You are a life-saver,' Stacy smiled. 'I was just going to the kitchen to get myself a cup.'

Maria bubbled her pleasure before adding, 'Weel the Señora Leedia be joining you?'

'Lydia?' Stacy's tone puzzled.

'Si. She just drive up een her car. I theenk perhaps she dreenk too.'

'I don't know——' Stacy began, but was interrupted by the opening and closing of the front door.

'Stacy, good morning. I'm so glad to see you're not busy,' Lydia smiled, entering the living room as Maria left. 'I hoped to have a little chat with you today, but I was afraid you'd be all tied up with Saturday's affair.'

'I'll have to be running off in a few minutes,' Stacy replied, not anxious to have another 'little chat' with Lydia. Their previous discussion was regrettable enough without enduring another.

Gracefully Lydia seated herself in the chair opposite Stacy, smoothing the skirt of her elegantly styled sundress before speaking. 'I don't see any engagement ring. Surely you've put that poor boy out of his misery by now.'

'If you mean Carter,' Stacy said coldly, incensed that Lydia was meddling in something that was none of her business, 'I've been rather busy lately. There's no rush, is there?'

'I wouldn't let him get away from you, if I were you.'

'That's the point, though, isn't it? You're not me.'

170

Lydia's cold eyes flickered ominously for a moment at Stacy's words.

'That's true, but I do have a better view of the situation than you,' she suggested solicitously.

'Why don't you come to the point?' said Stacy, irritated by the phoney concern that Lydia was attempting to project. 'We could talk in circles all day. Fortunately I have better things to do.'

Surprised at Stacy's unexpected audacity, Lydia rose from her chair, walked behind it, then turned her dark head with its glistening coronet of braids towards her.

'You're quite right,' her tone was sarcastic and contemptuous. 'There's no love lost between us, so why pretend? My point is really quite simple—don't withhold your answer from Carter in the hope that Cord will come through with a better offer, because he won't. Do you think that Cord is so blind that he doesn't realize that you've fallen in love with him?'

'Afraid of a little competition, or is your hold so slight over Cord that you can't take the chance?' Stacy retorted, standing to meet the glare of the older woman's challenge.

'Don't be ridiculous!' Lydia exclaimed. 'A more mature woman would be able to recognize the difference between affection and pity. You moped around all Sunday evening and then lit up like a Christmas tree the minute Cord danced with you. Can't you tell that he feels sorry for you, that his over-active sense of responsibility forces him to do these things? I don't know where your sense of pride is or whether you haven't outgrown that cow-eyed teenage stage yet, but either way your presence has managed to influence the plans that Cord and I have made. As ridiculous as it sounds, he doesn't feel he should make his true feelings known for fear of hurting you.'

'As I told Cord and I'll tell you, I'm leaving right after the auction,' retorted Stacy. 'I'll be returning with Carter, so that should end your concern. In a few more days I'll be out of your lives for ever and you and Cord can do whatever you like. In the meantime, I prefer that you leave this house now and stay out of my way in the future,' Stacy's voice trembled with controlled anger. But the truth of Lydia's words cut deep.

The click of triumphant heels echoed through the living room as Lydia left. Numbly Stacy heard her satisfied tone as Lydia exchanged greetings with Carter just entering the house. Walking into the living room, Carter studied Stacy for a second, noting the clenched fists at her side.

'What happened? She looked as if she just tried on the glass slipper and it fitted.'

'Really?' Stacy remarked with unnatural bitterness. Seeing the formation of a question in Carter's eyes, she hurried on, 'I have a meeting now. There's some mail lying on my desk. Will you see that it gets out today?'

Gathering her notebook, she hurried out the door.

The following evening Stacy and Carter went for a late ride after dinner. On their return Stacy chattered away happily with Carter refreshed and relaxed by the sunset ride.

'If you don't mind, I'm going to wash off some of your precious Texas dirt,' said Carter as they reached the front door of the hacienda. 'I'll meet you on the patio for a drink in half an hour.'

'A deal,' Stacy smiled, preceding him upstairs to her own room.

A short time later she joined him on the veranda. He was sitting quietly on one of the settees rubbing the ears of the German Shepherd abstractedly as he stared off into the deep ebony of the night. Seeing his mistress, Cajun pattered happily over to her side as Carter rose to meet her. Taking the hand extended to her, the chestnut-haired girl contentedly let herself be drawn into the settee beside him.

'It didn't take you very long,' Carter smiled. 'I thought I'd be able to sneak in an extra drink before you got here,' indicating a tray of tall glasses on the side table.

'At least you saved one for me,' Stacy teased, cradling an icy drink in her hands as she gazed into the midnight curtain of evening. 'It's a gorgeous night. I wonder where all the stars are?'

'If I were a proper lover, I would say they were all in your eyes.'

'Oh, Carter!' Stacy laughed protestingly, leaning against the back of the cushion.

Tenderly he cupped her chin in his hand, his face sombre in its study of her sobering expression.

'I wish I could say that and know it to be true,' he said, releasing her and rising abruptly.

Stuffing his hands in his pockets, Carter walked over by the pillar and gazed into the distance. Stacy fidgeted nervously with the pocket on her orange and yellow shift. The truth of his statement brought back the despair she fought so hard to subdue.

'Do you know how I've planned for this evening ever since I arrived?' A strange, bitter quality was in his voice that Stacy had never heard before. 'Here we are, all alone with not a soul to bother us. The setting is perfect, the black night shutting out the world, a couple of stars winking their encouragement, and a beautiful girl, her dark eyes filled with anticipation at the words that are to be said.' The light brown head turned to look back at Stacy. 'Only your eyes aren't

173

filled with anticipation, are they?' He looked down at her. .

Salty tears trickled down her cheeks to her tightly pressed lips as she bent her head from his accusing blue eyes.

'I was going to do it all properly tonight—get down on my knee and say, "Stacy, I love you and I want you to be my wife",' said Carter, his voice almost a monotone. 'Corny, isn't it? I love you, but you see, I'm a proud man. I don't want to possess something that doesn't belong to me. I suppose there are men who would have asked you anyway and taken the chance that they wouldn't be turned down. I'm not asking for an entirely different reason. I'm afraid you might accept, and I couldn't live with you knowing that you're in love with some rancher in Texas.'

Shame and humiliation shook Stacy's slim shoulders at the pain and bitterness she had brought into Carter's world. Rousing out of his mist of self-pity, Carter looked at the silent, sobbing form and walked over to where she sat, a hand moving unsurely towards her head.

'Oh, Stacy, why, why does it have to be this way?' His voice choked as he swept her off the chair into his arms.

'Carter, I wanted to tell you, but I couldn't,' she moaned into his shirt. 'I couldn't hurt you, not when I knew what that pain was like.'

'It'll be all right,' he smiled, drawing comfort from the easing of her pain. 'You know the saying "It only hurts for a little while." '

'I wouldn't have said "yes". I wouldn't have done that to you.'

'No, I think I knew that,' holding her away from him as he wiped her moist cheeks with his hand. 'Inside I knew you were made of a stronger stuff.'

174

'You will stay,' Stacy asked, 'and take me home after the weekend?'

'Of course. Don't you know, my pet, that you can use me any time?' Carter grinned, his smile taking the sting out of his words.

'I don't know what I would have done if you hadn't come when you did. I hadn't the pride to leave nor the strength to stay,' she confessed, nestling under his arm as they walked towards the yawning light from the glass doorway.

A troubled sigh echoed her words as Carter stepped forward to open the door. Hesitating just inside, Stacy turned to wait for him. He had stopped a step behind her, his attention riveted ahead of her. The brittle iciness of his blue eyes startled her and she turned to where he was looking. Cord was standing slightly to her right, a book in one hand and a cigarette in the other. His dark eyes were narrowed in an inscrutable expression as he looked passed Stacy to Carter. Abruptly, Cord turned his head and walked over to an ash-tray where he snubbed his cigarette out viciously.

'You young people are turning in rather early tonight, aren't you?' he taunted.

'It's been a hectic day,' Stacy murmured, starting to the stairway.

'All the arrangements are going along smoothly for the sale on Saturday, aren't they?'

'Of course. If you'd like to go over them now——' Stacy began, stung by the hint of neglect in his words.

'No, that won't be necessary,' Cord interrupted, his dark eyes examining the pinched lines in her face. 'There's time enough in the morning.' His tone curt and dismissive.

'Good night, Mr. Harris,' Carter offered, a little sarcastically.

'Yes, good night, Cord,' Stacy hastened at the sharpening of the rancher's eyes.

'Good night.' His voice followed them out of the room.

CHAPTER TWELVE

'HELLO!' came the call from the hill.

Stacy looked up in answer to see Carter's long legs carrying him down towards her. 'Hi yourself,' she replied with a grin.

'I should have known I'd find you down here,' Carter reproached. 'Don't you realize what time it is? You've been going since eight this morning.'

'It's only half past seven and I have a few things to finish up before tomorrow,' Stacy replied, ignoring the mild rebuke in his voice. 'Linda and Diane decided to set up the tables tonight instead of tomorrow morning. I thought I'd give them a hand. Did you get the things from Molly that Mrs. Grayson needed?'

'And delivered to her already. She shooed me out before I even got to sneak a taste of her famous barbecue sauce,' Carter concluded with a mock grimace. 'What's left to do?'

'Nothing, I hope,' Stacy answered with a nervous look around at the long row of folding tables. Waving a good-bye to the two women who were walking away, she turned to Carter apprehensively. 'Tomorrow will tell the tale. All my mistakes will be blatantly obvious.'

'Where's that girl who always rolls with the

punches?' Carter teased with a twinkle in his eyes. Wrapping an arm around her shoulders, he turned her towards the hacienda, adding, 'Day's done. Let's go and have something cool to drink.'

Stacy laughed in spite of her nervousness. A little relaxation would be in order, especially in the face of the ordeal ahead of her tomorrow. A twinge of pain laced her brown eyes as she considered what this week would have been like if Carter hadn't come. Studying his tanned face out of the side of her eye, she examined the new lines at the corner of his lips. Outwardly there was no change in Carter's attitude towards her and no reference had been made to Wednesday's ill-fated evening.

'Regretting the end coming?' Carter asked quietly, his hand squeezing her arm in comfort.

'No,' Stacy sighed. 'I'll be better off when I'm away from here.' 'And only haunted by Cord's memory,' she added to herself.

The couple skirted the front entrance, going directly to the patio at the side of the adobe structure. While Stacy settled herself on one of the chairs, Carter entered the house to get the drinks. The lowering fiery globe of the western sun failed to lighten Stacy's darkening brown eyes as she gazed around her morosely at the surroundings that had become her home these past few weeks. Drawn by a compulsion she didn't understand, she found herself staring intently at the knoll rising above the house. Distantly she heard the phone ringing in the living room and Carter answering it. Numbly she rose and began walking towards the small hill and the as yet unseen cemetery at the top. She didn't hear Carter call her name nor see his still form standing on the cobblestoned veranda with their drinks in his hands.

She didn't stop until she reached the black, wrought-iron fence that enclosed the graveyard. Ignoring the smaller crosses and markers, she made her way directly to the stone bearing the words 'Elena Teresa Harris'. Slowly she knelt in front of the tombstone until a denim knee touched the earth. One brown hand reached out tentatively and traced the letters gently. Two bright tears trickled down her cheeks as Stacy tried to draw comfort from those Cord had loved. Grief and anguish gripped her heart as she leaned against the silent grey stone.

Again Cord's voice echoed in her ear, but this time it sounded so real that she turned her brown head to look. Her eyes had to be playing tricks on her, for there before her stood Cord. It had to be a dream because when she looked up into his face there was the most peculiar light in his eyes. Suddenly Stacy became conscious of the encroaching shadows among the graves. Looking quickly to where the sun had been, she saw only a crimson glow marking its departure. She wasn't dreaming! The realization that it really was Cord standing before her jumped into her eyes as she turned back to face him. At the change in her expression, the large muscular arm that had started to extend itself towards her returned to Cord's side as she hastily scrambled to her feet.

'What are you doing up here?' Cord questioned, a hint of the softness remaining in his voice as he surveyed the pained, almost guilty look on her face.

'I came up here to——' The truth of her intention almost escaped her lips before Stacy could stop it. Nervously she glanced to the grey stone that marked the grave of Doña Elena before her eyes slid to the marker beside it. 'Your father's grave,' she ended lamely, conscious of the narrowing eyes upon her. 'I was remembering my father and somehow I thought coming up here would make him seem closer.'

Whether he accepted her muffled explanation or not, Stacy couldn't tell. Gripping her arm in his hand, he steered her out of the small cemetery without any further comment. Uneasily Stacy glanced into his face. Whatever he was thinking wasn't reflected there. The few minutes of silence were unbearable for her.

'How did you know where I was?'

'Your boy-friend saw you walking this way,' Cord answered, sarcasm seeping through his voice as his long strides carried them down the hill.

'Oh,' Stacy added faintly, as the steel grip propelled her before him.

She permitted herself a quick look down to the veranda before returning her concentration to the uneven ground beneath her. When they reached the edge of the cobblestones, Cord released her arm as if in distaste. A tight-lipped Carter handed Stacy her drink, his blue eyes examining the white pallor of her face.

'Are you okay? Where were you?' he asked quietly.

Stacy managed to nod an affirmative to the first question before Cord interrupted her. Swallowing a big drink from his glass, he stated in his derisive mocking tone, 'She was using my father's grave as a stand-in for her own.'

Carter's blue eyes studied Stacy's intently for a brief second before dismissing the explanation. But Cord wasn't finished.

'Giving in to self-pity is a luxury that this land doesn't allow, not for the people who live here.' The cold harshness of Cord's dark eyes penetrated Stacy's heart, sending the blood rushing to her face from the wound.

Cord turned away and started walking towards the

area north of the stables where the preparations for the barbecue were going on. Stacy and Carter followed a few steps behind. None of the three spoke on the way. Cord seemed to ignore the fact that they were behind him and Carter only glanced Stacy's way once.

The trio passed the long lines of tables gleaming eerily in the waning light and continued towards the red glow emanating from a nearby stand of grease-wood trees. Cord slowed his pace so the three approached the fire at the same time. A long pit had been dug in the grove and a fire started in it. In the hazy glow, a form moved to shove another log into the fire. Stacy recognized Hank with a smile.

Adjusting her eyes to the flickering light, she studied the ingenious arrangement of the barbecue with interest. Curiosity overwhelmed the feeling of tension that had previously held her silent. 'Are those old beds the meat's on?'

'Army cots,' Cord smiled in answer. 'We wrap the legs in foil to retain the heat. The hands take turns tending the fire through the night and basting the meat with barbecue sauce.'

'Heavens!' Stacy exclaimed as she saw the enormous amount of meat on the metal slate. 'Aren't you going to have too much to eat?'

'We Texans have big appetites,' Hank snorted. 'We don't mess around with those tiny sandwiches like folks back East. If yore gonna sit here and watch the fire, I'll get some other things done,' he finished. As he turned away from the fire, he added to Carter, 'Might as well come along and give me a hand, I ain't as young as I used to be.'

Without waiting for an answer he tottered off into the dark. A twinge of fear clutched Stacy as she realized that Hank intended to leave her alone with Cord.

She knew Carter was staring at her, waiting for her to say something to indicate that she didn't want him to go. She couldn't think of anything to say. With a stifled exclamation, Carter stalked off through the trees after Hank.

Cord was the one who finally broke the silence, his low voice drawling out, 'Well, you'll be leaving in another day. I suppose you're starting to look forward to it.'

'Not really,' Stacy answered truthfully in a quiet and unemotional voice. 'I've really enjoyed myself here.'

There was a slight pause as if Cord was mulling over her reply. 'I imagined you'd be glad to be going back where you belong.'

Involuntarily Stacy stiffened at Cord's phrase. A flash of her old anger returned at his pompous attitude of always knowing what would be best for her. She quelled the urge to make a retort and continued gazing into the fire.

'Have you and Carter set a date for the wedding?' Cord asked, flicking a twig into the fire.

'No. That's something we'll probably do when we get back,' Stacy replied, not letting the hurt seep into her words. Her pride said it was better to let him think that there was going to be a wedding.

'You'll send me an invitation?'

'Of course,' she answered, straightening her legs and leaning back on her hands as she scowled into the fire. 'Are you going to send me one to yours?'

'Mine?' Cord queried, straightening slowly at her words.

'I forgot I wasn't supposed to know,' Stacy answered airily. 'Though why you wanted to keep it from me, I don't know. It's pretty obvious the way Lydia's always

181

over here that there's more than just the burning embers of an old flame.'

'I see,' an amused expression on Cord's face as he stared at the charred legs. 'I suppose Lydia told you.'

'More or less,' she replied. 'She did all but write it on the wall,' she thought to herself. 'Now that you're released from your responsibility for me, you can go your merry way and I can go mine.'

Seeing his dark head turn towards her in surprise she added, 'I know about the letter from Carter's father too.'

'Carter's father? And how do you know?'

'You left the letter in one of the desk drawers. I must say you went to great lengths to see to it that I kept under your watchful eye. It's too bad you didn't let me in on it. We might have got along better if I'd known what was going on.'

'It didn't occur to me. You were a very headstrong girl. I only hope that Carter is successful in combating your more egocentric ideas.' Cord seemed to be secretly amused, which greatly irritated Stacy.

'Carter understands me,' she replied forcefully, lifting her chin defiantly.

'Oh, I'm sure he does,' Cord laughed. 'It's too bad he doesn't have more control over you.'

'If he had, I never would have come here and all this would never have happened.' Stacy's voice trailed off as a hint of melancholy crept into her voice.

'No, it wouldn't have,' Cord agreed quietly, falling silent with her.

The crackling of twigs and rustling branches sounded the return of Hank and Carter.

'Ready to head back?' Carter asked her.

'Might as well,' said Cord, rising and extending a

hand to Stacy before Carter could intervene. 'It's going to be a long day tomorrow.'

The ranchyard was packed with vehicles of every description from elegant El Dorados to broken-down ranch pick-ups. The auction itself had been over for two hours and the exodus of cars had just begun.

Stacy surveyed the long table that had been heaped with food earlier. So little was left of the vast quantities of meat, baked beans, potato salad, coleslaw, and breads that she sighed with relief that the appetites had been gauged so accurately. Already her group of ranch wives had started to clear the tables of left-over food.

'Are you through for the day?' Molly asked, a plump arm reaching out to fill the iced tea glasses.

'I've just been fired,' Stacy laughed, 'and ordered to join the fun.'

'Good. It's mostly all neighbours left now,' said Mary, hooking an arm in Stacy's and propelling her away from the table. 'You're going to witness a good, old-fashioned party.'

'Hey, where are you taking my hostess?' came the questioning laugh from behind them.

Halting abruptly. Stacy paled at the possessive tone in the voice. With a trembling heart, she felt the masculine hand rest on her shoulder.

'Cord!' Mary cried, 'It's about time you got around to your guests. You've been with those horses all day.'

'I see you've managed to extricate Stacy,' he replied, smiling down at the silent form beside him. 'You did a wonderful job, Stacy. I'm sorry I haven't had a chance to tell you earlier or to give you a hand which you didn't need.'

'Thank you,' Stacy stammered, a flush filling her

cheeks at his unqualified praise. 'But everyone has been good to me. I'm sure they covered a lot of my mistakes.'

'You're too modest,' Molly admonished. 'With someone as sweet as you, people just naturally take you to their heart and do everything they can for you.'

Tears pricked the back of Stacy's eyes at the woman's words. Knowing this to be her last day here, Stacy replied softly, 'You've all made me feel as if this is my home and I'll never forget any of you for that.'

Cord's hand tightened on her shoulder and the sudden pain forced Stacy to look into the tanned face. The questioning and confused look in his dark eyes rested on her face momentarily before turning to the other two women.

'This evening's party is doubling as a farewell party for Stacy. She's leaving us in the morning,' Cord stated grimly.

In the midst of the barrage of protests and objections, Stacy experienced a pang of regret at the ambiguous statements she had made about her leaving, always saying 'some time after the barbecue'. If only they knew how little she really wanted to go!

'Why are you leaving so soon?' Mary asked. 'I thought you'd be staying at least another week.'

'Carter has to be back the first of the week, so we decided to go together,' Stacy explained, ignoring the chill coursing through her as Cord removed his hand from her shoulder. 'We can share the driving and the trip won't seem so long.'

'The two of you are going alone?' Molly asked, frowning a little as she glanced at Cord.

'Tch, tch, Molly, you're showing your age,' Cord mocked. 'Remember this is the enlightened generation. Our moral codes are a little old-fashioned for them. Excuse me, I think it's time I mingled with some of the other guests.'

Despite the light tone of Cord's voice as he had chided Molly, Stacy caught the underlying thread of bitterness in his words. Embarrassed by the implication, she faced the two women self-consciously, ignoring the retreating broad shoulders moving through the crowd.

'Have you decided to marry Carter?' Mary asked lightly as the sounds of guitars and fiddles drifted towards them.

'No,' Stacy replied without thinking.

'Speak of the devil,' Molly muttered as Stacy glanced around to see the sandy-haired Carter walking towards them. 'So you're taking our favourite girl away from us tomorrow,' Molly scolded.

'How else will I ever get her all to myself?' Carter asked, wrapping an arm around Stacy's shoulders. 'Besides,' he added, noting the hidden pain in Stacy's eyes, 'a change of scenery might be advantageous.'

Stacy missed the glance exchanged between mother and daughter as she looked up into Carter's questioning, blue eyes.

'If you ladies don't mind, I think I'll dance with our hostess,' smiled Carter, possessively moving Stacy in the direction of the strumming guitars.

At the edge of the dance floor, he turned her into his arms. He allowed a few steps to the tempo before speaking.

'What happened back there? I saw Cord leave before I arrived.' His blue eyes studied the troubled look on her face. 'What did he say to make you look like that?'

'It wasn't anything he said,' Stacy murmured absently, catching sight of Cord watching them from the fringe of the crowd. 'It's me, I guess,' she sighed, forcing her eyes to Carter. 'I just don't want to leave. I know it's the right thing to do.'

'Stacy, are you even sure you're in love with him? If I thought I had a chance——' Urgency crowded out all caution as Carter gripped Stacy's shoulders. 'Marry me, honey. I can make you happy, you know that.'

'No, Carter.' The chestnut head shook negatively, agitation and indecision in her voice.

'He's so much older than you. How do you know you're not using him to replace the father you lost?' Carter's voice grew desperate and demanding. 'If I hadn't let you come out here, we'd have been married by now. Can't you see that, Stacy? You need an anchor. Let it be me. Say you'll marry me, Stacy, say it now before you regret it the rest of your life.'

'No!' Stacy fairly shouted, trying to stem the whirlpool of persuasion Carter's words were drawing her into. 'No,' she repeated more emphatically, turning from his arms to face the happy dancing throng before them.

'Think about it, Stacy. How can you be sure?' Carter rushed.

'There you are, Stacy,' came a masculine voice. 'Don't you know it's not proper for the hostess to run off in the middle of the party?'

Through blurring eyes, Stacy recognized the stocky form of Bill Buchanan.

'Doctor!' a frantic trill to her words as he grasped her outstretched hand.

'You don't mind if I steal her for a dance, do you, Carter?' Bill asked, a merry twinkle in his eyes. 'I'm too old to stand in line, and when the rest of the men get a good look at her that's just what I'd have to do.'

The doctor whisked Stacy into the clearing where a

lively tune was filling the air. As Stacy matched his bouncy steps, she momentarily glanced back to where Carter was standing. Her attention was caught by the tall figure standing steps away from him, separated only by the same trees in which she and Carter had sought seclusion moments ago. Forgetting her partner completely, Stacy stood motionless as terror raced through her at the realization that the turbulent fury flashing through Cord's eyes could only be caused by his overhearing her conversation with Carter. Suddenly Cord was moving through the dancers towards her. Hurriedly Stacy turned to her partner, ignoring his puzzled expression as she frantically hoped to lose herself among the other couples.

It was too late. The firm brown hand was gripping her shoulders as Cord expressed an abrupt apology to Dr. Buchanan and, without giving Stacy an opportunity to protest, forced her through the whirling couples. Away from the crowd, Stacy attempted futilely to pull away from Cord's hold.

'Let me go!' she cried desperately.

'Just shut up,' Cord replied sharply. 'You've done too much talking already.'

'It's none of your business what happened between Carter and me.' Stacy's temper flashed in her brown eyes.

'I'll decide what's my business.' The muscle in his jaw twitched as Cord turned her towards the hacienda.

'What do you want from me?' Her voice trembled.

'Some straight answers for a start,' said Cord firmly, his voice threateningly low as a couple crossed in front of them.

Walking on to the veranda, Cord muttered an imprecation as he caught sight of guests gathered by the pool. Without a hesitation in his stride, he turned her towards the knoll above the house. Realizing they were headed for the cemetery, Stacy glanced back at him suspiciously.

'Why are we going up here?' she demanded, slightly winded by the swift pace he was setting.

'It's probably the only place on this damn ranch where there aren't any people,' was the curt answer.

Reaching the top of the rise, he moved ahead, dragging her behind him, until they were out of sight of the people below. They stopped a few feet from the iron fence. Releasing her arm, he took hold of a breathless Stacy's shoulders.

'Why did you lie to me and let me believe you were going to marry Carter?' he demanded.

'What does it matter?' Stacy moaned, trying to wrench herself free of his hold.

'Do you want to go back? Do you want to leave here?' When she failed to answer, he shook her. 'Answer me!'

'No!' she sobbed, fighting the answers he was seeking and the truth she couldn't bear him to know. 'Please, Cord, don't!'

'Why don't you want to leave?'

'B-because——' she stammered. 'Oh, Cord, please let me go.'

'Stacy, I can't, not this time.' His voice was suddenly tender and pleading. 'Not until you tell me the truth. This time you've got to tell the truth.'

Tears ran unchecked down her cheeks as she gazed into his tanned face with disbelief. Desperately she searched for assurance that the loving tone she had heard was not a mockery. He pulled her closer, as one side of his mouth lifted in encouragement. He whispered, 'Don't look at me like that until you've answered me. Why don't you want to leave me?'

'Because——' she began, a flush filling her cheeks as a warm glow spread over her. 'Because I love you. Cord, I——'

But his lips silenced the rest of her words. All resistance was gone as previously checked passions were unleashed in a burning embrace. When at last the fiery urgency was satisfied Cord's lips left Stacy's to travel to her eyes, cheeks, the curve of her neck as he whispered his endearments in the glory of love.

'Oh, Cord, Cord, I can't believe it,' Stacy gasped, thrilling at his every touch. 'You really love me?'

'I've loved you for an eternity.' His deep voice choked with emotion like hers.

'You were so hateful to me,' she accused, amidst another shower of kisses meant to silence her.

'I fell in love with you the day I found you lying unconscious on the plains. I knew then if anything happened to you my life wouldn't be worth living,' Cord's voice was husky. 'When you recovered and said you were leaving in a few weeks, I knew I had to find a way to make you stay, to make you love this land as I do.'

'I do, Cord, I do,' murmured Stacy.

'I know. I've never told you how proud I was of you and the way you took your place with the men on the drive and did your share of the work, except on occasions,' he grinned.

'Were you jealous of Jim?' Stacy teased.

'I was jealous of anyone who touched you. Even your letters from Carter irritated me,' he confessed.

'Look at the way you paraded Lydia around. She told me you were going to marry.' Stacy's upturned face was earnest as she added, 'That night on the veranda I thought you were pretending I was Lydia.'

'How I wanted you that night, darling.' His calloused hand traced the curve of her cheek. 'When you recoiled from me——'

'Not from you, Cord. Never from you.'

'Oh, the tangled webs we weave,' Cord smiled.

'If you hadn't overheard my conversation with Carter and forced me to admit to you my love, would you have let me leave tomorrow?'

'I would have shown you no mercy, Miss Adams,' Cord mocked gruffly.

'No quarter asked,' Stacy replied with a smile, lifting her face for his kiss.

'And none given, Stacy,' Cord murmured, inches away from her lips. 'Now that you're finally mine, I'll never let you go. And there'll be no fancy wedding. We're going to be married as soon as we can. You understand that,'

'Yes, Cord, yes,' Stacy answered fervently, yielding once again to his embrace.

THE INDY MAN

"YOU MUST BE JOKING, SUSAN."

Warren's voice vibrated with rage. "You can't mean Mitch Braden is going to be living in the same house as you!"

"I'm perfectly serious," Susan replied in a forced calm voice.

"Your parents actually invited him to stay?" Her fiancé shook his head in disbelief. "Didn't you tell them what kind of man he is?"

"What could I tell them? That he pays me outrageous compliments? That he flirts with me? They would have laughed and invited him anyway. They like him." The impatience she felt toward the whole mess made her voice sharp. "So what would you have me do, Warren—move out?"

Warren looked grim. "I have a feeling there's going to be trouble," he muttered.

And Susan echoed the thought ... but only to herself.

CHAPTER ONE

THE candle flame flickered briefly despite the colored pear-shaped glass that rose protectively around it to keep away the drafts. It was a touch of intimate atmosphere in an otherwise well-lit lounge.

As Susan sipped the drink from her stemmed glass, the wavering light caught and reflected a red fire in the sleek curls of her dark brown hair. Salt rimmed the edges of her glass with crystal white thickness, some of it clinging to her lips when she replaced the glass on the small table. Unconsciously her tongue moistly cleansed the lower lip of its salt traces.

Her soft brown gaze swung to the man sitting

opposite her. For the thousandth time Susan studied his aloof, almost arrogant features, the firm jaw, the thin hard mouth, the aristocratically straight nose, the impassive dark, nearly black, eyes beneath thick brows of an equal shade. His hair was as dark as hers, but in this light it had a raven black sheen without the red casts hers possessed.

Warren Sullivan was not looking at Susan, though. His dark gaze was shifting about the lounge in that ever alert manner of his. He seemed suddenly withdrawn and remote, not actually with her but apart.

Leaning forward, Susan reached out with her hand to touch the long masculine fingers that held his glass. The movement caused the ruffled vee of her white blouse to open, revealing a tantalizing glimpse of her lacy bra. The nearness of her hand to the candle flame illuminated the gold ring with its diamond fire. Her fingernails were impractically long and manicured, the way Warren liked them.

The touch of her hand against his brought the dark gaze to center on her face, cameo-smooth in tenderness. A semblance of a smile curved his mouth as Warren released the glass to let his fingers close over the tips of hers. Susan ignored the lack of warmth in his smile because she saw the look of approval in his eyes.

'We're going to have a good marriage, Susan.' The matter-of-fact announcement was issued quietly as if he had been pondering the question and was now satisfied with his conclusion.

Susan smiled, letting her dark lashes flutter down. She had become accustomed to Warren's statements. They were rarely romantic, but she didn't mind. He had never proposed to her, merely told her they were getting married. Her acceptance of his decision was taken for granted.

'May I ask the learned attorney what prompted him to reach such a verdict when the jury is still out?' she murmured, her lashes sweeping up so she could gaze at him with undisguised tenderness.

His mouth moved again into that thin line that was never quite a smile. 'Because, my dear, during the day you are level-headed and efficient. There's only the slightest trace of the womanly, feminine creature that you are at this moment. That is why we will have a good marriage: you are like me in that you don't want private emotions entangled with business.'

'Or business entangled with private emotions.'

'That, too, of course.' His broad shoulders moved in an agreeing shrug as if that was of secondary importance. Susan held back a sigh.

There were times when she wondered if Warren really loved her. Fortunately there were times when he convinced her of it very thoroughly. She silently wished they were not here in this public place so that he would take her in his arms and convince her again.

Her fingertip trailed around the salted edge of

her glass. Glancing up, she saw his gaze wandering about the room again. Almost as if he felt her watching him, he met the soft adoration of her look.

'I often wonder,' he mused, 'how long it might have been before I noticed you if my father hadn't become ill and I was not forced to stand in for him at the Christmas party. You had worked there for—how long—two years?'

'Four years,' Susan corrected gently. 'Two years in the typing pool and two years as your secretary.'

'I always thought you were very attractive,' Warren continued, not the least bit perturbed that he had not known how long she had been employed. 'But you were always so cool and practical that I never guessed such a warm, vibrant woman lived beneath that cloak of efficiency, not until you shed it that day at the party . . .'

'You have no idea, darling,' Susan murmured huskily, 'the cheer that went up that day when the female staff members of Sullivan, Sullivan and Holmes learned that you were going to attend the Christmas party.'

'Including from you?'

'My cheer was perhaps the loudest of all,' she smiled deeply. 'I told you I've been infatuated with you since almost the first day I saw you. But with all the socialites that paraded through your life, I never thought I had a chance.'

'Those empty-headed pieces of fluff,' he laughed in derision. 'I was never interested in any of them.

I was looking for someone like you, intelligent and understanding, capable of appreciating the demands of my career and supporting my ambitions. Until I came to know you, I thought all women threw tantrums or became piqued if business interfered with the time I spent with them.'

'You should have dated a doctor's daughter before,' Susan laughed. 'I don't remember taking part in any school function that my father was able to see through to the end. Invariably some woman decided to have her baby in the middle of the performance. Not that I wasn't hurt sometimes, but my mother taught me patience and understanding. She had had plenty of time to learn.'

Susan knew Warren was listening to her, yet his head was half-turned to glance around the lounge. They were not expecting to meet anyone tonight and she wondered fleetingly why he was so interested in the other occupants. The budding curiosity didn't last longer than it took his look to return to her.

'I'm glad you're understanding,' he stated. Was it her imagination, or was his expression sterner than before? 'It's going to be a trying time at the office next week with my father going into hospital for surgery.'

'I'm certain the doctors will find that the tumor is benign,' Susan offered, realizing Warren's harshness had probably been a show of concern for his father's health. They were very close.

'Of course it will be,' he nodded curtly, sliding a glance again to the side, his mouth tightening grimly. 'Though naturally they'll have to run a biopsy on it to be certain.'

'Warren,' Susan tilted her head to the side, a tiny frown drawing her brows together, 'what's wrong?'

Impatience laced his expression. 'The man at the second table— No, don't look now,' he reprimanded in a low sharp voice. 'He's been rudely staring at you for the last ten minutes.'

'At me?' she repeated in disbelief. 'Are you certain?'

'Very,' Warren retorted.

'Maybe I know him. Maybe he's someone I went to school with,' Susan suggested hesitantly. 'The second table, did you say?'

'Yes. Take a look, but for heaven's sake don't be obvious about it,' he commanded.

An order that was much easier given than carried out. With forced nonchalance, Susan leaned back in her chair. She let her gaze wander idly about the lounge until it was caught by the man at the second table and held by his intent regard. There wasn't any doubt in Susan's mind that he was looking at no one else but her.

The man was alone at the table, leaning somewhat indolently back in his chair. A thumb was hooked in the waistband of his suit trousers, holding the jacket open to reveal a vest in the same unusual tobacco brown color as his suit. Even at this distance Susan could recognize the expensive tailoring.

His hair was a tawny shade, brown unusually

gilded with dark gold, a trifle long judged by the clean-cut standards Warren adhered to, and its careless style gave the man a look suggesting the untamed. The lean, handsome face held deeply grooved lines around his mouth and eyes that said he smiled often. Boyish was an initial adjective that Susan wanted to use to describe the man, but he was much too virile and too masculine. That faintly boyish charm she detected was really the rakish air of a rogue. The stunningly handsome face and devastating smile had probably over-whelmed many women.

Her inspection finally stopped at his eyes, blue and glinting with undisguised amusement. Susan couldn't shake the feeling that there was some-thing about him that was vaguely familiar. She stared at him a minute more while she tried to place what it was.

The stranger used that minute to inspect her in-solently. As his blue eyes ran over her figure, Su-san felt her clothes being stripped away little by little. The caressive quality of the sensation sent flames shooting through her veins but without any feeling of revulsion. She glanced away before she could ascertain why she had thought she might know him.

'Well?' Warren demanded impatiently.

A black anger was in his expression and Susan knew he had recognized the stranger's intimate appraisal of her at the last. Perhaps the only major fault that Warren possessed was his foul, brooding temper. She almost wanted to say that she knew the man, but at this point she didn't think Warren cared whether she did or not.

'I don't think I know him, although I have the feeling I've seen him somewhere before,' she replied evenly. It wouldn't do to let Warren see she had been embarrassed.

Warren flashed another glance at the man, his jaw tightening ominously as he let his gaze slide back to her. 'I can't believe the insolence of that man!'

'Just ignore him,' Susan shrugged.

'How can you ignore such a blatant disregard of good manners?' he snapped. 'It's about time someone taught him some.'

'Then you would be behaving as boorishly as he is,' she pointed out. Logic was the only way to penetrate Warren's temper. 'Besides,' she glanced out of the corner of her eye and saw the movement of the man rising to his feet, 'he's leaving anyway.'

Warren wasn't satisfied with Susan's word that the man was leaving and had to look for himself. His eyes were dark as pitch as they swung back to narrow on her face.

'Are you quite certain you don't know that man?' he demanded.

'I——' Susan hesitated, then invisibly shrugged away that vague sensation of something familiar about him. 'I'm quite certain,' she concluded with a firm nod of her head.

'Then would you tell me why,' Warren continued in the same ominously low tone, 'he's walking to our table?'

Her brown eyes widened in surprise. A hand moved bewilderedly to a wing of dark hair at her temple, smoothing it back to glance surreptitiously at the man. He was approaching their table with a rolling, supple walk totally unlike Warren's firm, almost military stride.

There was the faintest suggestion of a smile on the man's mouth, but his eyes were decidedly crinkled at the corners, a wicked glitter in their blueness. She had barely met his mocking look and she was glancing swiftly away.

Her mind raced. She didn't know him, did she? How could anyone forget someone like that? She didn't know him, she was sure of it. Yet why was he coming to their table? Warren never forgot a face or a name, so it couldn't be him the stranger was coming to see.

When the man stopped beside the table, Susan wasn't able to raise her head in inquiry. Her hands were trembling and she clasped them together, silently praying that Warren wouldn't notice how unnerved she was, and that he wouldn't make a scene.

'Excuse me,' the man spoke in a voice that was low and musically pitched.

Unwillingly Susan lifted her chin, determined to show the man how completely indifferent she was to his presence. But the laughing blue eyes weren't looking at her. The man's falsely solemn expression was directed at Warren, whose head tilted challengingly toward the man.

'You don't know me,' the man continued, erasing at least one of Susan's doubts. 'My name is Mitch Braden.' A bell rang in her mind, but not loudly enough for her to know why. A hand was extended toward Warren in greeting. 'I came over to offer an apology for my rudeness. I'm afraid I might have offended you by staring at your date.'

For only a brief second did the man's gaze swing to Susan before it centered again on Warren. The hand remained outstretched. In the face of Mitch Braden's apology, Warren grudgingly shook the man's hand, not mollified by the apology but unable to disregard it without displaying bad manners himself.

'Your apology is accepted,' Warren responded curtly, releasing the man's hand almost abruptly.

'Thank you, Mr.—I'm sorry, what was your name?' A smile flashed across Mitch Braden's face, deepening the grooves around his mouth and proving as devastatingly attractive as Susan had thought it would be.

'Sullivan, Warren Sullivan,' was the reluctant reply.

At that moment Warren had released the man's gaze so he missed the sudden twinkle that sparkled in the man's eyes, but Susan saw it. As if feeling her gaze, the man named Mitch Braden looked at her.

'I don't suppose you need me to tell you what a very beautiful woman your date is, Mr. Sullivan.

Obviously you've had more opportunity to appreciate her looks than the few moments I have spent admiring her. It isn't often that a face as beautiful as hers has a figure to go with it.'

Susan breathed in sharply, unable to believe the man could speak so audaciously. Warren seemed momentarily stunned by the man's boldness as well.

'Mr. Braden,' he said cuttingly, 'I don't like your comments.'

An eyebrow of golden brown, the same color as the man's hair, raised in surprise. 'Don't you think she has a beautiful shape? I would say she's almost perfectly proportioned. Maybe you haven't taken a good look at her recently——'

'Susan is very beautiful,' Warren interrupted angrily, black fire flashing from his eyes. 'But I certainly don't appreciate you saying things like that——'

'I see,' Mitch Braden interrupted calmly. His laughing gaze swung to Susan's face, taking note of her heightened color. When he was looking at her, the man didn't attempt to conceal his mockery with pseudoinnocence. 'You're afraid too many compliments will go to her head, isn't that it? That's a pity, because she has such a pretty little head.' He glanced back at Warren's smoldering expression. 'Susan, did you say her name was Susan?'

'It happens to be Mrs. Sullivan. She's my wife!' Warren snapped.

Partially angered by the man's flirtatious remarks deliberately intended to rile Warren, Susan had still found herself hiding a smile. The tiny dimple in one cheek vanished at Warren's announcement.

'Congratulations,' Mitch Braden responded easily to the news, not displaying disappointment or surprise. 'You're a very lucky man, Mr. Sullivan.'

'Thank you,' Warren returned acidly.

When Mitch Braden glanced again at Susan, his vocal blue eyes said it was such a pity she was married, but his smiling voice spoke of something else.

'May I buy you two a drink and we can toast the happy couple?' he offered with a flashing smile.

Susan's heart accelerated slightly. 'No, thank you, Mr. Braden,' she refused in a swift, husky voice.

'We were just going into the dining room to eat,' Warren inserted to rescue her. 'Thank you just the same.'

The man inclined his head in shrugging acceptance. 'It was the least I could do to make up for my earlier bad manners.'

Warren rose to his feet. Susan was faintly surprised to see that Warren was an inch or so taller than Mitch Braden. The man's presence had so completely dominated the table that she had presumed him the taller of the two. Even now Mitch Braden was the more compelling.

'Your apology has been accepted, Mr. Braden,' Warren said coolly, touching Susan's shoulder to prompt her to her feet. 'Now please excuse us!'

'Of course.' The stunning smile seemed permanently carved on the handsome face, the sparkling blue eyes directed at each of them in turn. 'I hope you two have a long and happy marriage. If not,' the wicked glint returned as his gaze rested momentarily on Susan, 'I hope I'm around to pick up the pieces.'

Susan slipped her hand under Warren's elbow. 'We shall have a long and happy marriage, Mr. Braden. Good evening.'

With a curt nod in the general direction of Mitch Braden, Warren turned Susan toward the door. The muscles in his arms were rigidly hard as his striding walk practically carried her out of the lounge. She guessed at the taut hold he had on his temper. There was no need for her to turn around because she could feel Mitch Braden's eyes watch them leave.

Free of the room and Braden, Warren's rein on his temper relaxed. 'That man is insufferable!' he muttered beneath his breath. 'He apologizes, then tries to steal you from under my nose. It didn't even faze him when I told him you were my wife!'

'That was going to a bit of an extreme, wasn't it?' she suggested gently. 'I mean, we aren't married yet.'

'Simply because it isn't convenient right now,' Warren snapped. 'And August is only a little over two months away and we're getting married then.'

'Yes,' Susan agreed, but Warren's white lie bothered her.

Warren continued as if he hadn't heard her. 'Do you know this is the first time I've wanted to invite a man to go outside with me since I was in high school and beat up the local bully?'

The story had been told to her several times before, so she merely nodded and was secretly relieved that Warren had not embarrassed her tonight by trying to repeat a high school episode. Warren, embarrassing her? The idea was so ludicrous considering how proper and polite Warren was that she nearly laughed aloud.

'Let's forget about that man,' she suggested instead, and wondered why she didn't believe her own words.

'You're right, of course.' The taut lines of anger vanished as Warren looked down his nose at her.

'There isn't any need to let his impudence spoil our evening. Shall we dine here as planned? I don't think that man will bother us again.'

Susan wasn't as certain about that as Warren seemed to be, but she agreed with his suggestion anyway. Besides, she told herself as the dining room hostess led them to a table, she should look on the bright side of the otherwise unfortunate episode. At least she had learned that Warren was capable of being jealous. Sometimes he was so self-contained that she wondered if she aroused any feelings in him at all.

They were studying the menu when a group of loud, laughing voices invaded the dining room. Susan's back was to the entrance, but she didn't need to turn around to learn who had entered.

'Good lord!' Warren exclaimed irritably. 'It's that man Braden again with a motley collection of men! The hostess is leading them this way. Pretend not to notice them, Susan.'

How could anyone fail to notice the boisterous group coming nearer? Susan tried to obey Warren's crisp command by concentrating on the menu, but as the men filed past their table, she couldn't resist peering above the leather-bound menu.

There were six men in the group, counting Mitch Braden. If he had noticed Susan and Warren, there was no indication of it now. He was laughing at some comment that had come from the gangly youth bringing up the rear.

It was an odd assortment, average men running from short to tall, skinny to thin, young to old. None of them possessed the strikingly handsome looks of the man leading the way.

The large table the hostess led them to was not far from Susan and Warren. Susan breathed a silent sigh of relief when Mitch Braden took a chair that faced away from them. She doubted if she could have eaten with him watching her at his leisure. Warren, too, seemed to relax.

After receiving Susan's preference for her meal, Warren gave the waiter their order, spending a few minutes choosing a wine from the dining room's wine list. He prided himself on being a connoisseur with very discriminating taste. Susan had difficulty telling one wine from another.

When the main course was served, the waiter

uncorked the chilled bottle and offered a tasting portion to Warren. 'Sir——' the waiter began.

'This is not the wine I ordered,' Warren interrupted immediately, not allowing the man a chance to finish. He reached for the bottle still in the waiter's hands. 'This wine was not even on your list.'

'No, sir,' the man agreed. 'It's from the owner's private stock. Compliments of the gentleman at the large table.'

Mitch Braden. Both Warren and Susan darted a look at him. He had turned in his chair and briefly inclined his head in acknowledgment.

'The owner?' Susan breathed, glancing curiously at the waiter.

'He is a friend of the owner, I believe,' was the courteous answer.

Indecision held Warren silent for an instant. Susan guessed that he wanted to refuse the wine. It must have been a very excellent vintage because he did not.

'Please thank the gentleman for us,' Warren said tautly.

'Of course, sir.'

Perhaps if Mitch Braden had not sent the wine to their table, Susan might have been better able to ignore his presence in the dining room. As it was, her eyes strayed often to his table, focusing on his lean masculine form and the dark golden-toast shade of his hair. Never once during the entire meal did she encounter the laughing blue eyes with the crinkled lines at the corners.

Always from the table of six there was laughter and constant chatter. In comparison the silence between Susan and Warren seemed unnatural. But Warren didn't care for any discussions during a meal. The time for talk was before or after, but never during a meal. By the time coffee was served, a tiny pain had begun to hammer at her temples, from tension, Susan guessed.

Laughter punctuated the air, coming naturally from Mitch Braden's table. Warren cast a censorious look in that direction.

'It would have been an excellent meal if the atmosphere had been more peaceful,' he commented.

Lifting her chin slightly, Susan refused to let her gaze wander to the other table. 'I imagine about the only place you can be fairly certain of obtaining a quiet meal is in your own home.'

'Very true,' Warren agreed, dry-voiced. 'Are we ready to leave?' At Susan's nod, he signaled their waiter for the bill.

When he rose and walked to the back of her chair, Susan noticed one of the men nudge Mitch Braden. She could barely see his lips move, but she knew instinctively that he was telling Mitch that she and Warren were leaving.

One shoulder lifted in an uncaring gesture and some comment was made in response by the man. A stout balding man laughed shortly and said, 'When did that ever stop you?' Mitch Braden's low answer brought laughter from the rest of the group.

Holding her breath for fear he might have heard the exchange too, Susan glanced swiftly at Warren. He merely looked inquiringly back and she smiled with false brightness.

From the restaurant, Warren drove her straight home with no stops in between. It was a week night, which meant they both had to be at the office in the morning. Warren did not believe in keeping late hours when he had to work the next day. For that matter, neither did Susan. On Tuesdays and Thursdays, the only week nights they went out, it was strictly for dinner, then home. The weekends were quite different.

This night Susan was glad to have the evening end quickly. It hadn't been as enjoyable as other outings. Mostly because of Mitch Braden.

Their goodnight embrace in the parked car outside her home did not last long. Lingering kisses were saved for the weekends when they had more time to indulge in them. At those times, Warren was masterful and passionate. Susan had never considered it odd that those were the times when she was most aware that she loved him.

Only when she was in the house and watching his car drive away did she wish for the first time that the pattern of their relationship hadn't become so predictable. A surprise now and then would be nice.

Of course, Mitch Braden, whoever he was, had provided a surprise this night and it hadn't been so nice. Oh, Warren had displayed jealousy, but Susan still wished the encounter had never occurred. Just why she wished that she didn't know.

'Is that you, Susan?' her mother called.

She turned away from the window. 'Yes, Mom, it's me,' she answered, shedding her spring coat and hanging it in the closet before walking down the hallway to the large family room.

'Hello, honey, did you have a nice time?' her father, Doctor Simon Mabry, greeted her as she entered the room. His burly frame was draped in a reclining chair, a medical magazine unopened on his lap.

'Of course,' Susan smiled.

'Is *he* here?' Her younger brother Greg, a week away from turning seventeen, twisted away from the television set to glance at her.

"No, Warren didn't come in tonight.' Susan picked up a pillow from the couch and threw it at her brother's lanky frame sprawled on the floor. Warren and Greg had disliked each other on first sight and the months since their first meeting hadn't changed either's opinion.

As Susan slipped off her shoes and started to curl her feet beneath her to sit on the couch, the pillow was thrown back. She caught it easily from long practice.

"Ouch, Mother! You're pulling my hair!' the youngest of the Mabrys exclaimed angrily—Amy, age thirteen.

'Well, if you would hold still——' Beth Mabry began, Susan's mother.

'You'd pull out every hair in my head!' Amy squeaked, her hands moving protectively to her long auburn hair.

'I have to get the tangles out somehow, unless

you'd rather do it yourself.' Beth Mabry firmly pulled the young girl closer to her chair. 'After all, you were the one who got it into this mess, climbing that tree like a tomboy.'

'I told you,' Amy protested with rounded brown eyes of speaking innocence, 'I had to get Peggy Fraser's kitten. Ouch!'

"Want me to comb it for you, Amy?" Susan offered, knowing the tug-of-war could go on continuously between mother and daughter.

As her mother had put it the night before when she and Amy had argued, Amy was 'going through that difficult stage,' crazy about boys and becoming a woman but not quite able to stop climbing trees.

'Oh, yes, please, Susan!' Amy agreed fervently.

'Will you guys pipe down?' Greg protested impatiently. 'I'm trying to watch this TV show!'

'Keep it to a low roar, Amy,' her father suggested with a gentle smile.

'Greg's much too bossy, Dad.' Amy stuck out her tongue at her brother as she walked to the couch where Susan sat.

Slowly and carefully working the snarls free from Amy's hair, Susan smiled to herself. It was no wonder that Warren found it difficult to relax when he came here. He had been an only child and the constant wrangling that went on between brother and sister and parent was something he couldn't accept. He would adjust to it when they started having children of their own.

The television program her father and brother were watching was a police drama. Susan managed to grasp most of the storyline without giving the picture her complete attention. The local Indianapolis news broadcast came on as she brushed the last snarl from Amy's long auburn hair. She listened to the news and the weather, but when the subject shifted to sports, Susan started to untangle her legs from beneath her and stand up.

A familiar face appeared on the television screen. She stared at it in disbelief. It was Mitch Braden, the man she had so disastrously met with Warren tonight. Only on television he wasn't wearing that perfectly tailored suit and vest. He wore a tee shirt that stretched like a second skin over his chest, and snug-fitting Levis. The film was taken outside and the wind was ruffling the dark tawny gold of his hair.

'Is . . . is that Mitch Braden?' Susan forced the question out, too stunned to hear what the sports announcer was saying.

'Yep,' Greg replied.

The smiling, handsome face left the screen and a rundown of baseball scores started.

'Who is he?' Susan asked hesitantly.

'He's Mitch Braden.' Greg frowned at the dumbness of her question.

'But—what does he do?'

'What does he *do*?' Greg exclaimed with a taunting hoot. 'He's just about the most famous race car driver around. He's in town for the Indianapolis 500 race Memorial weekend. What does he do! Boy, what a dumb sister!'

'I thought he looked familiar,' she commented, but more to herself than as a direct comment.

'Well, you just saw him on the television screen.' Greg shook his head in despair at her strange remark.

'No, I mean, tonight at the restaurant,' Susan explained absently, still slightly stunned that Mitch Braden had turned out to be such a famous personality.

'You saw him! You saw Mitch Braden!' Her brother bounded to his feet. 'Did you get his autograph? Did you talk to him?'

'Well, yes, I talked to him in a way, but I didn't recognize him. I knew he looked familiar, but I didn't know why.'

'You didn't get his autograph!' Greg moaned.

'What did he say to you?' Amy asked curiously. 'Is he as handsome as he looks on television?'

'Mostly he talked to Warren,' Susan answered truthfully, wishing suddenly that she hadn't even mentioned that she had seen him. 'He's good-looking.' More so than on camera, she thought silently, because film couldn't capture the magnetism he exuded.

'I wasn't aware that Warren was acquainted with anyone in racing circles,' her father included himself in the conversation.

Greg's hair, a dark brown like Susan's, fell shaggily across his forehead. He flipped it away from his eyes with his hand. 'Neither was I,' he agreed forcefully.

Susan bit into her lower lip. She wasn't about to explain what had really happened. 'Warren doesn't know him.'

'You said he talked to him,' Greg reminded.

'They were simply in the same restaurant at the same time.' Susan rose to her feet to bring an end to the conversation. 'It was just a case of two strangers exchanging casual conversation. I wouldn't even have mentioned it if I'd known I was going to get the third degree.'

She started for the hall with Greg trailing on her heels.

'I don't suppose Weighty Warren knew who Mitch Braden was either.'

'Will you stop making those insulting references about my fiancé?' Susan demanded impatiently. 'And no, he didn't know who he was any more than I did.'

'That figures,' Greg responded derisively.

'There are more important things in the world, Greg,' Susan stamped her bare foot on the floor, a childish action for someone approaching her twenty-fourth birthday, 'than knowing some idiot who drives around a racetrack at a hundred and fifty miles an hour.'

'Yeah?' her brother challenged.

'Greg!' came her mother's warning voice.

'Ah, gee, Mom,' he turned impatiently away from Susan. 'There's only a chance in a million of meeting someone like Mitch Braden and my sister blew it!'

Susan didn't wait to hear what arguments Beth Mabry offered in her behalf. She escaped to her room while she had the chance, knowing that she probably hadn't heard the last of her brother's recriminations or Mitch Braden's name.

CHAPTER TWO

'SUSAN, is my son busy?'

Glancing up from her typewriter, Susan encountered the solemn face of Robert Sullivan, the senior partner of the law firm and Warren's father. The resemblance between the two was striking. Both were tall and ruggedly handsome. Warren's hair was jet black while his father's had turned iron gray.

'Yes, he is,' she nodded. 'You can go on in, Mr. Sullivan.'

She gestured fleetingly toward the closed interoffice door behind her, wondering if she would ever be able to address the man less formally even after she and Warren were married.

Robert Sullivan always seemed so remote and untouchable, the way Warren did sometimes.

With a sigh, Susan turned backed to the typewriter, rereading the last page of the corporate agreement for typographical errors. Satisfied that there were no mistakes, she removed the original and carboned sheet from the carriage. The hall door opened as she started to staple the several-page document together.

'Hi.' Greg ambled into her office, hands stuffed in the pockets of his thin jacket.

'Hello.' Her surprise at his unexpected appearance was in her voice. 'What are you doing downtown?'

'I had to take care of my car insurance,' he answered with a shrug of his shoulders. 'I thought I'd stop by to see if you wanted a ride home.'

Susan glanced at her watch. It was only a few minutes before five o'clock, which was her normal leaving time.

'Warren was going to take me home, but——' She looked to the closed interoffice door. With his father in there, there was no telling how long he would be tied up.

'Oh, that's okay. I just thought I'd check.' Greg started to turn back toward the hall door.

'Greg?' The atmosphere had been tense between Susan and her brother since she had lost her temper two nights before after his disparaging reference to Warren. She guessed his offer of a ride was a conciliatory gesture. He stopped and pivoted toward her. 'I'm not sure——' she began, only to come to a halt as the door to Warren's office opened.

'Susan——' Warren walked in, an absent frown clouding his wide forehead. At the sight of her brother, he paused and nodded. 'Hello, Gregory. I didn't expect to see you here.'

Susan felt her brother's wince. He disliked the use of his full name. No matter how tactfully she mentioned it to Warren, he still persisted in using it.

'I stopped to see if Susan needed a ride home,' her brother explained tautly. His chin was thrust defiantly forward and there was a belligerent darkness in the brown gaze that met Warren's.

'Well, that's opportune,' he smiled coldly, and Susan despaired of the two ever becoming friends. Warren's obsidian dark eyes looked toward her. 'I was just coming in to suggest that it might be better if you left without me. My father and I have some business to go over, cases I might need to handle while he's in the hospital. It might take considerable time.'

'I understand,' she smiled. 'I'll go home with Greg.' She hesitated, disliking to mention dinner that evening since he hadn't. 'What about dinner tonight?'

'I'll phone you at home. I'm not certain how long I'll be,' he answered, not expressing any regret in words or his tone of voice that their plans for the evening might be canceled.

'Of course.' Susan turned away, a barely audible sigh of disappointment escaping with the words she spoke.

'Since Gregory is already here and it's nearly five, you might as well leave whenever you've straightened up,' Warren stated in dismissal.

'I've finished the Hoxworth proposal,' she said, picking up the document she had just stapled together. 'Did you want it now or in the morning?'

'I'll take it now.' He reached for the papers in her hands, briefly leafing through them as he turned again toward his office.

'I understand you met Mitch Braden the other night,' Greg spoke up unexpectedly.

Warren stopped short and glanced piercingly over his shoulder at Susan, condemnation in his look.

'I forgot to mention to you, Warren,' Susan hastened to explain how Greg had known about their meeting with Mitch Braden, 'why he looked so familiar to me. Mitch Braden is a racing car driver. He's in town for the Indianapolis 500 race.'

'A racing car driver?' There was a faintly contemptuous curl to Warren's mouth. 'I suppose that explains his behavior.'

When the door to his office had closed behind Warren, Susan could feel Greg's eyes watching her. 'What did he mean by that?' he asked finally.

She didn't look up but continued clearing her desk in preparation to leave. 'Let's just say that your idol Mr. Braden behaved a little rudely the other night and leave it at that.'

'With a snob like your boyfriend, I wouldn't blame him,' her brother retorted.

Susan counted slowly to ten. 'You don't know

what you're talking about, and Warren is not a snob,' she replied patiently. 'And I have no intention of arguing about it or discussing it any further. Okay?'

'Okay,' Greg submitted grudgingly.

A quarter of an hour later, Susan was gingerly sliding into the passenger seat of Greg's vintage Chevrolet, a tactful term for a worn-out used car. She carefully avoided the jutting edge of broken plastic ribbing on the seat that was trying to snag her pantyhose.

'I thought you were going to buy new covers for the seats,' she commented as she brushed her plaid skirt of olive green and black on white.

Her brother grinned and turned the key in the ignition. 'I'm hoping Mom and Dad will buy them as a birthday present. Then I can use the money I saved to buy some hubcaps.'

'You might be further ahead to save the money for a down payment on a new car,' Susan suggested when the motor grudgingly growled to life. 'It might prove a better investment.'

'This car is practically an antique. It's going to be worth a lot of money some day.'

'Yes, but will it be worth as much money as you invested in it? That's the question,' she teased, but with a thread of seriousness.

'She runs like a top,' Greg defended.

Her brother was practically a fanatic about the car. He and his friends spent hours tinkering with it after school and on weekends.

As they joined the rush hour traffic on the free-

way en route to their home on the outskirts of Indianapolis, Susan admitted that outside of a grumbling reluctance to start the car ran quite well.

They were nearly halfway home when Greg
murmured a worried 'Oh, oh!' and began to edge
the car into the outside lane of traffic. Susan
glanced curiously at his troubled frown.

'What's wrong?'

'The engine is overheating,' he answered, slowing the car to a stop on the wide shoulder of the
freeway.

'Why?'

'That's what I'm about to find out,' Greg answered grimly as he opened his door and walked
to the front of the car to raise the hood.

A misty gray cloud swirled into the air when the
hood came up. Alarmed, Susan quickly opened
her door and joined her cursing brother now
standing several steps from the front of the car.

'Is it on fire?' she asked anxiously, not seeing
any flames that might be causing the smoke.

'No, that's steam,' he sighed heavily. 'The radiator hose has a leak.'

'Can you fix it?' Susan followed Greg as he
moved closer to inspect the problem when the
bulk of the steam had dissipated. She was careful
not to come too close to the front of the car in case
the condensing steam stained her skirt or the
well tailored blazer-style jacket of matching olive
green.

'Even if I could fix it temporarily,' he grumbled,
'there isn't any place to get water to replace what

the radiator has lost, which looks like about all of it.'

'Which means?' Susan prodded.

'Which means,' his hands were disgustedly propped on his hips as he looked past the car in the direction they had just come from, 'I'm going to have to hike to that service station a mile and a half back and see if they don't have a wrecker that can tow us in. And that means I'm going to have to spend the money I was saving for my hubcaps.'

'Greg' I'm sorry,' Susan offered sympathetically. 'I'll pay the towing charges as part of your birthday present. I——'

'Hello, Susan. Are you having trouble?'

Whirling around, Susan's heart skipped a beat as she met the winning smile of Mitch Braden. His supple, rolling walk was carrying him from the cobalt blue sports car parked ahead of them.

There was an absent recognition that his twinkling eyes matched the color of his car or vice versa, but mostly Susan simply felt stunned amazement. The traffic had been so heavy that she had not noticed any cars even slowing in response to their breakdown, let alone hear any stop.

'How . . . How did you know it was me?' she breathed, still in a state of confused astonishment.

His gaze swept her from head to toe and back. 'I pride myself on never forgetting a figure,' he grinned wickedly, 'or a face.'

His suggestive reply disturbed her heartbeat, making it pulse much too fast. Susan turned away, momentarily unable to counter his remark.

Out of the corner of her eye, she caught a glimpse of her brother's slightly open-mouthed stare, as if he couldn't believe his eyes. For that matter neither could she. Who would ever have dreamed of Mitch Braden stopping to help?

A sickening thought knotted her stomach. What if he mentioned in front of Greg her supposed marriage to Warren? She would never be able to endure that man's mockery if he learned Warren had been lying.

'What's the problem?' Mitch Braden was directly behind her, his voice low and amused.

'Oh . . . er . . . a leak in the radiator hose.' Greg pulled himself out of his trance with a supreme effort.

Mitch Braden leaned forward to look under the hood and verify the problem. Susan moved quickly to the side of the car. The man was a wolf. She didn't intend there to be any 'accidental' physical contact between them—he would be too quick to find a way to take advantage of it.

Mitch Braden straightened, his expression serious as he darted her a twinkling look. 'It's a busted hose all right.'

'I'm Greg Mabry, Susan's brother,' Greg rushed, the shock at meeting the race driver wearing off. 'Boy, I can't believe I'm actually meeting you in person, Mr. Braden. I've watched you drive hundreds of times, on television mostly, but— wow, this is really a thrill for me!'

'I'm happy to meet you, too, Greg.' Mitch Braden offered his hand, which Greg shook with obvious enthusiasm.

224

'This was worth breaking down for,' her brother grinned, a quaking excitement trembling beneath the surface of his voice as if he was mentally pinching himself to be certain this was really happening to him.

'Greg, it's getting late,' Susan thinly prodded him back to the problem at hand.

'What?' He looked at her blankly for an instant. 'Oh, yeah.'

The grooves deepened around Mitch Braden's mouth as Susan's glance ricocheted away from his face. 'Why don't you let me give you a lift to the nearest wrecker service, Greg, and we'll make arrangements to have your car towed in?' he offered.

'Would you?' Greg breathed excitedly. 'I mean—wow, that would be terrific!'

Susan felt an overwhelming desire to give her brother a hard shake. His blatant hero-worship of the man was getting on her nerves. More than that, however, she wanted to bring this meeting to an end.

'Lock up your car and we'll go,' the man ordered easily.

'There's no need to do that,' Susan inserted quickly. 'I'll stay here and keep an eye on it until Greg comes back with the wrecker.'

'I can't let you do that.' Mitch Braden moved his head to the side in disagreement, a mocking glint in his blue eyes. 'A beautiful woman like you, stranded on a highway, that would be asking for trouble. I would never be able to face your husband if something happened to you while your brother and I were gone.'

Husband. There it was. And Greg picked up on it immediately as Susan's heart sunk to her toes.

'Husband?' he frowned. 'Susan isn't married.'

There was no mistaking the reason for the gleam in Mitch Braden's eyes as they swung to Greg. 'She isn't? This Warren——'

'That creep!' her brother grunted.

'Greg!' Susan warned through gritted teeth.

He paid no attention to her. 'She's engaged to him all right,' her brother acknowledged in the same contemptuous voice, 'but she isn't married to him yet.'

'It doesn't sound as if you're very much in favor of the marriage,' Mitch Braden observed.

'That's putting it mildly,' Greg replied, indifferent to his sister's daggers.

'Maybe you and I will have to join forces to see what we can do about it,' he suggested with a crooked smile.

'That's a good idea,' her brother laughed, suddenly seeing himself in the role of a matchmaker and liking the idea of Susan and Mitch Braden together.

'If you don't mind——' Anger trembled through her into her voice.

'You're right.' Mitch Braden nodded, his brown hair glinting golden as it caught the fire of the setting sun. 'This conversation isn't getting your car fixed.'

'Right,' Greg agreed. 'I'll lock up.'

He shut the hood and walked around to the driver's side to lock the doors. Susan wanted to dig her heels in and refuse to leave the car. Meeting Mitch's challenging look, she knew she couldn't leave Greg alone with him. There was no telling what kind of a scheme he would talk her gullible brother into trying.

Her brown eyes snapped with frustrated anger as she stalked past him toward the blue sports car. Of all the motorists on the highways, why had he been the one to stop? She paused beside the passenger door of the low-slung sports car and Mitch Braden was instantly beside her, his lazy, rolling stride covering ground with surprising swiftness.

'You'll have to wait for your brother,' he murmured in a mocking tone. 'It'll be easier for him to crawl into the back cubbyhole than for you with your skirt.'

She stared through the tinted glass window at the bucket seats in front of the half-seat behind them. What he said was irritatingly correct, and Susan wondered why he couldn't drive a car with full seats in front and back. Impatiently she glanced back to see her brother jogging toward them. His eyes widened in admiration as he approached the sports car.

'A Ferrari Boxer!' Greg whistled, touching the shiny blue surface almost reverently.

'She's a beauty, isn't she?' Mitch smiled understandingly as he opened the door.

'I'll say!' her brother agreed fervently, ducking his head inside to look around before crawling automatically into the compartment behind the bucket seats.

Susan's lips tightened grimly as she slid onto the leather seat, keeping her gaze straight ahead while Mitch closed the door. Greg leaned forward to inspect the dashboard panel and the gearshift on the floor between the front seats.

'I've only seen these babies in magazines,' he breathed in the same awed tone as before when Mitch slipped behind the wheel.

'This one has been all rebuilt to pass the emission control standards,' Mitch explained as the powerful motor sprang to life.

Susan refused to appear impressed, instead looking uninterestedly out of the window. The car accelerated quickly into the mainstream of traffic, the hand near her leg smoothly shifting the gears. She sat very still in prim silence.

'I saw you on television the other night,' Greg offered after they had traveled some distance.

'Did you?' Mitch responded absently as if it was a commonplace occurrence that didn't warrant any special mention.

'How do you think you'll do in the time trials for the Indy 500?'

'If the car keeps running the way it did today, it ought to finish somewhere up in the top ten,' he replied.

'The newspapers say you have the fastest car,' Greg observed.

'Maybe,' Mitch shrugged, 'but in a race as long as the Indy 500, there are too many unknowns that can happen for owning the fastest car to make you a sure winner.'

'Yeah,' her brother agreed with a smile. 'A lot

depends on the driver behind the wheel and you're the best driver on the circuit.'

'With you and luck on my side,' Mitch grinned over his shoulder, 'I won't need a cheering section to win. Of course, there are some other guys in the race who are just as intent on making that victory lap as I am.'

'Oh sure,' Greg admitted, 'but you'll win. I know it.'

A low chuckle followed her brother's positive statement. Susan reluctantly acknowledged to herself that it was an attractive sound, warm and caressing like his voice. Her fingers tightened convulsively on the handle of her purse, not wanting to like anything about this man.

Out of the corner of her eye, she studied the strong hands gripping the wheel. Muscles rippled in the tan arms, bare below the short sleeves of his shirt. She considered the strength that the fingers, hands and arms had to possess to manhandle a car traveling at upward of a hundred and eighty miles or more.

Yet something told her they could be gentle, too. The prospect of them ever touching her with that gentleness was disturbing and she mentally shook the thought away.

They had made the turnaround on the highway and were driving into the station that had been Greg's destination when he had intended to walk for help. Cutting the motor, Mitch stepped from the car and Greg scrambled over the driver's seat to follow him.

Taking a step, Greg turned back, glancing into

the car at Susan. 'You might as well wait here until I find out whether they can help me now.'

Susan had turned slightly, reaching for the door handle, but at her brother's words she subsided into the molding cushions of the leather seat. No doubt with Mitch Braden lending his voice to Greg's request, they would receive speedy service, she thought with a sigh.

The cynicism in the thought surprised her. What was there about the man that acted on her like two opposing fields of a magnet? She was unquestionably drawn by his charm and stunning looks. It was only natural that she found him physically attractive.

Yet something inside her insisted that she keep a safe distance from Mitch Braden. Susan wanted to believe it was a sense of fidelity to Warren, but that was only a part of it. There was a feeling of guilt, too, that she would be attracted to a man who was not her fiancé.

She brushed a wing of dark hair away from her cheek. Propping her elbow on the door, she rested her chin in her hand, trying to discern why she couldn't bring herself to trust Mitch Braden, and why she was so determined not to let herself like him.

The door on the driver's side was opened. Susan turned with a start as Mitch Braden slid behind the wheel and closed the door. The motor growled at the turn of the ignition key and he shifted the gear into reverse.

'Where's Greg?' Susan looked frantically around.

Deftly they had turned around, the car fluidly changing from a reverse motion to forward with barely a break. The car was responsive to Mitch Braden's slightest touch, its power an extension of the man who commanded it.

Turning in her seat to look out the rear window, she saw Greg waving a casual goodbye.

'It will be ten minutes before a man is free to take the wrecker out for your brother's car,' Mitch finally explained when her frantic gaze riveted itself on his profile. 'Then they still have to install the new hose. I offered to give you a ride home.'

'Don't I have some say in it?' Susan protested with astonishment at his high-handed manner.

'I have your brother's permission.' He sent her a wicked smile. 'And I thought by the time you had finished all your objections about why you didn't want to ride with me, I would have you home.'

Susan breathed in deeply and finally expelled the breath in an impotently angry sigh.

'What's the matter?' he mocked. 'Don't you think I will take you straight home?'

'Will you?' she returned acidly.

'No side trips,' Mitch assured her with a mock promise, his blue eyes sparkling with an audacious light. 'Of course with such precious cargo, I'll take my time.'

'I think, Mr. Braden, that you're impossible,' she retorted tightly.

'Call me Mitch. And what warm-blooded male would deprive himself of such beautiful company sooner than he had to?' he grinned.

Susan turned her head away, a faint warmth creeping into her limbs. She had to remind herself how easily he issued compliments. She mustn't let them go to her head.

'Would you please not talk to me that way?' she requested icily, her fingers nervously clutching the purse in her lap.

'You don't like me to say that I think you're beautiful, is that it?' he rephrased the compliment with infuriating calm.

'That's it,' she tried to reply in the same vein.

'Okay,' Mitch agreed with a faint shrug.

They drove for a time in a silence that was unnerving for Susan. She simply couldn't seem to relax. Every muscle was taut with her inner tension.

'Do you know something, Susan?' he spoke finally in a thoughtful tone. 'You're the first woman who's kissed me today.'

'That must be a record,' was her initial reply, until she realized what he had said. Her head pivoted sharply to stare at him. 'I haven't kissed you!'

'Haven't you?' A wicked light flickered in his brief glance. 'That's okay, there's still time.'

'You will have a long wait for that time,' she snapped. 'In case you've forgotten, Mr. Braden, I am engaged.'

'But you're not married,' he reminded her. 'Why do you suppose your fiancé told me you were?'

An uncomfortable flush began to warm her

cheeks, and she averted her face so he wouldn't see.

'I really wouldn't know,' she answered haughtily.

'Maybe he didn't feel secure enough about your affection to risk any competition?' Mitch suggested.

'Warren is very much aware of how much I love him and how eagerly I look forward to our marriage,' Susan told him in no uncertain terms.

'But to claim you were married?' An eyebrow arched with faint arrogance. 'Surely it would have been enough to admit that you were engaged.'

'Unfortunately Warren couldn't guess that you wouldn't respect the bonds of matrimony any more than an engagement ring,' she flashed.

'Hey!' he laughed softly. 'You are aiming those blows below the belt, aren't you?'

She tilted her head to the side in defiant challenge. 'I thought I was only speaking the truth.'

'You don't think much of me, do you?' drawled Mitch.

'Actually, I don't think of you at all,' she said coolly.

'Ooh——ouch!' he smiled with a mock grimace of inflicted pain. 'Now you really are trying to upset my ego!'

'I think it's of sufficient size not to suffer any lasting harm.' Susan directed her gaze out the window at the rows of homes on the residential street. 'Our house is the two-story brick home, the second from the corner on the next block.'

Mitch Braden didn't comment as he swung the

car into the driveway, stopping in front of the two-car garage. Her hand had closed over the metal door handle when her other wrist was seized.

'Will you let me go?' She looked at him coldly.

'You remind me of a racing car,' he said thoughtfully, his gaze sweeping her in absent appraisal. 'All classic design and beautiful to look at, with a lot of fire under the hood. Fire that could be amazingly responsive with the right man at the controls.'

Her pulse thudded a little faster. It was impossible to remain passive any longer and she strained to free her wrist from his firm grip. Applying only the slightest pressure, Mitch pulled her toward him.

His other hand reached out to cup the back of her neck, entangling itself in the silky curtain of her dark hair. 'You forgot to kiss me, Susan,' he said softly.

Susan forgot to struggle as the sensual line of his mouth moved closer. Then it was closing warmly over hers and her lashes fluttered down, the craziest sensation rocking her body. Almost before the kiss began, he was ending it, moving away to his own side of the car.

She blinked at him once and turned hurriedly away, opening the car door quickly, needing desperately to escape his presence. It only occurred to her when she was standing in the driveway, the car door slammed shut, that she should have slapped him for taking such liberties when he knew she was engaged.

But of course she should have offered some sort of protest, too. Slapping him after the fact would have been equal to locking the door after the house had been burglarized.

The driver's door opened and closed, too. Susan stared in disbelief when Mitch Braden walked around the car to her side.

'I am home now. You can leave any time,' she said huskily.

The grooves around his mouth deepened although he didn't actually smile. 'I promised Greg I would stick around until he came back. I think he intends to invite me to dinner. Naturally I'll accept.'

Susan breathed in sharply, ready to demand that he leave. At that same moment a car pulled into the drive. A quick glance said it was her father. Recognition of Mitch Braden was already flashing in his face, and Susan knew any hope that she would soon be rid of this man was lost.

CHAPTER THREE

AN explanation why Mitch Braden had brought
Susan home had been required by her father as
well as an introduction. Then Susan had had to repeat the same thing again for her mother with an
added word from Mitch that Greg had asked him
to stay until he returned. The expected invitation
to stay for dinner had immediately come from
Beth Mabry.

The glitter in the blue eyes had mocked Susan's
tight-lipped expression as Mitch Braden had murmured politely that he didn't want to inconvenience Mrs. Mabry before he allowed himself to be
talked into staying.

It had irritated Susan, the way her mother

treated him like visiting royalty. Amy hadn't been much better, practically swooning at his feet when she saw him as if he were a movie star. Her father had seemed to be the only one in her family to react normally, but then few things had ever ruffled him.

As for Susan, she had made an escape to the privacy of her room as soon as she decently could. Changing out of her office clothes, she had donned a cotton robe of cranberry red, offering a silent prayer that Warren's meeting with his father would not cancel their dinner. The alarm clock at her bedside had ticked the minutes away with infuriating slowness.

Downstairs the telephone rang. She unconsciously held her breath until her mother called, 'Susan, it's for you!'

It had to be Warren. With fingers crossed, she hurried down the stairs, the long robe swinging about her ankles. Her mother was near the base of the stairs in the living room alcove that served as an entrance hall. The phone was in her hand.

'It's Warren,' she told Susan. 'You aren't going out tonight, are you? Not with Mr. Braden staying for dinner?'

'Mitch Braden is Greg's guest, not mine,' Susan answered airily, reaching to take the receiver from her mother's hand.

Her moving gaze was caught by the man seated in the living room talking with her father. She quickly turned her back on the secretly amused gleam as she brought the telephone to her ear.

237

'Hello, darling,' she spoke into the mouthpiece with forced brightness.

Her greeting was not returned. Instead, Warren's harsh voice demanded, 'What did your mother just say? What was that about Mitch Braden staying for dinner?'

'That's right,' Susan breathed softly and hesitantly.

'What's he doing there?'

'I'll . . . I'll explain later,' she stalled.

'Does he know— Of course he knows,' Warren answered his own half-spoken question in a disgusted voice. But Susan knew what he had been going to ask, whether Mitch had learned they weren't married. 'Has he been bothering you?'

'No, of course not.' That was a lie, but the last thing Susan wanted was for Warren to make a scene. 'What about dinner this evening? Will you be free?' There was a slightly desperate ring to her voice in spite of her effort to reassure him that everything was all right.

Warren hesitated. 'Yes,' he said, then more firmly, 'Yes, I will be free. I'll be at your house in the time it takes me to drive from the office.'

'I'll be ready,' she promised, knowing that didn't give her a great deal of time.

'I'll see you, then,' he said with his usual clipped shortness, and hung up.

After Susan replaced the receiver in its cradle, her mother approached again. 'Susan—?' she began.

'Excuse me, Mom,' Susan interrupted quickly,

'but Warren is on his way here now and I don't have much time to get ready.'

Without giving her mother a chance to reply, she hurried up the stairs to her room. The cranberry-colored robe was tossed onto the bed and a classically straight dress of beige knit was taken from the clothes closet.

Dressing in record time, Susan dashed to the single bathroom on the second floor to repair her makeup. Amy was there in front of the mirror, carefully stroking her eyebrows with a tiny brush.

'Do you mind, Amy?' Susan rushed impatiently. 'I have to get ready. Warren will be here any minute.'

Her sister stepped sideways so she would be occupying only one small corner of the mirror. 'No, go ahead. You can use the mirror, too.' She set the brush in the makeup tray and picked up a tube of lip gloss.

Susan shook her head in despair and made use of her larger portion of the mirror. Sharing the bathroom with her teenage sister was something she probably should start becoming accustomed to.

'Do you think Mom would notice if I used some mascara?' Amy asked thoughtfully as she touched the corner of her mouth where some gloss had smeared.

'I'm quite sure she would,' Susan answered, hiding a smile while she remembered how impatient she had been to wear makeup.

Amy sighed and picked up the hairbrush to run

it through her long auburn hair. 'He likes long hair. Did you know that?'

A tiny frown of confusion knitted her eyebrows as Susan glanced curiously at Amy's reflection in the mirror. 'Who's "he"?' she asked, retouching the light green eyeshadow.

'Mitch,' was the prompt answer. 'He asked me to call him Mitch.'

'He did?' Susan responded dryly.

'Yes.' Amy leaned forward to fluff her bangs. 'He said he had a fondness for redheads, too. Of course, he said there was nothing wrong with brunettes,' she hastened to add as if suddenly worried that Susan might have felt insulted.

'I think Mitch Braden likes women, period.' Susan added a touch of peach blusher to her cheekbones, unable to keep the sarcasm out of her voice.

'Well, women like him, so I guess that makes the feeling mutual,' Amy declared with an airy toss of her head. 'I suppose I'd better get downstairs. Mom is almost ready to put the food on the table.'

That was an understatement, Susan thought as her sister went out of the room. Mitch Braden's sex appeal seemed to know no age barriers either. Her thirteen-year-old sister had just toppled under the spell of his charm. Unless she was careful, there was no telling who might be next.

When she was finished, Susan didn't go downstairs to wait for Warren. She chose to watch for him from her bedroom window that faced the street. As soon as she saw his car drive up, she hurried downstairs to the front door, calling goodbye to her family in the dining room.

There was a chorus of answering goodbyes including Mitch Braden's mocking, 'Have a good time, Susan.'

Warren had just emerged from his car when she darted out the front door. She saw him eye the blue sports car in the driveway and the black scowl that had appeared instantaneously on his face.

'I suppose that's his car,' he commented contemptuously as he held the passenger door open for Susan.

'Yes,' she nodded.

'It's disgusting the amount of money those racing drivers win,' he muttered almost beneath his breath, closed Susan's door and walked around to the driver's side. He didn't speak again until he was behind the wheel and they were driving away from the house. 'Now tell me how you ran into that Indy man again,' he commanded.

For the third time Susan repeated the story about Greg's car breaking down and Mitch Braden's arrival to help. Then she tacked on Greg's request that Mitch wait at the house for him and her mother's subsequent invitation to dinner which was accepted.

'What did he say to you?' Warren asked when she had finished.

Susan glanced at his stern profile with some confusion. 'When?'

'When he found out about—the marriage thing?'

Taking a deep, considering breath, Susan knew she couldn't repeat Mitch's response, so she chose to lie tactfully instead.

'When he said he thought I was married, I simply told him that he had misunderstood you. That what you'd actually said was that I was to *be* your wife.'

'Good thinking.' The look in his dark eyes was almost grateful, except Warren was much too proud. 'I should have known I could count on you.'

The topic of Mitch Braden was dropped for the time being, although Susan longed to ask why Warren had lied in the beginning. Yet his name cropped up the entire evening, usually in derogatory comments made by Warren. Fortunately the blue sports car was gone when Warren brought her home.

At the office the following morning, Warren questioned her very thoroughly about what her family had told Susan concerning Mitch's visit. Since Susan had not questioned them herself, she could answer very little. She had gathered the impression that possibly Greg planned to see Mitch Braden again, but since she wasn't positive of that she didn't tell Warren.

By Saturday evening Warren seemed to have forgotten Mitch Braden's existence completely. That brought Susan considerable relief because she had been uneasy discussing him with Warren.

She constantly felt she had to be on guard in case something slipped. And she didn't want to have to watch her words when she was with the man she was going to marry.

After a quiet dinner, Warren had told her that they were going to have to attend a party being given by one of his clients. Normally Susan didn't object to the mingling of business with their evenings together.

After all, when they were married, she would need to know the people Warren associated with outside of business hours. Yet tonight she had wanted them to be alone so she could be the center of his attention.

Warren had indicated they wouldn't stay long, but they had already been at Grayson Trevor's house for an hour. Susan was standing on the fringe of a group of men gathered around Warren, all of them deeply embroiled in a political discussion.

She had been with some of the younger women, but had become bored with their never-ending gossip. She had hoped to catch Warren's eye and suggest that they leave. He had seen her, but he was quite plainly not ready to leave.

Beat music was coming from the glassed veranda of the ultramodern home and Susan gravitated toward it. She stood quietly near the wall watching the rhythmic, swaying motions of the couples dancing on the tiled floor. Hidden by her long black skirt, a toe tapped in time with the music.

A young attractively dressed woman entered the room, ash blonde hair coiled in a sophisticated bun at the nape of her neck. Susan smiled in warm recognition. Anna Kemper was two years older, married with two small children. Since Susan had started dating Warren, she had met Anna at many functions such as this.

Anna spotted Susan at almost the same instant. 'Hello. Where's Warren?'

'In the other room talking politics,' she answered, smiling wryly. 'Where's Frank?'

'By now he's probably joined Warren,' Anna laughed.

'How are the children?'

Susan never learned the answer. At that moment a man came up behind her friend, his arms circling her waist. Brown hair flashed golden as the man bent his head to place a kiss in the hollow of Anna's neck. Susan's mouth opened in disbelief.

'Anna—still breathtakingly lovely, I see,' Mitch Braden murmured as he allowed the ash blonde to turn in his arms.

'Mitch!' she exclaimed gaily. 'I might have known it was you. How are you? All in one piece?'

'I'm fine,' he smiled lazily, and loosened his hold so Anna stood free. 'I can see for myself that you are, too.'

Anna turned to Susan, her hazel eyes dancing with pleasure. The words of introduction were forming on her lips, but Mitch didn't allow her to get them out.

'I knew if I looked long enough I'd find the

most beautiful girl in the house,' he stated softly. 'Hello, Susan.'

'Mr. Braden.' Susan stiffly tilted her head in acknowledgment, placing emphasis on the formality of her greeting.

'Do you two know each other?' Anna asked with a frown of surprise.

'We have met,' Susan admitted in the same rigid tone, 'but I couldn't know he would be here tonight.'

'Didn't you know, Susan?' Mitch taunted mockingly, his eyes crinkling merrily at the corners. 'Well, listen, I'm the proverbial bad penny. I always turn up.'

'So I'm beginning to learn,' she said coolly.

'Do I dare ask,' Anna hesitated, laughing nervously, 'what the problem is between you two?'

'There isn't any problem as far as I'm concerned, but you might ask that question of Susan later when the two of you are alone,' Mitch suggested, the directness of his gaze compelling Susan to look at him. His voice became husky, losing its amused quality to become caressing. 'Dance with me, Susan.'

It was neither an order nor a question. Not even a challenge. There was a small, negative movement of her dark head.

'No, thank you,' she refused, but the firmness in her voice wavered.

He reached out and lightly closed his fingers over the wrist of one of the hands clasped in front of her. There was something very winning in the boyishly pleading tilt of his handsome face.

'What's one dance going to hurt?' he shrugged in a coaxing gesture.

'Warren——' Susan began, glancing self-consciously over her shoulder.

'Warren isn't here.' With slight pressure, he disentangled her hands and drew her toward him. 'And while he's away, the cat is going to play— with the mouse.'

Susan cast a helpless look to Anna, seeking aid from her friend as she unresistingly allowed Mitch to lead her away. But Anna was lost in some silent speculation of her own and missed the wordless plea for help.

At the edge of the impromptu dance floor, the beat song ended and the music changed to a slow, romantic tune. 'This couldn't have worked out better if I'd planned it,' Mitch smiled slowly, and drew Susan around into his arms.

For several steps, she allowed her mind to concentrate only on following his lead. Then gradually her physical sense began to register impressions in her brain and she was unable to ignore him.

There was a clean, fresh scent about him that was definitely pleasing. His fingers were spread across the small of her back, molding her gently against him until she could feel the muscular strength in his legs and narrow hips.

She was staring at the knot of his black tie, yet she was very conscious of the strong-columned throat and the width of his shoulders beneath the black evening suit. The caressing warmth of his breath was near her temple. There seemed to be a steady increase in the rate of her heartbeat.

Her hand stiffened against his shoulder in protest to the way he was affecting her. 'Would you please not hold me so close?' she requested lowly.

'Why not?' he asked in the same low tone that sounded disturbingly sensual at these close quarters.

'Because it isn't right,' Susan answered, trying to breathe normally.

There was a testing movement of his hand on her back. 'It feels right,' murmured Mitch.

'Well, it doesn't look right,' she replied in an almost desperate whisper.

He tipped his head downward, his mouth moving against her dark hair as he spoke. 'To whom?'

'To everyone.' Her heart was thudding against her ribs, a traitorous weakness flowing into her limbs. She glanced wildly around the room, pulling away from the warm breath that teased the hair at her temples, but only Anna appeared to be watching them. 'Mitch, please don't do that.'

A finger touched her chin to draw her gaze back to his face. There was no laughing curve in his mouth. The bronze tan of his cheeks, smoothly shaven from cheekbone to jawline, invited her caress. The teasing glitter was absent from his eyes, but their darkening blue fire made Susan feel warm all over.

'Do you have any idea how long I've been waiting to hear you say my name?'

'I——' Susan faltered. No man should be so

handsome! His gaze became riveted on her lips and she couldn't think straight.

'This is a fine time to be in the middle of a dance floor, isn't it, darling?' A faint, dry smile curved his mouth.

She breathed in sharply. 'Don't call me that!'

'Why not?' he asked complacently. 'That's the way I think of you. Honey, darling——'

'Stop it!' Susan quickly lowered her gaze to the white of his shirt collar. 'You forget I'm engaged.'

'I haven't forgotten.'

'Then would you please leave me alone!' she protested, filled with a strange anger that she didn't understand.

'Do you mean here, right this minute?' A quick glance revealed his expression was serious in spite of the teasing lightness in his voice.

Susan looked around at the other couples, knowing eyebrows would rise if she and Mitch parted company in the middle of a song. Her wandering gaze was caught by Warren standing in the veranda doorway. His withdrawn expression was cold with displeasure. At that moment Anna approached Warren and Susan's gaze was released.

She swung it back to the black cloth of Mitch's jacket. 'Warren is here,' she muttered nervously.

'Am I supposed to quake in my shoes?' he asked in an amused tone.

'Oh, Mitch, would you be serious?' Susan demanded impatiently.

'Believe me, I'm very serious.'

She let the double meaning of his comment sail

over her head. 'I don't want there to be any trouble.'

'You mean that you don't want any fights started,' Mitch defined. 'Most women would feel complimented to have two men coming to blows over them.'

'I wouldn't, so please don't . . . don't rile him.'

'Are you afraid I might get hurt?'

She had felt the sinewy strong muscles in his chest, arms and thighs. Warren might have a weight advantage, but Mitch Braden was in much better physical condition.

Susan shook her head. 'I just don't want any trouble.'

'I wouldn't worry,' Mitch replied. 'Your fiancé is an attorney. He fights with words.'

'And you believe that actions speak louder?'

He shrugged indifferently. 'Let's just say that former opponents have indicated that I'm experienced with both.'

There was little doubt in her mind that he spoke the truth. She remembered the first meeting when his mock-serious comments had demolished Warren's composure to the point that he had lied about his and Susan's being married.

'Please, Mitch, don't start anything, for my sake,' Susan requested humbly.

The glint of humor left his gaze as it traveled over her upturned face. His solemn expression made her suddenly aware of an unrelenting quality in his handsome features. Beneath the surface charm and roguish air was a man of iron determination, incapable of wavering once he had set his mind on a goal.

'You have my word,' he answered evenly, 'for this once.'

And Susan knew instinctively that Mitch would keep his promise. She breathed an inaudible sigh of relief and smiled. A corner of his mouth quirked in response.

Their steps automatically ceased as the last note of the song faded. The lull in the music made Susan aware of the voices and laughter that filled the house.

The smile left her face before she turned to make her way toward Warren, Mitch's arm curved lightly across her back for his hand to rest on the side of her waist. The light possession was removed when they reached Warren.

'Hello, Warren.' Susan smiled with an attempt at naturalness as she moved to his side and slipped a hand beneath his elbow. His dark eyes gave her a sense of guilt even though she knew she had done nothing wrong.

'Susan,' he acknowleged her with a cool smile.

'I've returned her to you safe and unharmed, Mr. Sullivan,' Mitch commented, inclining his head with mock condescension.

'Thank you, Mr. Braden.' Susan could feel Warren's tense anger.

'And thank you for the dance, Miss Mabry.' Cynical laughter glittered in the blue eyes that were turned to her. 'Is that polite enough for you?'

'Y—you're quite welcome,' Susan acknowledged before glancing anxiously at the puckering frown of confusion in Warren's face.

'Forgive me, Mr. Sullivan,' Mitch apologized. 'Susan has been giving me a lesson in manners.'

A black brow arched inquiringly at Susan, the imposing arrogance of Warren's stance commanding her attention. Then his dark gaze slid back to Mitch Braden.

'I hope you didn't find it too difficult to learn,' he offered complacently.

'It wasn't easy to accept, Mr. Sullivan, believe me,' responded Mitch, dry-voiced. He glanced to Anna and her husband Frank Kemper. 'Anna, Frank,' he greeted them with a nod of his head. 'Excuse me, won't you? I think I'll go find the refreshment bar.'

With that Mitch moved away, walking lightly on the balls of his feet like an athlete. An uneasy silence followed his departure, one that neither Susan nor the couple standing next to her were willing to break.

'How did he succeed in crashing the party?' Warren muttered, staring after Mitch.

Frank Kemper ran a hand through his curling brown hair, hiding the glitter of amusement that appeared briefly in his brown eyes. 'I would guess he came with the Colesons. Their son is one of his chief mechanics and design engineers.'

'Are you acquainted with him, Frank?' Warren glanced curiously at his friend.

'Yes, although actually he's more Anna's friend than mine.'

The reply had Warren arching a brow of surprise at Frank's ash blonde wife. Anna glanced hesitantly at her husband as if asking him just how she should explain before replying.

'Mitch and I grew up in the same small town in Michigan. Of course, he's older than I am, but our parents were always good friends. We've been more or less like cousins,' Anna concluded.

'I see,' Warren drawled.

But Susan wasn't certain if she did. That hadn't been exactly a cousinly kiss Anna had received on the neck from Mitch. At the same time they had been more than cousins. Susan didn't have time to consider the thought further as Warren claimed her attention.

'I certainly hope you put him in his place once and for all,' he said.

'I doubt if anyone could do that,' Anna commented. 'That's supposing Mitch Braden had a place.'

Susan agreed, but she did so silently.

'Are you ready to leave, Susan?' Warren's hand closed possessively over the slender fingers resting on his arm.

'Yes, if you are.' She glanced into his face, seeing that the remoteness and coldness were gone. The ardent light in his dark eyes said she was forgiven for whatever it was that she had done wrong.

'I am,' he smiled, his rugged features possessing a wondrous softness with the action.

'So soon?' Anna sighed, then smiled understandingly at the engaged couple. 'Very well, I'll walk with Susan while she gets her coat.'

'I won't be long,' Susan promised Warren before leaving to get her wrap. As she and Anna left the glassed veranda for the main living area of the house, she took a deep, calming breath. 'You never did tell me how the children were.'

'And you never did tell me how you met Mitch.' A pair of hazel eyes twinkled back.

Susan paused for a second. 'It isn't a pleasant memory.'

'I can't believe that,' her friend laughed shortly. 'Tell me about it.'

After relating an accurate version of the first encounter in the restaurant, Susan tacked on a shortened version of Mitch stopping to aid them on the highway. She didn't know why she hadn't refused to discuss it with Anna.

'No wonder Warren was livid with jealousy when he saw you dancing with him,' Anna declared with decided amusement. 'Only Mitch would walk up to a total stranger and tell him how beautiful he thinks the man's date is.'

'Since you know him, I wish you'd tell him to leave me alone,' Susan sighed.

'Does he bother you?'

'It's embarrassing to have him following me around. I mean, I'm engaged.'

'Don't ask me to believe you don't find him attractive,' Anna smiled widely. 'No woman is immune to his looks and charm.'

Susan tipped her head to the side, gazing at her

friend with curious speculation. 'Including you, Anna?'

Nonplussed, the blonde glanced away. 'That's a question that requires a delicately phrased answer from a married woman like myself. I'm not immune to Mitch,' she sighed ruefully. 'He can still make me feel like I'm very much a woman, but not in that special way that Frank does. I'm very much in love with my husband and I wouldn't trade him for anyone else even if I could.'

'But you and Mitch were more than just make-believe cousins once?' Susan voiced the impression she had received earlier.

They entered the guest room being used as a powder room for the party that evening. Susan paused near one of the mirrors, waiting for the response to her half-statement and half-question. Anna lowered her voice so she couldn't be overheard by the other chattering women in the room.

'There was a time,' she acknowledged, frankly meeting Susan's gaze, 'when I was very much infatuated with Mitch. I could have easily fallen in love with him if I'd received the slightest encouragement. But he let me down easy, never once hurting my feelings or damaging our friendship.'

Guilty at having pried into something that was none of her business, Susan looked away. 'I'm sorry, Anna. I had no right to ask that. You should have told me not to be so nosy.'

'I don't mind.' Anna shook her head, absently watching as Susan retrieved her spring coat. 'Mitch has been racing for several years now.

Well, actually he's been racing cars since he was in high school, but only in the last few years has he been winning consistently. With his looks and personality, the press automatically tagged him as the bachelor playboy of the circuit. But he isn't a shallow person, Susan. He's very warm and very sincere and very intelligent. Frank says Mitch has an uncanny knack for making the right investment and a very astute business mind.'

'Why are you telling me all this?' Susan frowned.

'Because . . . ' Anna shrugged uncertainly, 'because of the attention he's paying you, I guess.'

'I'm flattered, of course, but——'

Anna interrupted. 'What I'm really saying is that if I'd received the encouragement you have, I'd already be in love with him.'

Nervously Susan turned away, her fingers fidgeting with the lining of her coat. 'You're forgetting that I'm already in love with Warren and we're going to be married in August.'

'Yes, I suppose I was,' the other girl agreed with self-conscious brightness. 'Speaking of Warren, he's probably worried that Mitch has waylaid you somewhere.'

Draping the light coat over her arm, Susan turned, an equally false smile on her face. She didn't like the vague stirrings of uneasiness she felt.

'We'd better be getting back,' she nodded.

As the two girls retraced their path to the veranda, Susan spied Mitch standing in the far corner of a room talking with two men. His gaze flicked to her at almost the same instant. There was an almost imperceptible nod of his head to acknowledge her look but no flashing smile to make her heart quicken.

When Susan walked through the room again at Warren's side, she refused to let her gaze be drawn to that corner of the room. Mitch Braden was physically attractive, but there was room for only one man in her life and that was Warren. She didn't intend to complicate things by encouraging Mitch, however unconsciously.

In the car she snuggled close to Warren, needing his nearness to chase away the shivers of apprehension that danced over her skin. When the car was started and they were on the road, he slid his arm around her shoulders and nestled her closer.

'Love me, Susan?' he asked, taking his attention from the road long enough to brush a kiss against the side of her hair.

'You know I do, darling,' she answered fervently, and wondered why she was so desperate to convince Warren of the fact.

CHAPTER FOUR

WARREN bent over Susan's desk, adding the typed notes she had given him to the stack of papers clipped together in his hand. He barely glanced at her as he issued instructions with a preoccupied air.

'I shall probably be with my father all afternoon. Hold all my calls unless Con Anderson phones. Put him straight through,' he ordered crisply.

'I will,' Susan acknowledged.

Warren straightened. 'I'm beginning to look forward to my father entering the hospital tomorrow.' A sardonic smile lifted the corners of his mouth. 'Maybe the office will settle into some semblance of routine again.'

A faint, agreeing smile appeared briefly on her lips, but Warren was already gathering his papers together and starting for the hall door.

Susan sighed and glanced at the small desk calendar. A silent prayer of thanks was offered that the three-day Memorial weekend was only two days away. She would welcome the time to recover from this hectic pace that seemed to require a constant juggling of appointments and schedules.

The hall door closed behind Warren as Susan swiveled to her typewriter, reaching for the earpiece of the dictaphone. The ringing of the telephone checked her movement.

'Warren Sullivan's office,' Susan answered in her courteous, professional voice.

'Hello, beautiful,' was the immediate response.

Susan froze, unable to breathe or speak. It couldn't possibly be Mitch Braden. He would never call her at work, would he?

'Did you wish to speak to Mr. Sullivan?' she asked coolly.

'Hardly,' Mitch chuckled.

The hall door opened and Susan quickly placed her hand over the receiver mouthpiece as Warren strode into her office. 'Forgot my notepad,' he said in explanation, walking to her desk and retrieving the legal size pad of yellow paper. He glanced at the telephone in her hand. 'Is that for me? Find out who it is. I might not be in.'

'No,' she said hurriedly. 'It's for me.' A curious light entered Warren's dark eyes. It was a rarity for Susan to receive a personal call at the office. 'It's . . . it's my mother,' she lied. 'She wants me to pick up some things at the store on my way home.'

With a satisfied nod, he turned to the hall door. 'Give her my regards,' he tossed over his shoulder absently.

Susan let out the deep breath she had been holding and slipped her hand away from the mouthpiece of the telephone. She didn't speak until the door was firmly closed behind Warren and she heard his footsteps echoing down the outside hall.

'What was it you wanted, Mr. Braden? I'm very busy,' she inquired with cool hauteur.

His tongue clicked reprovingly in her ear. 'Lying to your boss is one thing, Susan, but lying to your fiancé? Shame on you!' he mocked.

An embarrassed red warmed her neck. 'If you've merely called to——' she began angrily.

'To invite you on a guided tour of the race grounds tonight,' Mitch interrupted lazily, 'with a stop for dinner afterward.'

'I'm busy.'

'Tomorrow night isn't possible, I know,' he said with remarkable indifference to her sharp tone. 'Tuesday, Thursday, Saturday and Sunday nights are when you have your appointments with Warren.'

'They're dates,' Susan corrected.

'All right, they're dates,' Mitch conceded. 'Now,

when are you and I going to have a date? It's been four days since I saw you last. Haven't you missed me?'

'Was I supposed to?' The coldness of her voice was to help freeze away the image of his handsome face that kept trying to dance into her mind.

'I hoped you would,' he replied with a warm huskiness in his voice that made his words almost a physical caress. Susan swallowed, trying to ease the tightness in her throat. Her pulse was skipping erratically. 'I want to see you tonight, Susan. I promise I'll be a good little boy.'

'I told you, I'm busy,' she hurried, feeling the pull of his masculine attraction even over the telephone lines. 'I have to wash my hair and——'

'Can't you think of anything more original?' his amused voice laughed in her ear. 'No man believes that excuse any more.'

'You're right,' Susan said with sudden determination. 'I don't need to make excuses. I won't go out with you tonight or any other night, Mitch. I'm engaged to be married.'

There was a short pause before he responded in a quiet voice. 'Is that your final word?'

A muscle constricted painfully in her chest. 'Yes,' she answered, trying to ignore the hurt.

'Okay,' Mitch sighed, reluctantly accepting her reply. 'Maybe I'll see you around some time,' he said in a shrugging tone that indicated he doubted the possibility. 'So long, beautiful.'

'Goodbye, Mitch.'

Something seemed to be burning her eyes as she

hung up the telephone receiver. Nervously she ran a shaking hand through her dark silken hair, and blinked rapidly.

Drat the man! Why had he bothered to call? He must have known she would refuse to go out with him. And she had just begun to convince herself that she had heard the last of him. In fact she had even started to forget about him, at least partially, until this telephone call.

Why had she talked to him? she asked herself angrily. She should have hung up the phone the instant she recognized his voice. Or why hadn't she told Warren who was on the phone and let him deal with Mitch?

Since the first time she had met him, Mitch Braden had been disrupting her life, her senses, her emotions, and her relationship with Warren. She wanted to feel the peace and contentment she had known before she met him. Every time she thought she was about to obtain it, Mitch Braden popped up again, disrupting things all over again.

Now he had even confused her to the point where she was sorry that she would never see him again. What was worse, she seemed powerless to stop the sadness from invading her heart.

It was a good thing she wouldn't be seeing or hearing from him again. And it was a good thing that the race would be run this weekend and Mitch Braden would be leaving town within a few days after its conclusion.

Without him around to disrupt her, her life would settle into its previous pattern. The ripples his unexpected arrival had brought into her tranquil life would eventually disappear, without leaving any mark.

The logic didn't cheer Susan.

Her dark hair was caught in saucy pigtails on either side of her head, secured with ribbons of mint green to match the thin fabric of her short-sleeved polka-dot blouse. The wide legs of her white slacks swung about her ankles as she walked down the hospital corridor with Warren, the raised heels of her sandals clicking loudly in the hushed building.

'I told Father we might stop in this afternoon after our picnic,' said Warren. 'He's been waiting for me to bring you each time I've come to see him. I would have suggested it before, of course, except that the doctor thought it would be best to keep visitors at an absolute minimum the first couple of days after the operation.'

'I thought you said the operation took less time than expected and that your father had come through it in excellent shape,' Susan frowned.

'He did, but with his advanced years, it was still a shock to his system. We didn't want to take any risks of complication,' he explained. 'Here's his room.'

He indicated a door ahead and to Susan's right. She waited for him to open it, then walked into the semiprivate room. Robert Sullivan was partially sitting up in his bed, wire-rimmed glasses perched on the end of his nose. He looked over the top of them and closed the magazine on his lap. He looked pale but otherwise in good health.

'Hello, Susan.' He extended his hand toward her and she walked to the side of his bed to accept its firm clasp. 'You certainly are the picture of a summer's day!'

Blinking once in surprise at the rare compliment from the usually taciturn man, Susan smiled. 'Thank you. You're looking quite fit, too. How are you?'

'Stiff, sore, and uncomfortable, but that's to be expected I guess,' he replied, releasing her hand and turning to his son. 'Hello, Warren.'

Susan knew she had been dismissed and moved from the side of the bed to an armchair that stood near the foot. The partitioning curtain was drawn, concealing the second occupant of the hospital room, although the loud playing of a radio from the other side made Susan doubt that the patient would possibly be sleeping.

'That radio is awfully loud, isn't it?' Warren frowned in the direction of the curtain.

'Yes,' his father sighed heavily. 'I wish he'd turn the volume down.'

'Would you like me to ask him to do it?'

'No, no.' Robert Sullivan impatiently waved aside the offer. 'The man's half deaf. He can't hear it if he turns it any lower. Besides, I've already told him I didn't object. He doesn't have it on very often.'

With that explanation, Warren's father shifted the conversation to an article he had just been reading concerning a supreme court decision recently made. Susan wondered if he had any interest outside of his profession.

It didn't really matter, she decided, glancing at Warren and smiling to herself. They had had a wonderful time on their picnic. Warren had brought along a bottle of wine to go with the meal she had packed. He had taken her to a secluded spot alongside the rapids of a river. The setting had been idyllic, just the two of them alone, talking about their plans for the future.

Susan had been so contented lying on the blanket in his arms. She had hated it when they had to leave. Yet the rosy afterglow of the moment was still with her, maybe the aftereffects of the wine she had drunk.

Leaning back in her seat, Susan relaxed, not minding now that she wasn't the sole object of Warren's attention. From the other side of the curtain, the radio dial was turned, jumbling music together until it was finally stopped to the sound of a radio announcer's words.

'And now we'll go trackside with Jim Jensen and a report on the status of the Indianapolis 500.'

There was a roar in the background, followed by a second man's voice. 'Hello, ladies and gentlemen, this is Jim Jensen. Let me bring you up to date on the Indy 500. It will be no surprise to you racing fans out there when I say that the leader is none other than Mitch Braden.'

Susan clenched her teeth in frustration at the sound of his name. She wanted to rush over there and turn off that radio. The mention of the man's name seemed to destroy her contentment.

'He's been leading the pack since almost the beginning of the race,' the radio announcer continued.

'The first hundred miles Braden and another veteran driver, Johnny Phelps, jockeyed for the lead before Braden took command. He's been leading by a comfortable margin ever since.'

Trying to close her ears to the man's voice, Susan concentrated on the rainbow colors flashing from her diamond engagement ring. But her hearing seemed to grow more acute.

'The yellow caution flag has only been out three times. Except for those three minor mishaps, the race has been free of accidents. Twelve cars are out with mechanical malfunctions, but none of the drivers of those twelve cars were expected to be among the front runners today.

'If Mitch Braden does receive the checkered flag today,' the announcer's voice raised slightly as the background roar of racing engines grew louder, 'he's going to have to give a lot of credit to the outstanding performance of his pit crew today. They've been phenomenal. I say that because I see Braden is heading into the pits now. Let's take a few seconds to time him, and ladies and gentlemen, with that crew, a few seconds is all it's going to be.'

Suddenly the pitch of the man's voice changed. 'Braden is in the pits, slowing— An accident! In the pits!' Susan's eyes widened in alarm. 'It happened so fast! Braden was coming in, just starting to slow down, when Mark Terry, who was well back in the pack, accelerated out of his pit area. He couldn't have seen Braden coming in! His car ran right into the side of Braden's and rolled up on top of it!'

Her heart was in her throat, all the blood leaving her limbs until she felt chilled to the bone. It couldn't be happening! It wasn't really true!

'Terry has scrambled out of his car, seemingly unharmed, but there's no sign of Braden!' The announcer continued his eyewitness account in a fever-pitched tone. 'Emergency vehicles are already on the scene and I can see the familiar blue uniforms of Braden's pit crew. I don't see any sign of fire, but it's impossible to be certain. If Braden is trapped underneath Terry's car——' The thought wasn't finished, to Susan's horror, her imagination working much too vividly.

'I can see men working frantically on one side of Braden's car now! Yes, yes, they're pulling him out! He doesn't appear to be conscious. But of course we can't know how seriously he's been injured. That finishes the race for Braden, though. Johnny Phelps is the new leader. What a tough break, fans! They have Braden on a stretcher and are loading him into the ambulance. The Indy officials can be proud of the speed with which the rescue men reacted. I——'

'Susan. Susan?' Warren's frowning voice broke sharply in.

'Wh—what?' She looked at him blankly.

'You're as white as a sheet.' He walked swiftly to her side. 'Are you ill? What's the matter with you?'

She did feel sick. Her hands were cold and clammy when Warren clasped them firmly in his own. A black nausea was swimming before her eyes.

'I—I think I need a breath of—of fresh air,' she stammered. How could she possibly explain her reaction to the news of Mitch's accident? It didn't make sense to be so violently upset simply because she knew him.

Warren helped her to stand. 'Would you want me to go with you?'

'No.' Her knees were shaking badly as she shook her head in denial. 'I'll be all right in a moment, really. It's just a little stuffy in here. Ex—excuse me, please.'

Her rounded brown eyes bounced away from Warren's concerned gaze and she barely caught the frowning look from Robert Sullivan. She managed to force her legs to carry her into the hallway. Out of sight of the door, she leaned weakly against the corridor wall, breathing in deeply to quell the churning of her stomach.

The long gulps of air seemed to breathe strength into her limbs. The nameless terror that gripped her heart started to ease as her knees stopped their quivering.

'Susan?' Warren stood beside her, his eyes anxiously examining the pallor that remained in her face.

'You needn't have come.' She took another deep breath. 'I'm sorry I——'

'Don't apologize,' he interrupted, circling an arm under her shoulders and drawing her away from the wall. 'Let's get you outside in the fresh air.'

'I'm all right, really,' she protested weakly, but she let his strength carry her along. 'I just felt a little faint there for a moment.'

'Maybe it was the wine,' Warren suggested with a gentle smile.

'Yes,' she breathed, taking advantage of the excuse he offered.

The late spring air did its reviving act, returning color to her cheeks. The shock of Mitch's accident had dissipated, but a feeling of sick dread remained. When Warren suggested taking her home, she made only a halfhearted protest.

'Your father——' she began.

'——will understand perfectly. I'll call in to see him on my way to pick you up this evening, providing you're feeling fit enough to go out,' he said, helping her into his car. His solicitude made her feel even more guilty for not telling him the real cause of her upset state.

When they had driven out of the hospital parking lot, Susan glanced hesitantly at his carved profile. 'Do you mind if—if we turn the radio on?'

'Of course not.' He smiled at her crookedly, a frown of curious confusion drawing his dark brows together as he reached out to switch on the radio.

A news broadcast was on and Warren started to turn the dial to some music. 'No,' Susan rushed to stop him. 'That station is fine.'

Warren shrugged and left it there. Crossing her fingers in her lap that the news hadn't been on very long, Susan listened to a synopsis of the world news and swallowed when the announcer changed to the local scene.

Forcing a stoic expression into her face, she listened to a shortened account of the accident minus the terrorizing adjectives. A cautious glance at Warren caught him listening interestedly, too.

'—We do not have a report on the extent or seriousness of the injuries to Mitch Braden,' the announcer said. 'An ambulance attendant did say that Braden had regained consciousness in the ambulance. When we have more information, we'll pass it on to you.'

Susan's lashes fluttered down in temporary relief.

'Well, our Indy man seems to have had some bad luck,' Warren commented dryly.

Susan winced. 'Don't be flippant, Warren, please!'

'I didn't mean to sound callous.' He slid a questioning look in her direction. 'I may not like the man, but I certainly wouldn't wish him any crippling injury.'

Her heart catapulted into her throat. She hadn't considered the possibility that Mitch might be maimed or paralyzed. Her initial fear had been for his life. The prospect of that vital, handsome man chained to crutches or a wheelchair or a bed sent more sickening chills over her skin.

'I know you don't, Warren,' she replied, suppressing a shudder.

She leaned her head against the back cushion of her seat, closing her eyes and trying to achieve the indifferent interest Warren displayed.

'We'll be at your home shortly,' he said, misinterpreting her action and wanness as another sign of the dizziness she had suffered in the hospital and not connecting it with Mitch Braden's accident.

Soft music from the radio filled the silence. The soothing melody didn't penetrate Susan's thoughts, however. Her mind was replaying the last conversation she had had on the telephone with Mitch. She had been so sharp and so cold with him.

It hurt unbearably now to think that those might have been the last words she would exchange with him. She could have gotten the same message across with politeness and humor instead of being so indignant and rude.

The motion of the car stopped. Susan blinked her eyes open, recognizing the gracefully old brick home, and swung her head to look into Warren's dark eyes. He was half-turned in his seat, studying her quietly, his arm resting along the top of the cushion near her head.

With his forefinger, he reached out to touch the tuft of dark hair held by the green ribbon. 'You look more like a little girl who's had too many treats at the fair than a woman who's had too much wine,' he mused, then tilted his jet black head in concern. 'Are you sure you're going to be all right?'

'I'll be fine,' she smiled stiffly.

'You wait here,' Warren ordered, 'while I get the picnic hamper from the back.'

Susan did as she was told, remaining in the car until his supporting hand helped her out and guided her to the front door of her home. Only when they were inside did Warren release his hold.

'Oh, Susan, it's you!' Her mother appeared in the hallway, from the direction of the kitchen, wiping her hands on a towel. 'I didn't expect you home so soon.'

'Susan isn't feeling well, Mrs. Mabry,' said Warren.

'It's nothing, Mom, really,' Susan murmured quickly as Beth Mabry walked forward with concern in her brown eyes.

'You do look a bit pale, dear.' She pressed a hand against Susan's cheek. 'You don't seem to have a temperature, though.'

'You two are making a fuss about nothing.' Susan tried to laugh. 'It's just a little headache and dizziness. If I lay down for an hour it will go away.'

'I'll call you about six-thirty to see if you feel up to going out tonight,' Warren stated. 'If she isn't feeling better in an hour or so, Mrs. Mabry, I hope you'll have your husband take a look at her.'

'I will,' Beth Mabry promised. 'Let me take that picnic hamper for you, Warren. And Susan, you go and lie down.'

'You do as she tells you,' Warren added, touching Susan's cheek with his hand in a goodbye caress.

Susan stared at the front door for several seconds after Warren had closed it, wishing that she could have shared some of the anxiety she was feeling with him. But he wouldn't have understood. For that matter she didn't understand it very well herself.

'Would you like an aspirin or something, Susan?' Beth Mabry watched the unusual melancholy emotions flitting across her daughter's face.

'No, nothing,' Susan refused absently, and started toward the stairwell leading to the second floor.

A car pulled into the drive, the sound followed immediately by the slamming of doors and footsteps approaching the front door. Susan turned toward it, her hand poised on the banister. Her brother walked into the house ahead of his father. Greg's chin was tucked into his chest, hands shoved in his pockets and shoulders hunched forward.

In Susan's shock and subsequent worry, she had completely forgotten that Mitch had mailed complimentary tickets to the race today and that her father and brother had attended.

'Simon?' her mother exclaimed with some surprise. 'Is the race over already?'

'No,' he replied, glancing with concern at his

son's bowed head. 'There was an accident at the track. Mitch Braden has been taken to the hospital.'

'No!' Her mother's denial was given in astonishment and fear.

Amy appeared at the top of the stairs, a hairbrush in her hand. 'Mitch is hurt?'

'I'm afraid so, kitten,' her father affirmed grimly, and Susan noticed the tightness of his mouth.

For all his outward control, Simon Mabry was upset, too. In his short acquaintanceship, Mitch Braden had managed to touch all their lives.

'Was it . . . was it very bad?' her mother asked in a voice barely above a whisper. Susan guessed that she was envisaging a flaming crash and remembered her own surge of terror at that imagined picture. 'Is he seriously hurt?'

'It was bad enough,' Simon answered. 'He was trapped for a short time under another car. We heard a radio report on the way home that he had regained consciousness before reaching the hospital, but nothing about any injuries.'

'If something happens to him,' Amy wailed, 'I'll just die!'

Greg shifted his feet uncomfortably and Susan wanted to walk over and put an arm around his shoulders to say that she felt the same miserable pain he did. Fear of the unknown was eating at her heart, too.

'I think I'll turn on the radio,' he mumbled. 'Maybe they'll know something else.'

'Wait a minute, son,' Simon laid a hand on

Greg's shoulder. 'Maybe I can cut through some of the red tape.'

'What are you going to do, Daddy?' Amy raced down the steps past Susan, the long auburn hair that Mitch had professed to like shimmering like fire.

'I'm going to call emergency receiving and see if I can't find out something,' he answered in a decisive tone.

Susan gasped back the little sob that tried to escape and followed the others as they hurried after her striding doctor father. In the study, they all huddled around the desk where her father sat.

'I think Kate Johnson has the duty today,' he mused absently and flipped through his telephone list for the hospital number. 'She's an excellent surgeon,' he told them as he dialed the number.

It seemed an interminable time before anyone answered.

'This is Doctor Simon Mabry,' her father identified himself. 'I'd like to speak to Doctor Johnson.' There was another pause, filled by the drumming of her father's fingers on the desk top. 'Kate? Simon Mabry here. What? . . . No, no, I'm not bringing anyone in. I was calling about Mitch Braden, the race car driver they brought in from the speedway . . . I guessed that, but can you give me what you've got?'

Studying her father's expression intently, Susan didn't move, but waited motionless like the rest of her family. He listened quietly to the woman doctor on the other end of the phone, his silence occasionally punctuated by his grunts of understanding.

'Thank you, Kate,' he said finally. 'I appreciate this.' Then he said goodbye and hung up.

'Well?' Susan probed anxiously.

'So far,' he breathed in deeply, lifting his head to meet the gazes centered on him, 'they know he has a broken arm, some cracked ribs, and a concussion. They're still checking for internal injuries and the like.'

A sigh of relief seemed to come from all of them. Susan only knew she wanted to cry, her knees buckling slightly before stiffening to support her.

'I knew all the time he would be all right,' Amy declared brightly.

'He's tough,' Greg agreed with a tight smile, man-fully trying to conceal his emotions.

'I'm so relieved.' Beth Mabry shook her head as if astounded to discover how tense she had been. 'Every year you hear about a crash of some sort in the Indianapolis 500, but this is the first time we've ever known anyone involved, as more than just a name, I mean.'

'I think we all understand, Beth.' Simon Mabry glanced warmly about him at the smiling, relieved faces of his children.

Susan swallowed the tight lump in her throat and turned away from the group. Her fingers were still pressed against her stomach, but the nauseous churning had stopped. Mitch was going to be all right, said a joyous voice from her heart.

'Susan, in all the excitement,' her mother exclaimed, 'I forgot you were supposed to be resting.'

'Resting?' her father questioned. 'Aren't you feeling well, Susan?'

'I—I had a headache,' she answered self-consciously, not quite meeting her parents' eyes. 'It seems to have gone away, though.'

Which was the truth.

'With all the distraction, you probably forgot to feel ill,' her mother smiled. 'Warren was certainly worried. He'll be glad to hear you're all right.'

'Yes,' Susan agreed, with a faint answering smile.

Now that she was feeling better there was no reason not to go out with him that evening. But the dinner was an anticlimax. Susan couldn't seem to recapture the peace and contentment she had experienced earlier in his company.

Warren naturally blamed her restlessness on the lingering effect of her headache, and Susan let him, since she couldn't explain to herself why she couldn't find that previous sensation of closeness to him.

CHAPTER FIVE

NERVOUSLY adjusting the collar of her peach-colored jacket, Susan paused in the hospital corridor. Her palm was faintly damp and she pressed it against her skirt before clutching the leather case a little tighter. Her gaze darted swiftly into the open doorways of the hospital rooms in the hall as she started forward again.

'May I help you, miss?' a female voice inquired behind her.

Susan turned with a start, smiling self-consciously. 'No,' she answered quickly, glancing at the leather case in her hands. 'I was just bringing some papers to Mr. Robert Sullivan.'

The uniformed nurse, an older woman with

beautiful waving white hair and twinkling eyes, smiled and nodded. 'His room is three doors down to your right.'

'Thank you,' Susan turned away, her moving gaze flicking to the open doorway on the opposite side of the hall. There was a rustle of movement from the room.

'Hey, beautiful! Is that you?' Mitch Braden's voice rang clearly into the hall.

A red blush of embarrassment filled Susan's face as she turned instinctively toward the door in answer and caught the amused, raised eyebrow of the nurse.

Her step hesitated for only a second before she continued to the room. She told herself she wouldn't stay more than a couple of minutes, just pop in to wish him a polite get-well.

'Susan?' his inquiring voice called again as she walked through the open door of his hospital room.

He didn't see her immediately. He was trying to push himself into a more upright position in the bed with one arm. There was a wince of pain and his face went pale before he slumped back.

'Lie still,' Susan ordered quickly, walking swiftly to his bedside.

The blue eyes opened and Mitch simply looked at her for a long moment. 'Hello,' he said softly, lean dimples appearing in the tanned cheeks.

Her chest constricted at the dark glow in his eyes. 'Hello,' she returned with equal softness, a faint smile on her mouth.

'I heard your voice in the hall.' His compelling gaze refused to let her look away. 'I didn't think you would come in to see me.'

'What were you going to do?' she teased gently. 'Come racing after me?'

There was an urge to reach out and smooth the tousled gold-brown hair falling across his forehead. Susan moved away from the bed before she succumbed to it.

'I might have. My legs weren't injured, only this,' Mitch tapped the cast on his left arm, 'and a few ribs and a bump on the head.'

'The last certainly didn't knock any sense into you!' She let her hand trail over the foot of the bed and close over the rail, balancing the leather case containing the papers for Robert Sullivan beside it.

'Did you think it might?'

She could feel his eyes watching her. The intentness of his gaze began to affect her breathing and she shifted uncomfortably. Somehow the conversation had become too intimate. She had intended only to make an aloof, polite inquiry about his health, and here she was trading a kind of soft banter with him.

'I don't know,' she shrugged, and stared at the diamond ring on her wedding finger.

'Well!' Mitch breathed in. 'Have I lost track of time? Isn't this Tuesday? Shouldn't you be working?'

Her glance was almost grateful at his change of subject. 'It's Tuesday and I'm working. Warren's father is here in the hospital recovering from an operation. I was bringing him some papers to study.'

'I see.' He paused. 'Were you at the race? I looked for you, but I only saw your father and Greg. I sent enough tickets.'

'Yes, I know you did,' Susan answered nervously. 'I know they would want me to thank you for them, too. Warren and I had already made plans to go on a picnic.'

A wry smile tugged the corners of his mouth. 'It's probably just as well the two of you weren't there. Warren would probably have cheered when he saw the crash.'

'That's not fair,' she protested. 'All of us were upset when we heard about the accident.'

'Were you?' He shot her a piercing blue look.

Susan glanced away, afraid he might have some way of getting inside her mind and finding out how upset she had been. 'Of course,' she answered curtly. Tossing her head back, she let go of the railing and hugged the leather case in front of her. 'I really have to be going, Mitch. Mr. Sullivan is expecting me. I . . . I hope you're feeling better soon.'

'Wait.' His voice checked her movement toward the door. She glanced warily over her shoulder. 'You haven't autographed my cast yet.' He flashed her a smile that made her heart turn over.

Susan hesitated as she watched Mitch reach for a black pen lying on the table beside his bed. With a resigned sigh she walked back to the bed, taking the pen he extended toward her. The briefcase was awkwardly in the way and she set it on the bed. She bent slightly over him, the pen poised above the cast as she tried to decide what to write.

'You could put down "All my love" or "Love and kisses" ' Mitch suggested with a twinkle.

As quickly as the pen and cast would allow, Susan scrawled 'Get well soon' and signed her name. Straightening, she held the pen out to him, reaching for the case with her other hand. But instead of taking the pen, his right hand took hold of hers.

'Susan?' Her startled eyes met his faintly earnest gaze that searched her face. 'I would like you to come see me again,' he said, almost humbly.

'I'm afraid that's not possible.' She tried to withdraw her hand, but he wouldn't release it.

'Please, I——' He stopped, glancing down at her hand. 'It gets awfully monotonous being confined in this room hour after hour. Most of my friends are guys at the track, and they're pulling out for other races.'

'I'm sorry. I——' Susan frowned, wondering if it was loneliness she saw flicker across his face, so handsome and proud.

'I don't expect you to make a special trip to see me.' Mitch smiled ruefully, his thumb caressing the inside of her wrist in what appeared an unconscious motion. 'But if you have to come to the hospital to bring Warren's father any more papers, would you come in and say hello?'

The blue eyes held her mesmerized. 'I . . . I suppose I could,' she surrendered to their spell.

'Thank you.' He carried her fingertips to the soft firmness of his lips, making them tingle from the intimacy of the caress.

There was a rustle of a starched uniform behind Susan, followed by a brisk female voice. 'It's that time again, Mr. Braden.'

Susan pulled her hand free from Mitch's hold, hiding it guiltily behind her back as she spun toward the nurse she had met in the hallway.

'Madge, you have a rotten sense of timing,' Mitch sighed with a mock grimace at her interruption.

The nurse winked broadly at Susan before answering. 'We nurses pride ourselves on being a nuisance.'

'I'd better be going.' Susan quickly gathered up her briefcase as the nurse determinedly held out a thermometer.

'You won't forget to come again?' Mitch held her wavering gaze.

'No,' she admitted in a low voice, wishing she hadn't agreed as she hurried from his room.

There was too much of a risk that word might somehow filter to Robert Sullivan and from there to his son that Susan had seen Mitch Braden, for her to attempt to conceal the visit from Warren. His lips thinned with displeasure at the news, when she told him at dinner that evening.

'Did you really think it was necessary to see him?' he asked churlishly.

'It wasn't necessary,' Susan admitted, studying the rounded chunks of ice in her water goblet rather than meet his censorious dark gaze. 'But since I was right there, it seemed a bit unfeeling not to look in and wish him a speedy recovery.'

'Perhaps,' Warren submitted grudgingly, 'but considering that man's absence of manners, I would hardly worry about doing the polite thing.'

'His behavior is not my concern, nor any reason to behave the same way,' she explained patiently. 'After all, the man has no family here and his friends are mainly people from the race track. If they haven't gone already, they'll be leaving town in the next day or two. It's lonely, confined to a hospital room without any visitors.'

'Braden, lonely?' The disbelieving words were followed by a short, contemptuous laugh. 'I'm certain he has any number of female visitors flocking to his bedside without my fiancée among them!'

'I did not rush to his bedside!' Her nerve ends frayed at the edges. 'I think it's insulting of you to insinuate that I did!'

'I didn't mean to imply that you deliberately did, but I have little doubt that Braden and others would look at it in that light,' Warren retorted. 'Considering the way he's flirted with you so boldly in the past, I'm certain he sees your visit as a sign of encouragement to continue.'

'I did not encourage him,' Susan responded tautly.

Yet, remembering the light kiss on her fingertips, she wondered if unconsciously she had. And she had foolishly said she would see him again.

'Not intentionally, but as conceited as he is, he

will believe that you did. That's what I've been trying to explain,' he said with impatience.

'All right, you've explained, so let's stop arguing about this.'

'I'm not arguing.' His imposing, masculine features darkened in controlled anger. 'I'm simply forbidding you to see him again.'

Her eyes widened in astonishment, their soft brown color flaming into a snapping fire of temper. Her strong sense of independence asserted itself with a rush as Warren pushed her too far. Being willing to please the man she loved and was going to marry was entirely different from being ruled by him.

'Forbid me! Of all the arrogant——' Susan closed her mouth abruptly, choking on the anger erupting from inside. Uncaring of the possibly interested looks from the other people in the restaurant, she pushed herself out of her chair. 'You may ask me not to see him again, Warren, but nobody *forbids* me to do anything!'

Without a backward glance, she stalked from the table, disregarding his low-voiced command to return. The girl in the cloakroom had just handed her her coat when a glowering Warren appeared at her side. Susan turned to him, lifting her chin defiantly.

'Are you going to take me home, or shall I ask for a taxi?' she challenged.

'What do you think you're doing, making a scene like this?' Warren muttered angrily.

Susan pivoted away. 'I'll get a taxi.'

Her elbow was seized in a rough grip and she was propelled toward the outer door. His hold didn't lessen as he nearly forced her to his car in tight-lipped silence. The crackling tension remained through the entire journey to her home with neither of them uttering a sound.

When the car stopped in front of the house, Susan reached for the door handle. 'I—I believe I owe you an apology, Susan.' Warren seemed to have difficulty in getting the words out.

'I believe you do,' she answered coolly, turning slightly to give him a measuring look.

His hands tightened on the steering wheel as a muscle twitched in his jaw. 'All right, dammit, I'm sorry,' he snapped.

In spite of a faint irritation at his reluctantly offered apology, Susan smiled. The dimness of the car concealed it from Warren.

'And I'm sorry for walking out like that,' she said gently, meeting him halfway.

'The whole argument was silly,' he murmured, taking her into his arms and crushing her tightly against his chest.

'It hurt that you didn't trust me,' she whispered.

In answer, Warren kissed her long and hard as if to drive away the memory of their angry words. Susan responded with equal intensity to show him that all was forgiven, if not totally forgotten. Afterwards she lay curled contentedly in the hollow of his shoulder while his hand absently massaged the soft flesh of her arm.

'Please, darling,' Warren said in a low, husky

voice, 'I'm asking you not to see that man any more.'

Tensing slightly, Susan had the uncomfortable feeling that his apology and the subsequent kiss had been designed to lull her into the sense of security she was now enjoying. The end result would be that he would achieve the very thing he had set out to.

A tiny frown of uncertainty touched her forehead. 'I—I'm sorry, Warren, but I can't give you an answer. I simply won't promise that I might not see him again,' she murmured, darting a cautious glance into his passive, rugged features.

For an instant his expression seemed to harden and Susan thought the argument was going to begin all over again. Then he relaxed his mouth into a dry smile.

'The fact that you love me is the only answer I need, I guess,' he said softly.

A sigh of gratitude slid from her lips as she mentally chided herself for thinking such mean thoughts against his motives. She had hated accusing him of trying to use underhanded methods to extract a promise from her.

'Thank you, darling,' she whispered.

He placed a quick kiss on her lips. 'Come on,' he said, dislodging her from her comfortable nest in his arm. 'It's time you were going in the house. You have to be at work in the morning and you know what a tyrant your boss can be.'

'He's a regular monster,' Susan laughed as she moved to her own side of the car. Opening the car door, she glanced over her shoulder at his smiling face. 'Goodnight, darling."

'Goodnight,' Warren responded, his voice a gentle caress.

The next day the necessity arose again for Susan to transport some important documents to Robert Sullivan at the hospital. The words were there in Warren's eyes, asking her again not to see Mitch Braden while she was there. Susan looked away, unable to give him the answer he wanted.

All night and for the better part of the day she had been trying to come to a decision. As she walked down the hospital corridor to Robert Sullivan's room, she knew she had reached it.

After she had given the papers to Warren's father, she would see Mitch. She would see Mitch and tactfully tell him that it would be better for all concerned if she didn't see him any more. After telling Mitch she would look in, she would look in; she simply could not do it without explaining why.

Keeping her gaze averted from the door to Mitch's room, Susan intended to walk straight by. First she wanted to see Robert Sullivan, then she would go to Mitch.

'Susan!' Mitch's delighted voice interrupted her plan.

She paused, glancing over her shoulder to see him standing in the doorway. He looked disturbingly attractive in a knee-length robe of camel brown, one sleeve empty and the bulge of the cast beneath the tied front.

'Hello, Mitch.' She swallowed and curved her mouth into a taut smile. 'I was on my way to Mr. Sullivan's room with some more papers. I—I was going to stop in to see you on my way out.'

'I somehow didn't think there would be any errand that would bring you back today,' he smiled slowly.

'It came up suddenly.'

'I'm glad.'

'Yes . . . well.' Susan breathed in deeply, bowing her head to break away from the blue glitter of his eyes.

'Would it upset everything if you came here before going to his room?' Mitch asked, gesturing down the hallway with his right hand.

Susan hesitated indecisively. 'No, no, I don't suppose it would.'

But she walked very slowly toward Mitch, not quite knowing what she was going to say to him now that the moment had arrived sooner than she had anticipated. He stepped aside to let her pass, meeting her nervous sideways glance with a faint dimpling smile.

A few steps inside the room, she stopped short, meeting the curious and speculating gaze of the brawny man sprawled in the chair beside the bed.

'Excuse me,' she stammered, turning quickly to Mitch. 'You should have said you already had a visitor. I'll come back later.'

Mitch blocked her path to the door with casual ease. 'Stay,' he insisted. 'Mike was just leaving, weren't you, Mike?' Mitch glanced pointedly at the man with the thinning dark hair.

The man's mouth turned up at the corners, smiling at some secret thing as he pushed himself out of the chair. 'That's right. I was just leaving.' He didn't leave, but stood there expectantly waiting for an introduction.

'You needn't go on my account,' Susan said quickly.

'Honestly, miss, I was about to leave before you came,' the man assured her in an amused voice. Still he waited.

Out of the corner of her eye, Susan saw Mitch shake his head in resignation. 'Susan, this hairy-chested Irishman is Mike O'Brian, my pit boss and sometimes my friend. This is Susan Mabry, Mike.'

'I'm pleased to meet you, Mr. O'Brian.' Her hand was lost in the hugeness of his.

'Mike,' he corrected her formality with a friendly smile. 'I recognized you, Susan.' At her blank look, he added, 'From the restaurant.'

Her cheeks warmed as she realized he must have been one of the men who had joined Mitch the first time she saw him. A swift glance at Mitch caught the narrowing look he gave Mike, warning him into silence.

Mike released her hand. 'It was nice meeting you.' Then he turned to Mitch. 'We'll be pulling out in the morning, so take care.'

'I will,' Mitch nodded affirmatively. 'Don't enjoy your vacation too much. I shouldn't be in this cast very long.'

'You wait until the doctor tells you to take it off or I'll break it again for you!' Mike smiled his threat.

There was a brief clasp of hands between the two, then Mike left the room. Susan felt Mitch's gaze on her and moved toward the window.

'You're looking much better today,' she said to fill the silence.

'The dizziness seems to have gone, so the doctors let me up,' he replied. 'Now that you're here, I'm feeling much better.'

Susan fingered the leather case in her hands. 'Don't say things like that, Mitch.'

'What did I say?' His voice held false innocence.

'It wasn't what you said but what you implied,' she answered, pressing her lips together tightly.

He walked slowly toward her. She could hear his footsteps bringing him nearer, but refused to turn around.

'And you don't like it when I imply that I find the sight of you stimulating to the senses,' Mitch stated.

'No, I don't.' Susan stared at the whiteness of her fingers clenching the case handle. 'You can't keep ignoring the fact that I'm engaged.'

'I don't ignore it, exactly,' he corrected with faint amusement. 'But, since you don't like me to tell you how very beautiful you are, we'll talk of other things. Greg came to see me last night and your father looked in this morning while he was doing his hospital rounds.'

Susan sighed, a crazy kind of misery welling up inside. She turned from the window, meeting his level gaze. She wished for the calm possession displayed in his handsome face.

'This isn't going to work either,' she protested lamely. 'I can't make small talk. I was going to come here today because there was something I wanted to tell you.'

His gaze moved to the top of her head. 'Do you know when the light hits your hair just right it has a fiery glint, crimson red like flames? Yet your hair is such a very dark shade of brown.'

'Don't try to change the subject, Mitch. I'm serious.'

'So am I,' he agreed. 'In certain lights, your hair is definitely red.'

'I don't want to discuss the color of my hair. That's not why I came.' Frustrated, Susan turned back to the window.

'I know why you came,' Mitch said quietly. 'You came to tell me you aren't going to visit me any more.'

Her head jerked toward him in surprise. 'How did you know?'

'Call it a calculated guess,' he shrugged indifferently, and stared out the window. 'What happened? Did your jealous fiancé find out that you'd seen me and forbid you to come?'

'He didn't forbid me.' She wasn't about to tell

him that Warren had tried. 'And he didn't find out, I told him.'

'You told him and he didn't forbid you to see me? I find that hard to believe.' He grinned crookedly at her, his bronze features glowing attractively in the sunlight.

'I never said he liked the idea,' Susan protested as her pulse quickened under his glittering look. 'He doesn't altogether understand why I'm seeing you.'

'Do you?' Mitch taunted softly.

'Yes,' she looked quickly away. 'It's never any fun being in a hospital, and not having any visitors makes it even worse. I—I was trying to be kind and compassionate.'

'I see,' he drawled with an undertone of amusement. 'Now you've decided that to keep peace with your fiancé, it's best not to see me any more.'

'That's what I decided,' Susan agreed, unconsciously touching the diamond solitaire on her finger. 'I have to be fair with Warren.'

'I'm afraid you have a problem.'

'What?' She slid a wary sideways glance at his face.

Mitch continued to gaze complacently out the window. 'The doctor will be releasing me from the hospital tomorrow morning or Friday at the very latest.'

'And?' Susan frowned, not seeing how that news would present her with any difficulty.

'And,' there was a wicked light in the blue eyes when he looked at her, 'your father has invited me to dinner on Friday night.'

'No,' she denied in a small voice.

'Yes,' Mitch nodded firmly.

'But you can't go!' she protested.

'I have already accepted the invitation.'

'You can phone Dad and tell him you can't come,' Susan insisted. 'You can think of some excuse to refuse.'

'But I'm not going to refuse,' Mitch said patiently.

'You must.'

'Why? I like your family and I'm looking forward to one of your mother's home-cooked meals. I don't see any reason I should deny myself the pleasure simply because you have a jealous fiancé. He's going to have to learn to trust you more.'

'Warren trusts me,' Susan defended.

Mitch chuckled softly. 'Of course, it's me that he doesn't trust, and with good reason. He knows I want you.'

'Stop saying things like that!' She spun away from him, angry at him for not refusing the invitation and for the daring and disturbing statement he had just made. 'I'm engaged to Warren!'

'You are beginning to sound like a broken record,' he taunted.

'I'll repeat myself a thousand times if that's how many it takes before you accept what I'm saying!' Her eyes flashed angrily at his mocking expression.

Sobering, Mitch studied her intently for several long seconds, gazing so deeply into her eyes that she had the uncanny sensation that he knew what she was thinking. Then, slowly, his firm male mouth grooved into a smile, carving faint dimples into the smooth, lean cheeks.

'You only have nine hundred-odd times to go,' he told her.

'Oh!' Her foot stamped the floor in a childish tantrum. 'It's hopeless trying to reason with you! Warren said you were much too conceited, and he was right!'

'Do you mean Warren *isn't* always right?' Her outburst only deepened his mocking smile.

Blinking back the furious tears of rage that scalded her eyes, Susan stalked from the room.

'I'll see you on Friday night.' Mitch's parting jibe was followed by a throaty chuckle that whipped her already raw nerves. If she had looked back she might have gained some satisfaction from seeing his immediate grimace of pain because of his cracked ribs.

Almost an hour later, she tapped on the connecting door to Warren's office, waiting for his summons before entering. He glanced up from the papers spread before him, straightening against the tall-backed leather chair as he recognized her.

'Did you get the papers safely delivered to my father?' But his dark, inspecting eyes asked an entirely different question.

'Yes, I did.' Susan walked to his desk and handed him the keys to his car.

'Good,' Warren nodded, and paused expectantly.

Susan's arms were stiffly held to her sides. She

knew she could avoid answering his unasked question. She also knew she could avoid mentioning Mitch's intention to join her family for dinner on Friday evening. Unfortunately there was an excellent chance that her family, especially her brother, might not be so silent about it.

'I saw Mitch today.' Susan tried to make it sound like an unexpected happening that was of little importance. Warren said nothing and waited. 'I told him I wouldn't be visiting him any more.'

'Susan!' Warren breathed warmly. He leaned forward in his chair, a smile lightening his imposing and rugged features.

'Wait.' She held up a cautioning hand. 'There's something else I have to tell you.'

His dark head tipped to the side in wariness. 'What?'

'My father has invited Mitch Braden to dinner on Friday night and he has accepted.'

'Your father! Good God!' Warren breathed in deeply, a black mask stealing again over his face. 'Why?'

'How should I know why?' Susan shrugged with bewildered anger. 'I suppose it was a combination of reasons. My family have already met him. My father is a racing fan and I guess he got along rather well with Mitch the last time. Greg practically hero-worships him as you know. Mother agreed, probably because she felt sorry for him, because of the accident and all. In any case, he's coming to dinner and there isn't anything I can do about it.'

'I wouldn't be surprised to learn that he did everything but ask to be invited,' Warren muttered. 'And I'm tied up Friday night. I wonder if he knew about that, too.'

'Really, Warren, he isn't omniscient,' she chided.

'Sometimes I wonder about that Indy man.' He shook his head. 'I just don't like the idea of you being alone with him for an entire evening.'

'With Greg and Amy and Mom and Dad, I'm hardly going to be alone with him,' she pointed out.

'You know what I mean.'

'Yes,' Susan agreed, knowing that in some way Mitch would make his presence felt. 'If I thought I wouldn't have to do a lot of tall explaining to Dad, I would arrange to be out. Besides, I don't want it to look as if I'm running away from him.'

'You're right,' he conceded. 'You might as well plan to be home. He might as well see that you belong to me even when I'm not around.'

CHAPTER SIX

'MORE coffee, Mitch?' her mother offered as he sat back in his chair.

'Nothing more, thanks, Beth,' he replied, shaking his head and raising his hand in refusal. 'My ribs are already saying I've eaten too much.'

Susan's teeth grated against each other. Less than half an hour after Greg had brought him from his hotel, Mitch had been calling her parents by their Christian names. The easy friendliness between them irritated her.

'Mom remembered last time that you said Swiss steak was your favorite, so she fixed it especially for you tonight,' Amy said. 'And I helped.'

'I guess I have to divide my compliments to the

chef between the two of you,' Mitch smiled. 'I'm flattered that you remembered, Beth.'

'Thank you.' Her mother was momentarily flustered and Susan seethed inwardly.

'There's nothing that can replace a home-cooked meal,' her father stated.

'I'd forgotten what I'd been missing,' Mitch agreed ruefully.

'Yeah, but you lead such an exciting life.' Greg glanced at him enviously. 'Mom's a great cook, but ——' He shrugged his shoulders to indicate that food was not important compared to the adventures Mitch had known.

'I thought the same way when I was your age, Greg.' The mockingly raised brow held gentle understanding. 'But ten years of living in hotels and eating in restaurants can make a man reevaluate his thinking. Hotel rooms can be very sterile and lonely when you have to walk into them night after night.'

'Haven't you ever considered settling down?' Beth Mabry asked with maternal concern.

Through the veil of his spiky dark lashes, his blue eyes glittered at Susan. She met the look with determined indifference.

'Until recently, I was much too busy.' His gaze swung back to her mother. 'A time or two I've considered buying a house or renting an apartment so I could say I had a home base. But without someone to share it with, it would have been no different from a hotel room.'

'You're a very attractive man. I find it hard to

believe you haven't found anyone you were willing to share a home with,' Beth Mabry laughed with gentle disbelief.

'You have to realize I'm seldom in one place long enough to really get acquainted with anyone. And the chances of meeting someone—say, like your daughter——' Mitch looked at Susan again, but she kept her eyes downcast, knowing they were flashing with temper again, 'is unlikely in my profession.'

'And when you do, the girl is probably engaged, like myself,' Susan couldn't resist inserting in sugared tones.

'Exactly,' Mitch agreed.

'I still think it would be an exciting life,' Greg insisted. 'When I get older, that's what I want to do.'

'If you live that long,' Simon Mabry said dryly.

'You used to drive race cars, Dad. I'm just taking after you,' Susan's brother pointed out with a sly grin.

Mitch glanced to her father, his head cocked inquiringly on one side. 'You didn't mention that, Simon.'

'It was years ago, when I was in college,' he shrugged. 'At the time it seemed like an easy way to pick up some extra money. When you're young and foolish, you do a lot of things without thinking about the risks.'

'Why did you quit, Dad?' Amy forgot her young lady act and curled her feet beneath her on the straight-backed chair. 'You could have become a famous racer like Mitch.'

'Two reasons, actually,' he smiled and glanced at his wife, sitting at the opposite end of the table from him. 'The first being the fact that I met your mother. For a while, even after we were married, I rather enjoyed the image of being the dashing adventurer until she told me one night that Susan was on the way. That rather woke me up to the responsibilities I owed to my future family. I had planned to continue racing until Susan was born so I could have the extra money to pay the doctor and hospital bills. Then one day I was working on my car—I couldn't afford to share my small winnings with a mechanic—and the wrench slipped. I broke all the fingers on my left hand. At that point, I realized that what I really wanted to be was a doctor and I was terrified that the injury to my hand might have finished that dream for good. It didn't. The very next day after the accident, I sold the car.'

'When you get married, Mitch, will you give up racing?' Amy propped an elbow on her knee and rested her chin in her hand.

'No, I don't think so,' he mused absently. 'Eventually I'll have to, of course. Unlike your father, I want to race cars. It's my life.'

'Isn't that being slightly arrogant?' Susan said tightly. 'What you would be telling the woman you married is that this is your life and she can take it or leave it. Surely she has some say in your joint future?'

A steel blue gaze focused on her, his expression

unyielding yet not cold or angry. 'I'm willing to take her as she is and not attempt to change her. Is it wrong to expect the same in return? Or even arrogant?'

Susan looked away from the unwavering directness of his gaze. Her small bubble of indignation was pricked by his reasonable request.

'I suppose not,' she admitted with quiet reluctance.

'It would be rather like asking Warren to give up his law practice, wouldn't it?' her mother put in rhetorically. 'A woman would learn to adjust to the dangers of your job in the same way that I've accepted the life of a doctor. I never thought of it like that before, but it's true.'

'I don't see what all the fuss is about,' Amy declared airily, uncurling her legs and rising from the chair. She tossed her head, sending her long hair dancing about her shoulders and catching fire from the overhead light. 'I think it would be super to be married to a race car driver.'

Greg laughed. 'Everything with you is "super." The dinner was "super." The movie was "super," ' he mimicked.

'Oh, what do you know about it?' Amy accused, her temper flaring that her brother should make fun of her in front of Mitch.

Beth Mabry rose to her feet. 'I think it's about time we made washing the dishes "super." '

'Come on, Mitch,' her father grinned. 'That's a signal for us to leave the room before she ties an apron around our waists.'

'It was a delicious meal, Beth,' Mitch offered,

wincing slightly at the pain in his rib cage when he rose from the chair. Then he winked at Amy. 'Prepared by a pair of "super" cooks.'

Amy giggled and quickly covered her mouth with a hand as if wishing she had made a more adult reaction. Susan's mouth tightened grimly as she quickly began stacking the dishes on the table rather than watch her father and Mitch leave the dining room.

Her younger sister was dreamily watching him go. He seemed to have her entire family in the palm of his hand, Susan thought disgustedly.

'Amy, would you stop mooning over that man and help clear the table!' Susan snapped.

'I am not mooning over him!' Amy's eyes widened indignantly. 'And you don't have to be so grouchy!'

Sinking her teeth into her lower lip, Susan bit back an even sharper retort, knowing it wasn't fair to take her temper out on Amy. Her sister was at an impressionable age where her crushes were painfully deep and short-lived.

'Besides,' Amy lifted her chin to a haughty angle, 'it's my turn to wipe the dishes and it's your job to clear the table,' she declared before flouncing into the kitchen.

Susan glanced at her mother and sighed. 'Was I ever that hopeless?'

'We all were,' her mother smiled faintly, and picked up a stack of dishes, carrying them into the kitchen.

Susan followed within minutes carrying more

dishes. She opened the door in time to hear Amy ask, 'How long will Mitch be staying tonight, Mom?'

'I don't know. I imagine until your father drives him to his hotel. Why?' Beth Mabry replied, adjusting the temperature of the water coming out of the double sink taps.

'Couldn't I wipe the dishes after he leaves?' Amy pleaded. 'I mean, he's just got out of the hospital and all. He might be tired and ask to leave early.'

'I'm sure he'll stay until after the dishes are done,' her mother answered with a straight face but a decided twinkle in her eyes that met Susan's raised eyebrows of despair.

'We could leave the dishes altogether,' Amy suggested, unwilling to give up with one refusal. 'I promise I'll help you do them in the morning.'

'The answer is "no," Amy.'

'If you would help, Amy,' Susan put in with thinning patience, 'instead of standing around trying to think of reasons not to do the dishes, we might finish them sooner. Besides, I'm certain Mitch Braden can survive without your company for a little while.'

Amy whirled about. 'Just because you don't like him, Susan, it's no reason why I can't! And don't be telling me what I should do!'

'Susan,' her mother said with astonishment, 'don't you like Mitch?'

'Of course I like him,' Susan answered nervously, 'but I certainly don't think he's some Greek god who's come down from Olympus to walk with us mortals the way Amy does. He's just a man.'

'But what a man!' Amy retorted smugly. 'Compared to him, Warren is a stiff-necked prude.'

'Mother,' Susan breathed in deeply, 'if you don't do something about this daughter of yours, so help me, I will!'

'Stop it, both of you!' was the stern response.

Returning to the dining room, Susan finished clearing the table. She had resolved not to lose her temper with Amy, then lost it anyway. She herself had felt the force of Mitch's attraction. Amy was so young and vulnerable that it was only natural she should fall under his spell.

With the dining room straightened and all the chairs in the proper place at the table, Susan walked back into the kitchen straight to her young sister.

'I'll finish drying the dishes for you,' she said, taking the towel from Amy's hands. 'Go on into the living room.' She smiled at the joy gleaming instantaneously in her sister's face. 'And I'm sorry for putting you down.'

'Oh, Susan, you are super!' Amy hugged her quickly and dashed from the room. Susan could hear her footsteps slow to a more ladylike pace before she reached the living room.

The dishes were finished in short order and Susan was compelled by a sense of polite duty to follow her mother into the living room. She chose a chair apart from the others, curling up in a shadowed corner which allowed her an unobstructed view of her family and Mitch Braden.

Despite the armless sleeve and the bulging cast beneath his shirt, he looked leanly powerful, like the coiled muscular shape of a jungle cat. The lampshade kept the light from touching off the golden fire of his brown hair, but a blue light seemed to glow warmly in his eyes.

Her family was so at ease with him. The conversation wasn't stilted as it often was when Warren visited them. She had expected Mitch to dominate the discussion, but he had a knack of drawing others into the conversation.

Except herself, that was. He seemed to sense her faint hostility. She guessed he had been aware of it all evening and was now leaving her alone. Fine, she told herself, that was what she wanted, but she felt strangely left out, and it didn't help to remind herself that it was her own choice.

The cuckoo clock sang out the ten o'clock hour. Mitch glanced at his wristwatch as if to confirm the time.

'I'm sorry, I didn't realize it was so late,' he apologized warmly. 'I hadn't intended to outstay my welcome.'

'You aren't leaving already?' Amy moaned.

'It's late, Red,' Mitch smiled, then glanced to her father. 'There isn't any need for you to go out again tonight. I'll call a cab.'

'Nonsense,' Simon Mabry refused vigorously. 'The night air will do me good. I won't hear of you taking a cab.'

'I appreciate your kindness,' Mitch said with a nod of submission. 'I can't thank you enough for this evening. You've all made me feel very welcome.'

'I wish you didn't have to leave,' said Greg with obvious sincerity.

'So do I,' Mitch agreed as he carefully rose to his feet. 'My hotel room is going to seem awfully cold and silent after an evening in your home, Beth. Thank you.'

'Why do you have to go back there?' Amy frowned, a faint pout on her lips. 'I don't see why you couldn't stay here with us.'

'Then I definitely would wear out my welcome.' The lines around his mouth deepened with a gentle smile.

Susan breathed a silent sigh of relief at his instant refusal. For a second, she had thought he was going to make some wistful remark.

'That's an idea,' her father said thoughtfully and Susan's eyes widened in apprehension. 'We do have that guest room upstairs, Beth. Nobody uses it for anything.'

'Simon——' Mitch held up his hand.

'He's right,' Beth Mabry interrupted. 'We would be happy to have you stay with us, Mitch.'

'I couldn't take advantage of your generosity that way,' he shook his head in refusal.

'You wouldn't be taking advantage of us,' Beth insisted. 'If we didn't want you to stay, we wouldn't have asked. And one more person in this house isn't going to be any extra trouble. The way

306

Greg and Amy are always inviting their friends over I've become used to it.'

'It's a tempting invitation, Beth, but I don't think I should accept it,' Mitch refused again.

Susan, who had been staring in open-mouthed protest, finally spoke out. 'We understand, Mitch. We wouldn't want you to do anything you would regret. After all, you're used to coming and going as you please and you would probably feel your movements were restricted, staying here with us.'

His level blue gaze focused on her and a sudden merry twinkle came into his eyes. 'On the contrary, Susan,' he smiled, 'I was more concerned that your parents might regret inviting a stranger into their home.'

'You're not a stranger!' Amy denied vehemently.

'In truth I must agree,' Simon Mabry added. 'Speaking for myself, I feel as if we've known you for a very long time. We would be happy to have you if you would like to stay.'

'Well, if you insist on twisting my arm,' Mitch shrugged, smiling crookedly, 'I guess I have no choice but to accept.'

Amy cheered unabashedly while Susan trembled with impotent rage. How could she possibly live under the same roof with him for the three or four weeks he would be staying?

She was filled with the uneasy premonition that nothing would be the same after he left. Her life would be irrevocably altered.

Greg scrambled to his feet. 'I'll come along with

Dad and help you pack up your things at the hotel. You can move in tonight. Wow! Wait until the fellers hear about this!' his voice cracked in excitement.

'No, it's too late tonight,' Mitch stated. 'I'll have everything packed and ready to go tomorrow at noon. That will give you time to reconsider the invitation. And I promise I'll understand if you change your mind.'

'We won't,' Amy declared as if making a solemn vow.

Unmindful of the startled looks she received from her family, Susan muttered a hurried 'Excuse me' and walked quickly from the room. She had no particular destination in mind. She wasn't even conscious of where she was when she came to a stop in front of the kitchen sink.

Yanking open a cupboard door above her head, she removed a drinking glass and filled it with cold water from the tap. She was just lifting it to her lips when the kitchen door opened. She counted to ten before turning toward it, expecting to see the reproving face of her mother.

'Do you always sulk when things don't go the way you want?' Mitch asked in a low voice laced with curious amusement.

'How could you do this?' Susan hissed angrily.

'Do what?' he repeated with deliberate blankness. 'All I've done is accept a neighborly invitation,' he drawled lazily.

'Yes,' she was so angry she could hardly speak, 'all you did was accept an invitation you did everything but get on your knees and ask for!'

'Are you implying that I tricked your parents into inviting me to stay here?' His hurt, affronted look might have seemed genuine if it wasn't for the sparkle in his eyes.

'Yes,' she snapped.

'You really believe I could be that devious?'

'Yes!'

A brow raised briefly in resignation. 'Time is running out on me. I have to take advantage of every minute that I can.'

'What does that mean?' Susan demanded guardedly.

'You're a smart girl, I think you'll figure it out,' he smiled. 'Good night, beautiful. I'll see you tomorrow.'

He was being deliberately mysterious to confuse her and sidetrack her from the issue. Her fingers tightened around the glass of water in her hand, then paused.

'I wouldn't throw that glass if I were you,' he warned in a silently laughing tone. 'I think you'd have difficulty explaining to your parents how dropping a glass splattered water all over the walls and door.'

The second time the door opened, it was Beth Mabry who entered. Susan raised the glass to her mouth and took a long gulp of water.

'What's the matter?' her mother asked quietly.

'It's just going to be awful.' Susan avoided the gentle gaze studying her.

'What is?'

309

'Mitch Braden living here, that's what.' She set the partially empty glass on the counter with an impatient movement of her hand.

'Now, why do you say that?' Her mother's curiosity was overridden with surprise as she walked to the counter where Susan stood.

'Because——' Susan glanced up, her expression stretched taut to control the desperate anger that wanted to erupt. 'Because Warren is jealous.'

'Jealous? Of Mitch Braden? For heaven's sake, why?'

This time Susan related the exact circumstances surrounding her first meeting with Mitch Braden and the subsequent encounters, not omitting the way Mitch constantly flirted with her.

'Does Warren know all of this?' Beth asked when Susan had finished. Her expression was gentle with understanding, but there was a faint gleam of amusement in her eyes that Susan found irritating.

'Of course he doesn't know all of it. He would be positively furious if he knew everything. But I swear, Mother, he isn't going to understand why you've invited Mitch to stay here. For that matter, neither do I.'

'Yes, you do,' her mother smiled. 'Perhaps if I'd known about the way things were between Mitch and Warren I might have considered the invitation more thoroughly before inviting him to stay here. But we certainly can't retract it now even if we wanted to, not unless you want to explain this whole story to the others.'

'Greg would have a field day with it,' Susan

310

sighed, running a weary hand through the dark hair near her ear.

'Besides, you and Warren are engaged. And since you've done nothing to encourage Mitch,' there was a faint pause as Susan suddenly averted her head, 'then I think Warren should learn to trust you and to accept that you can handle the situation. Mitch isn't staying for ever, just a few weeks.'

'It's going to seem like an eternity,' Susan sighed.

'You're beginning to exaggerate like your younger sister,' her mother teased dryly.

Smiling ruefully, Susan pushed herself away from the counter. 'If it wasn't so painful being thirteen, then I'd wish I was Amy's age. Good-night, Mom.'

'It will all work out for the best, Susan.'

'Sure,' she answered in a doubting-Thomas voice.

Early on Saturday afternoon, Mitch moved in bag and baggage. The house was in a gleeful turmoil the entire afternoon. Mr. Mabry had decided the garage had to be cleaned out to make room for Mitch's sports car. He had driven it over for him since Mitch couldn't manage the gearshifts with his broken arm.

Susan tried to stay out of the mainstream as much as she could, but the excitement rippling through the house touched her in spite of her attempts to remain outside its sphere.

Each time she caught herself about to join the

laughter and chatting voices of her family and Mitch, she would remind herself of Warren's reaction when he came to pick her up for their date that night.

It was difficult being miserable when everyone else was having fun.

As Susan dressed for her date with Warren, she considered Mitch's attitude toward her that day. He had seemed to pay little attention to her. She had expected him to be smugly triumphant, ready to remind her mockingly of his presence in her home at every opportunity. Yet he had been as friendly with her as he had been with the rest of the family.

It wouldn't last, she sighed into the bathroom mirror. He was merely biding his time. She couldn't afford to relax her guard even for an instant.

The sound of a car pulling into the drive drifted through the screened windows, opened to admit the warm breeze of the early summer's night. Adding the finishing stroke of lipstick, Susan hurried to her room, picking up the crocheted shawl from her bed before hurrying out again for the staircase. Warren was early.

The doorbell rang when she reached the top of the stairs. Before her toe touched the first step, a voice called out from the living room below.

'I'll answer it!' Mitch stated.

Susan's heart nose-dived to her shoes. Her legs were paralyzed, unable to carry her down the flight of steps before Mitch reached the front door.

Whistling absently, he appeared below her, the empty white shirt-sleeve tucked into the waistband of his trousers.

The door was swung open and Susan could just barely see the dark gray of Warren's trousers. She could visualize the stunned look on his face.

'Hello, Warren. Come on in,' Mitch greeted, inviting him in as if he had done it a thousand times before, just as if he was a permanent member of the household.

He stepped to one side to allow Warren entry, brown head turning toward the stairs where Susan waited in dread.

'Susan, it's for you!' Mitch called loudly, then paused as he met her gaze. 'Sorry, I didn't see you standing there.'

'I just bet you didn't,' Susan thought savagely when she saw the wicked glint in the blue eyes. She averted her gaze to the steps before her as the paralysis left her legs and she started down.

'Warren is here to pick you up,' Mitch announced unnecessarily.

'I can see that,' Susan snapped tightly.

One look at the glowering mask of rage on Warren's face told her in no uncertain terms what he thought of the freehanded way Mitch was making himself at home. Susan hurried her pace, fearing an explosion at any second.

With infuriating calm, Mitch waited at the bottom of the stairs with Warren, his mocking gaze watching her descent and knowing the reason for the flush of anger in her cheeks.

Deliberately she ignored Mitch to look directly at Warren. 'I'm ready if you are,' she said, reaching out for Warren's arm.

'You two have a nice time,' Mitch offered as Warren pivoted sharply around to leave. 'Don't keep Susan out too late. She needs her beauty sleep.' There was mocking emphasis on beauty before he closed the door behind them.

Warren began striding toward his car, indifferent to the fact that Susan had to practically run to keep up with him. 'Would you kindly explain to me what he's doing there?' His voice vibrated with checked rage.

'You aren't going to like it,' Susan said in a very hesitant voice.

He held the car door open for her, his dark gaze sweeping her apprehensive face, its coldness chilling her to the bone.

'There's nothing about the man that I like, and I have the feeling I'll like this even less.'

Susan waited until he was in the car before dropping her bombshell. The response was what she expected and dreaded.

'You can't be serious! You can't possibly mean he's going to be living in the same house with you!'

'I'm perfectly serious,' she replied in a forced calm voice.

'Your parents actually invited him to stay!' Warren shook his head in disbelief. 'Didn't you tell them what kind of man he is?'

'What could I tell them?' Susan reasoned. 'That

he pays me outrageous compliments? That he flirts with me? They would have laughed and asked him anyway. They like him.'

'So you're just accepting it?' he accused grimly. 'You're not making any attempt to change the situation?'

'What would you have me do, Warren?' The impatience she felt toward the whole mess she was in and Warren's lack of understanding about her helplessness to correct it made her voice sharp. 'Move out?'

'You could at least consider it,' he snapped.

'He isn't going to live there permanently, only for a few weeks,' she reminded him.

'I have a feeling there's going to be trouble,' Warren muttered.

Susan echoed the thought, but only to herself.

CHAPTER SEVEN

SUSAN walked into the kitchen. 'Is there anything I can help you with, Mom, before Warren comes?'

Glancing up from the salad bowl in front of her, Beth Mabry cut the last tomato into wedges and let them join the others in the red mound on top of the lettuce. She surveyed her daughter quickly, taking in the freshness of the yellow sun-dress with its varying sized circles of white polka dots.

'Yes, you can toss this salad together while I scrub some potatoes to bake,' she answered, drying her hands on a terry dish towel. As Susan moved toward her, Beth paused. 'On second thought, you'd better have Greg take the charcoal out and get the barbecue grill started. I think he's in the garage tinkering with his car.'

'I'll finish the salad when I come back, then,' Susan nodded, and walked toward the kitchen door that led directly into the garage.

As she opened the door, she heard Mitch say, 'Try it again, Greg.'

Her brother was partially sitting behind the wheel of his car, the door open, and Mitch was bending to look under the hood. Greg turned the key in the ignition. There was a whining growl and nothing happened. With an impatient grimace, Greg stepped out and walked to the front of the car where Mitch was intently studying the motor.

'Greg, Mom wants you to take the charcoal out back and get the grill started,' Susan told him, her gaze unwillingly drawn to Mitch, who didn't even look up at the sound of her voice.

He was wearing a pair of soiled overalls in a deep shade of azure blue, the plaster cast on his arm concealed behind the zippered front.

'Not now, Susan,' Greg muttered with a dismissing glance. 'I'm busy.'

'If you want to eat before dark, you'd better go do it now,' she replied. 'It won't take you that long.'

'You might as well.' Mitch straightened. 'This isn't something we're going to fix in a few minutes.'

And still he didn't look at Susan. Ever since Saturday night he had seemed to take her existence for granted, as if her presence in the house didn't warrant any special attention. Mitch hadn't ignored her, but he had treated her no differently than he had the rest of the family. He could have been her older brother.

'Oh, all right. I'll start the stupid grill,' Greg grumbled, his lanky frame moving with a long stride to a corner of the garage where the bag of charcoal briquets sat. Picking it up, he roughly shoved open the rear door leading into the back yard and kicked it shut with his foot.

Mitch started to fiddle with something under the hood and Susan turned to leave, not really certain why she had waited.

'Would you mind lighting me a cigarette, Susan?' Mitch asked absently. 'My hand is all greasy. The pack is sitting on the work bench. The lighter should be there, too.' He waved in the general direction of the counter built into the rear wall of one side of the garage.

Susan hesitated briefly, then walked to the counter, littered with various kinds of garden and mechanical tools. She took a cigarette from the pack and lit it, surprised to find the hand that held the lighter was trembling slightly. She turned to give it to him as he walked toward her, an absent frown of concentration on his handsome face.

Instead of reaching for the cigarette, his right hand removed a rag from the work bench. His head tipped sideways toward Susan, indicating she should place the lit cigarette in his mouth. She did so reluctantly, but he barely seemed to notice her at all.

'Thanks,' he offered, speaking through the cigarette between his lips. He tried, ineffectively, to wipe the worst of the grime off his hand. Then he sighed. 'How does a man with one hand wash the dirt off that hand?'

'That's a good question,' Susan laughed shortly. The amusement that glittered in his eyes was casually friendly. It was impossible to take offense at his comment when he was directing it against himself. 'I suppose you'll have to have someone else do it for you.'

'I suppose so,' he agreed, squinting his eyes against the smoke before gingerly removing the cigarette from his mouth with two still darkly soiled fingers. He arched his back slightly and winced at the pull the movement exerted on his injured rib cage.

'You really shouldn't be working on that car,' Susan said reprovingly, 'not in your condition.'

'I'm only giving Greg a hand.' Mitch smoothly dismissed the idea that he might be overtaxing himself. 'He's doing all the heavy work.' He leaned against the counter and ran an appraising eye over her dress. 'This is Tuesday night, isn't it? That means you have a date with Warren.'

It was a casual comment without an undertone of mockery. 'That's right,' she admitted cautiously. 'He'll be here to pick me up in a little while.'

'You don't sound very enthusiastic.' He tipped his head to the side, a pose of vague curiosity.

'I—I don't know what you mean.' Her chin lifted slightly as if she sensed a coming need for a defensive attitude.

'The man you're engaged to is going to be here

in a little while, and you sound so matter-of-fact about it,' he explained with indifference.

'Well, it is a fact,' Susan shrugged, a faint frown of bewilderment clouding her forehead.

'Aren't you excited about seeing him again?'

'I just saw him when I left the office at five,' she reminded him. 'It isn't as though I haven't seen him for a couple of days.'

'Of course,' Mitch agreed with a wry smile. 'I guess I was letting myself be influenced by a lot of romantic nonsense. I assumed that you would miss him no matter how short the time since the last time you saw him.'

'Naturally I miss him,' Susan retorted, almost too quickly.

'Naturally?' A brown brow arched with arrogant mockery. 'You sound very offhand. Are your dates becoming too routine?'

'What do you expect me to do? Fling myself in his arms every time I see him?'

Mitch smiled. 'I'm not expecting anything. I was only commenting on the fact that you seem to display little emotion where Warren is concerned.'

Her head lifted to a haughty angle. 'I save any emotional display for when we're alone,' she informed him icily.

'Then the two of you do indulge in a little necking?'

'I don't see that it's any of your business.'

'It isn't, not really.' The laughing blue eyes moved to her mouth, thinned into a disapproving line.

'Then you shouldn't have brought it up,' Susan replied with biting arrogance.

'I couldn't help it. You have a very kissable pair of lips, and I didn't like to think of them going to waste,' he mocked.

'I assure you they don't.'

Her heartbeat skipped erratically as he studied the movement of her mouth when she spoke. It was unnerving. Susan could feel a warmth start in her midsection and slowly begin to spread through her veins.

'I wonder if anyone taught Warren to share when he was a little boy,' Mitch mused absently, his gaze not wavering from her mouth.

Her breathing became shallow and restricted. She knew she had to escape and quickly. That indefinable magnetism was reaching out for her.

She averted her face sharply. 'I have to go and help Mom in the kitchen.'

One step was taken and Mitch moved fluidly to block her way. An arm was stretched out to rest a hand on the garage wall to obstruct one avenue of retreat while the length of his body took care of the second. Behind Susan was the work counter and to one side was the wall. She was very effectively trapped.

'Will you please step out of my way?' But there was a betraying tremor in her voice.

'Bribe me.' The grooves around his mouth deepened, faint dimpling lines appearing in his lean cheeks.

Susan swallowed nervously and took a step

321

backward. Mitch didn't follow. He didn't have to because there was nowhere she could go to escape him.

'Let me through, please.' It sounded more like a plea than the order she had intended to issue.

'Warren will never know I stole one of your kisses from him unless you tell him,' Mitch reasoned, flashing her one of those devastating smiles that made her heart turn over. 'What's the harm in one kiss? Neither of you will miss it.'

'No!' Susan made a small, negative movement with her head, not taking her wary eyes from him.

In her mind, she was considering the chances of successfully pushing her way past him. His movements to stop her would have to be hampered by his injuries.

As if reading her mind, Mitch spoke softly. 'It would be a shame if that pretty dress you have got soiled by this combination of grease, oil and dirt. Then you'd have to change clothes and make poor Warren wait. You have a choice, beautiful. You can try to force your way by me, in which case I'll simply take my kiss. Or you can willingly give it to me and not get all messed up.'

'*You* are a blackmailer,' she accused in a low, taut voice.

The wicked glint in his eyes only grew brighter. 'Which is it to be?'

Wildly Susan searched for a third alternative and couldn't find one. With snapping fire in her brown eyes, she stepped toward him. Mitch obligingly bent his head, a suppressed smile of mockery grooved in his cheeks. Lightly she brushed the warmth of his lips with her own and withdrew immediately.

The golden brown head moved to the side in patient despair. 'I said a kiss, not a brotherly peck,' he scolded mockingly.

Susan breathed in sharply. 'That isn't fair!'

'I haven't time to play fair. Are you going to do it right?' Now the blue eyes were daring her to kiss him, silently chiding that she didn't have the nerve.

Nibbling uncertainly at her lower lip, Susan wondered if she did. Then she threw caution to the wind and moved toward him again. Her gaze scanned his handsome face, taking in again the challenging glitter in his brilliant blue eyes.

Her lashes fluttered down as her lips trembled against his mouth. Although she didn't draw away, it was still a mock kiss, a stiff touching that only outwardly resembled a kiss.

'Like this, honey,' Mitch said against her lips.

His mouth closed warmly over hers, melting the rigidity that had held Susan back. The soft persuasion of his kiss had her yielding before she realized what she was doing, and by then the sensations rushing through her were too firmly in command to try to check.

The sweet possession of his mouth had her reeling. Her hands spread themselves against his chest to steady herself. The beginnings of a fiery response had just started to be offered when a door opened.

The sound brought Susan sharply back to reality as she realized what she was doing. Quickly she pushed herself away from Mitch, her head jerking toward the rear garage door. Her fear-widened eyes met Greg's stunned expression before swinging with accusing embarrassment to Mitch's calm face.

A faintly triumphant smile touched the sensual male lips that had seconds before rocked her common sense. Mitch returned his outstretched arm to his side and stepped back to let her go by him. She stalked angrily away from him.

'Wow,' Greg whistled. 'Wait until old Warren finds out about this!'

Susan stopped in front of her brother, tears of shame and frustration gathering in her eyes and turning them liquid brown. 'If you say one word of this to Warren, Gregory Allen Mabry, so help me I'll . . .'

But no suitably chastizing threat came to mind. Her mouth snapped shut and her trembling legs carried her swiftly to the connecting kitchen door.

The memory of that kiss haunted Susan for days. Each time she saw Mitch after that her gaze unwillingly strayed to the firm masculine lips, and again the impact of their touch would flood through her. It was frightening to remember her physical reaction to the essentially forced kiss.

What was worse, Mitch knew she had been disturbed by his kiss. The light in his eyes reminded Susan of it every time he looked at her, although she made certain no occasion occurred that would leave her alone in a room with Mitch.

If only she could explain to herself the strange ambivalence of her emotions. She was engaged to a man she loved and respected, yet she had experienced physical desire for another man. How was it possible?

She sighed dispiritedly.

'What's the matter, darling?' Warren probed softly.

'Hmm?' She glanced at him blankly, forgetting for a few minutes where she was and whom she was with. She shook her head slightly, his question sinking in. 'Oh, nothing. Just tired, I guess.'

'You've been preoccupied nearly all week,' he commented, turning the car into the driveway of her home and switching off the engine.

'Nonsense,' Susan lied with a shrugging smile as she moved contentedly into his arms when he half turned in his seat.

His mouth closed masterfully over hers. It was an experienced kiss meant to arouse the response that it did. But Susan was disappointed again at the lack of chemical combustion. An ache throbbed painfully in her heart because she couldn't stop herself from comparing Warren's kisses with Mitch's. It wasn't right to do it and she hated herself for it.

'I wish I didn't have to go in,' she murmured as he nuzzled the lobe of her ear.

'You're certainly having trouble making up your mind,' Warren spoke in a curiously amused tone. 'A minute ago you said you were tired and now you say you wish you didn't have to go in.' He drew his head away, gazing at her intently. 'That Indy guy hasn't been bothering you, has he?'

'Oh, Warren, don't be silly,' Susan denied with a brittle laugh. 'Of course he hasn't.'

'Well, he'd better not.' The unspoken threat was obvious and Susan shifted uncomfortably in his arms. 'Come on. It's after one o'clock,' Warren announced. 'You'd better be getting in the house or else you'll find yourself getting ready for Sunday morning church without any sleep.'

He didn't allow Susan an opportunity to express her opinion as he moved her out of his embrace and stepped from the car. She stared at the darkened windows of the house and wondered how she was going to get through the whole of tomorrow— no, today it was now—with Mitch underfoot all the time.

Still silently considering that problem, she accepted Warren's hand out of the car and walked to the front door nestled under the crook of his arm. At the door, he stopped and turned her into his arms.

'I wish we were already married,' Susan sighed wistfully as she raised her head for his goodnight kiss. 'Why do we have to wait until August, darling? Why don't we get married now, in June?'

'Because we've already made all our plans with the intention of getting married in August,' he said patiently. 'Father will be fully recovered by then and I'll be able to take time off for our honeymoon. Besides, all our friends know of our plans. I respect you too much, Susan, to suddenly throw our plans aside and elope. That would raise too many eyebrows.'

'I suppose so,' she agreed submissively, and knew she had only been seeking a coward's way out of her dilemma. Mitch would be leaving before the month was out anyway and he would be taking that fleeting physical attraction she felt with him. It was only a matter of time.

'Good night, darling.' Warren kissed her tenderly.

'Good night,' she whispered when he released her and walked to the car.

She stood in front of the door, lifting a hand in farewell as he reversed out of the drive. Then she reached for the doorknob, the door unlocked as she knew it would be.

Stepping inside, she closed the door and leaned against it for a few weary seconds. She breathed in deeply and exhaled a long sigh before straightening and turning to lock the night-bolts. They had just clicked into place when someone rapped lightly on the door.

Susan froze. 'Who is it?'

'It's me,' a quiet voice answered. 'Mitch.'

Quickly unlocking the door, she opened it, staring at him with curious wariness. He was leaning lazily with one arm propped against the door frame. Her brows drew together when he failed to walk in.

'What are you doing out there?' she asked.

'Walking and thinking.' Susan thought she detected a weariness in his voice. 'I wouldn't have bothered you except that I was afraid you would lock me out. I would hate to wake up the whole household in the middle of the night so someone could let me in.'

Glancing at the navy shirt that matched the check of his slim-fitting trousers, Susan noticed that he had worked the long sleeves over the cast on his left arm although it was still held in a sling.

'It's awfully late,' she said with faint curiosity.

'I wasn't waiting up for you, if that's what you're thinking,' Mitch smiled wryly. 'I couldn't sleep. My arm was bothering me too much. Healing pains, I guess.'

'Oh,' Susan offered in a tiny voice. 'Would you . . . would you like me to get you something for it?'

'You mean a pain pill? No, thanks,' he refused. 'The pain isn't so bad that I can't endure it. It's a beautiful night. I'll just wander around out here for a while and see if I can't take my mind off it.' He straightened from the door, the moonlight glistening with a silvery sheen on his brown hair.

Sympathy surfaced instantly. 'Are you sure there's nothing I can do?' Susan offered.

Mitch hesitated. 'Well, you could——' Then he shook his head and stepped away. 'No, never mind. You wouldn't want to anyway. Don't lock me out, Susan. Goodnight.'

'Wait,' she called hesitantly. 'Was there something I could do?'

He shrugged slightly. 'I was going to ask if you would want to walk with me for a while, just so I could have someone to talk to instead of thinking about this throbbing in my arm. But I know you're probably thinking that I had something else in mind. I know you don't trust me, so let's just forget about it.'

'What would we talk about?' she asked.

Mitch looked back at her. The expression on the handsomely tanned face was solemn and serious. There was no mockery, not even a suggestion of it lurking anywhere near the surface.

'We could compare the new Offy with the Cosworth engine,' he stated indifferently, 'or the price of tea in China. It doesn't matter, Susan. Forget I mentioned it.'

'We would just talk?' she asked for his confirmation of his earlier statement again.

'I won't promise that, Susan,' Mitch sighed heavily. 'With you, I never know from one minute to the next. Right now all I can think about is the needles stabbing my arm. If you want to walk with me, then all right, let's go. If not—well, I understand why and we'll forget it.'

'I'll come,' she said quietly, and stepped through the door, shutting it behind her, 'for a while,' she qualified.

'I'll try to behave,' Mitch smiled faintly with a half-promise.

It was a warm summer's night, quiet and lazy. Midnight dew glistened with tiny diamond drops on the grass and leaves. Crickets chirruped in somnolent competition with the cicadas in the trees. The houses lining the streets were dark. There wasn't a moving thing in sight.

Stars shimmered softly, sprinkled over the nearly black sky. The moon, lopsided in three-quarter stage, was a pale gold, changing to silver.

In a mutually agreed silence, Susan and Mitch wandered into the back yard where the spreading limbs of a maple tree shaded Beth Mabry's rose garden. Beneath a thick limb was a bench swing, ivory white in the night shade. The scent of roses filled the air.

Susan chose one side of the swing and Mitch the other with a comfortable space in between. 'You were right,' she murmured. The quietness was so peaceful that it seemed almost wrong to break it. 'It is a beautiful night.'

'Thank you. I ordered it specially.' Mitch leaned back, an absent smile curving his mouth as he gazed through the maple leaves to the night sky.

'Specially for what?' Susan countered.

'For sleepless nights.' The swing rocked gently as he shifted into a more comfortable position, easing the arm sling on to his lap. 'Talk to me about something, Susan.'

'What about?' she responded uncertainly.

Mitch slid a sideways glance at her, his mouth curving slightly. 'Tell me what it's like to grow up a doctor's daughter.'

It was her turn to smile faintly. 'I doubt if it's any different. My childhood was very normal.'

But she sensed that it was words he wanted to

330

hear to distract his thoughts from the pain of his knitting arm. He was hurting. She could tell by the stiffness of the smile he had given her a second ago. It had been an absent, almost indifferent movement of his mouth without the warmth it usually reflected.

'Begin at the beginning, then,' Mitch instructed, 'with your very normal entry into the world.'

'Well let's see.' Susan leaned back in the swing, staring into the night sky as Mitch was doing. 'The stork brought me the first year that Mom and Dad were married. Dad was still in college. He hadn't begun his postgraduate work in medical school yet. My unplanned arrival on the scene was a hardship for them, I know. But Mom said she never regretted having me. She said she didn't know what she would have done if I hadn't been around to keep her company when Dad was putting in those long hours of internship. She worked, of course, and the landlady, a Mrs. Gibson, took care of me. Greg arrived the year Dad started his own practice. Amy came four years later.'

His eyes were closed when she looked at him. Susan wondered if he was asleep or merely resting. Then Mitch spoke to fill the silent pause.

'I was certain I was going to hear about all the contests you won as a baby,' he mocked lightly without lifting the spiky fan of lashes. 'You had to have been teacher's pet at school.'

'Pet or pest?' Susan laughed softly.

Quietly she began to relate anecdotes of her childhood in school and at home. While she talked, she studied him. His closed eyes kept her inspection safe from discovery.

In repose, his face—minus crinkling laughter around his eyes and the dimpling lines in the smooth lean cheeks—was still extraordinarily handsome. The roguish air, associated with a playboy, was gone.

Indomitable strength was roughly and arrogantly carved in Warren's features. Mitch Braden possessed the same strength, but in him it was tempered with determination and consideration. Mitch did not overpower people with the force of his personality. He charmed them to his side.

Concluding a story about a pet rabbit she had received one Easter, Susan noticed his breathing had become quite even and how relaxed his posture had become.

'Mitch?' she murmured.

'Yes,' he answered in a clear, quiet voice.

'I thought my talk might have bored you into falling asleep,' she explained, directing the wryly amused tone of voice at herself.

Mitch opened his eyes, blue and jewel-bright, focusing his gaze unerringly on her face. Steadily he looked at her.

'I don't think there's anything about you that would bore me, Susan,' he replied quite seriously.

Unnerved by the smooth way he had countered her jesting comment with a disturbing compliment, Susan turned away. The atmosphere of moonlight and roses was too romantic for her to be completely untouched by his statement.

'It's your turn now to tell me about yourself,' she said, trying to change the subject.

'What do you want to know?' Mitch inquired curiously. 'Shall I tell you of all the snips and snails and puppydog tails I collected as a mischievous boy?'

Susan didn't want to know about his childhood. She was reluctant to hear about the personal details of his past life. It was better not to learn too much about him.

'Tell me about racing.' She chose a safer topic. 'Why do you do it?'

'That's like asking why a man climbs a mountain or why a matador enters the bullring,' he chuckled softly at her question. 'It's the constant challenge, I suppose.'

'What's it like to drive in a race?'

He considered her question for several seconds before answering. 'Your heart pounds to send adrenalin surging through your system and your senses are more alert than you can ever remember. It's the high level of energy that sustains you when the gravity force exerted on you in the turns tries to pull you apart. It keeps you going when you're so bone weary and exhausted that you want to drop. There's a crazy kind of peace and freedom you feel when you're out there on the track. I don't know where it comes from,' he mused thoughtfully. 'It isn't from the cheering of the crowd or the deafening roar of a powerful engine. It isn't even from being the first car over the finish line. It comes from inside, I guess. You are competing with yourself, driving yourself to the limit of what you can endure, then discovering you can go farther.'

'Aren't you ever frightened?' Susan asked, suddenly fascinated by the insight into a sport she had never really considered in such a philosophical way.

'A man would be a fool if he didn't admit to being aware of the danger and the risks,' Mitch smiled. 'But you don't have time to be frightened, not at the speed you are traveling. By the time your mind can concentrate on the thing that frightens you, whether it's a particularly steep bank or the car ahead of you that's gone out of control, you're already past it or the worst has happened.'

His calm acceptance of the hazards made Susan shiver. Her heart was in her throat just visualizing Mitch in a race. There was the instinctive knowledge that she would live with fear if she ever watched him race.

'I think it's time we went into the house,' Mitch announced. 'It's beginning to get cool, and you must be tired.'

Susan didn't correct his assumption that her shiver had been from the growing coolness of the night air. She accepted the hand he offered to help her out of the swing.

'How is your arm?' she asked. 'Is it still bothering you?'

'Hardly at all now.' A lazy smile spread across

his features, crinkling the corners of his eyes. 'Thanks to you.'

Mitch didn't release her hand as they retraced their steps to the front of the house. The warmth of his grip was comforting as if he was silently assuring her not to worry about him.

CHAPTER EIGHT

INSIDE the house, Mitch released her hand and turned to lock the front door. Susan waited for him a few steps inside. She didn't know why except that it seemed the polite thing to do.

'Are you tired?' he glanced at her inquiringly.

'A little,' she admitted. 'Aren't you?'

'Unfortunately, no.' His shoulders lifted in a rueful gesture. 'Do you suppose your mother would object if I fixed myself some cocoa? I can't stand hot milk.'

'Of course she wouldn't mind.' Susan hesitated, then admitted, 'I'll fix it for you, if you like.'

There was a merry sparkle in his look. 'To tell you the truth, I was hoping you'd volunteer. I didn't like the idea of having to poke through the cupboards trying to find things. You'll join me, won't you?'

The boyish honesty and engaging smile were too much for Susan to combat. Besides, although she was tired, she wasn't ready for the evening to end. She didn't want to examine the reason for that thought too closely.

'Yes, I'll join you,' she agreed. 'Do you want to have it in the kitchen or shall I bring it into the living room?'

'The kitchen is fine. We'll be less likely to disturb the others there.' Mitch started for the hallway leading to the kitchen. 'I'll give you a hand. Of course, I only have one hand that I can use.'

In the kitchen, Susan put the milk on to heat and stirred in the cocoa and sugar. She pointed out the cupboard where Mitch could find the mugs and another one where the marshmallows were kept.

As the cocoa mixture began to simmer, Susan glanced over her shoulder at Mitch. He was walking toward her, carrying the two mugs by a finger curled through the handles.

'There are sugar cookies in the cookie jar if you want a snack,' she offered.

'No, thanks,' he refused, and watched as she carefully poured the hot chocolate into the mugs and floated a pair of marshmallows on the hot liquid in each mug.

They each carried their own cup to the narrow

breakfast table in front of the glassed windows looking into the back yard. Mitch waited as Susan sat down in the chair at the head of the table, then he took the chair to her left.

'How long have you known Warren?' he asked casually.

'Why?' Susan tipped her head to one side, surprised by his unexpected question.

'Just curious,' Mitch shrugged.

Susan couldn't think of any reason not to answer his question. 'I was formally introduced to him when I went to work for the law firm in the secretarial pool. Two years ago I became his personal secretary when his previous one left to get married.'

'That's quite a long courtship, isn't it?' he grinned crookedly.

'Oh, no,' she hurried to explain. 'We didn't start dating until after the Christmas party last year.'

'Not until then?' he frowned in faint disbelief.

'Well, Warren didn't actually notice me as more than his secretary until then.' She sipped self-consciously at her steaming cocoa.

'The man must have been blind,' he laughed in short disbelief. 'What about you? Had you noticed him?'

Susan stirred the melting marshmallows into her hot chocolate. 'Secretaries are always in love with their bosses without their bosses being aware of it.' She tried to make it a joke, unable to meet the mocking glint in Mitch's eyes. 'I thought everybody knew that.'

'And after the Christmas party, it was a case of love at first and very late sight for Warren, is that it?' Mitch inquired with decided cynicism. 'I mean, you already believed you were half in love with him.'

'I guess it was like that,' Susan admitted nervously.

'Then how long have you been engaged?'

'Since April.'

'April Fools' Day?' he asked mockingly.

There was a defiant tilt of her chin. 'He gave me the ring over the Easter weekend, if you must know.'

'I would have thought you would have planned a traditional June wedding,' Mitch gazed thoughtfully at the cup in his hand, 'instead of waiting until August. But then I guess the idea to marry then wasn't yours.'

Warily Susan studied his bland expression, a thought just occurring to her and one that she probably should have had earlier.

'You were hiding somewhere listening to Warren and me tonight, weren't you?' she accused in a low, angry voice.

'Inadvertently,' he admitted without apology. 'I didn't intentionally eavesdrop. I heard the car drive in and assumed it was you. I wanted to be certain you didn't lock me out of the house. Warren usually doesn't walk you to the door, or at least he hasn't lately.'

Susan remembered suddenly that the guest bedroom that Mitch used had a clear view of the front door. He must have been spying on her ever since he had come.

'You could have let us know you were there,' she retorted bitterly trying to remember what she and Warren had said.

'The topic sounded very personal. I didn't think either of you would appreciate my opinion on the matter,' Mitch explained, the wicked glitter back in his blue eyes. 'Does he make love to you?'

The spoon clattered from her hand on to the table. Fire flashed in her eyes.

'If you're asking whether I sleep with him, then you're just going to have to wonder, because I have no intention of answering such an objectionable question!'

'Temper, temper, Susan!' He clicked his tongue at her in mock reproval. 'Obviously the man doesn't.'

'Obviously?' she echoed angrily. 'Why obviously?'

'There are several things that made me reach that conclusion,' Mitch answered lazily. 'You might have wanted to set the wedding date ahead because you were becoming frustrated sexually. And everything is so precise between the two of you. Certain nights you have dates. On the week nights he has you home at a certain hour. Everything fits into a prim pattern. Believe me, Warren isn't a man overcome with passion. He's doing everything by the book, including waiting until the wedding night.'

Trembling, Susan stared at him while he casually drank his cocoa. 'You sound as if that's something to be ashamed of!' she accused.

'Of course not,' Mitch denied with a deprecating laugh. 'But wouldn't you feel better if his control broke just once? Wouldn't it make him a little more human?'

'I don't know what you're talking about.' She looked away hastily, staring at the foamy residue clinging to the sides of her mug. 'Besides, Warren is in love with me, whether you want to believe it or not.'

'In his way, yes,' he nodded agreeably.

'What do you mean by that?' she asked with an irritated sigh.

'If I were a girl engaged to a man and that man held me in his arms and declared how very much he respected me, I would be insulted,' he answered simply.

'I see.' Her fingers drummed a war beat on the table top. 'What you're really saying is that you wouldn't respect the woman you married. Isn't that right, Mr. Braden?'

'Naturally I would respect her, or I wouldn't marry her.' Mitch met the angry glitter of her gaze with good-humored patience. 'But that certainly isn't the emotion I would want to feel when I held her in my arms.'

'No, I suppose you would feel lust,' Susan retorted sarcastically.

'Why not? I'm a lusty man.' Amusement touched his mouth, her barbs bouncing off without inflicting one prick.

'I think you're impossible!' she declared with a frustrated shake of her head as she looked away.

Out of the corner of her eye, she saw him rub the back of his neck, with a slight stretching motion of his shoulders. 'And because I would enjoy making love to the woman I want to marry, that makes me impossible?' he chided.

'You make it sound as if it's all your decision,' Susan replied. 'I should think the girl might have something to say about it.'

'If she loved me, she would be willing.' His hand moved to wearily rub his mouth and chin. Susan's stifled gasp of indignant outrage drew his gaze from the mug to her. 'You don't believe me, do you?'

'I think that statement smacks of conceit!'

'Maybe,' Mitch acknowledged nonchalantly. 'But if I were Warren and you professed to love me as much as you say you love him, and if I chose to take advantage of that love—which I admit is what I would be doing—then I could have you in bed with me within twenty minutes and you wouldn't have made a single word or gesture of protest.'

'Of all the——' Susan sputtered.

But Mitch wasn't listening. His hand was covering a yawn that brought a watery brightness to his eyes. When it was over, he glanced at Susan, sending her a sheepishly rueful grin.

'That's a boastful statement to make, isn't it, for a man who's too tired to back it up,' he said with half a sigh. 'I guess the hot chocolate did the trick.'

Pushing the chair from the table, he rose to his feet and carried his empty coffee mug to the sink. Susan stared angrily at him for a few seconds, then picked up her own mug and followed him.

'Would you like me to help clean up?' Mitch offered when she shoved her mug in the sink and walked stiffly to the stove for the pan.

'No thanks,' she snapped.

He stood beside the sink, a hip leaning against the counter, and watched the suppressed anger in her movements. But Susan refused to meet his gaze.

'I upset you, Susan,' he said slowly. 'That wasn't my intention. I should have been thanking you for so considerately spending some time with me. Instead I started needling you about your engagement to Warren. I was jealous—I still am. I suppose that's why I was so brash. I'm sorry, truly.'

Susan stood in front of the sink, the pot nervously clutched in her hands. She was aware of his gaze studying her bent head. The sincerity in his voice had taken away most of her outraged anger. She swallowed down the lump in her throat.

Why did he constantly have to confuse her? One minute she was trembling with anger at his taunts and another she would be feeling the force of his attraction. Part of her liked the idea that Mitch was attracted to her and showed it, while the other half was indignant that she should feel that way when she was already engaged to marry another man.

343

'I accept your apology,' she said tightly, not ready to wholeheartedly forgive him for provoking her so. She glanced at the wall clock above the sink. 'It's a minute after two. You need some sleep.'

'Are you positive you don't want me to help with those dishes?' Mitch repeated his offer, still trying to catch her downcast gaze.

'I'm only going to stack them in the sink and wipe off the counter and stove. I can manage that on my own, thank you.' Her clipped voice was deliberately cool and indifferent.

His hand closed over her chin, his grip firm but not harsh. He turned her head so he could look into her face. Resentment still smoldered in her dark eyes as she met the patient blueness of his.

'I'm sorry for making you angry, Susan.'

'So you said.'

'And I want to thank you again for keeping me company tonight. I appreciate it,' Mitch finished in a level, serious tone. Then he leaned forward and lightly touched his lips to hers. 'Good night.'

Her chin was released and he was walking away before Susan could offer a protest at his action. When the kitchen door closed behind him, she touched a fingertip to her lips. They still tingled with the warmth of his light caress.

Jerkily she brushed the dark hair away from her temple and set about the task of cleaning up, a minor one that hardly took any time. All the time she kept wondering how long it would be before this physical chemistry between her and Mitch would fizzle out. For the sake of her peace of mind it couldn't be too soon.

Two minutes after Mitch had left the kitchen, Susan followed, making her way up the darkened stairs to the unlit hallway of the second floor. Unerringly she turned in the direction of the bathroom to clean off her makeup and brush her teeth before changing into night clothes. Her steps took her past the guest bedroom.

From inside came a stifled gasp of pain and a few savagely muttered oaths. Her eyes darted curiously to the strip of light beneath the door just as it swung open to catch her in full light.

Mitch's tall frame was in the center of the doorway, his navy blue long-sleeved shirt unbuttoned. He started to stride into the hallway, saw Susan and stopped, a dark frown on his forehead.

'Give me a hand, would you?' It was a crisp demand rather than a request as he pivoted around to reenter his room. 'I can't get my shirt off with this cast on my arm.'

Susan hesitated in the hallway, watching as Mitch impatiently tried to shrug his right arm out of the long sleeve. He glanced over his shoulder, the look in his eyes asking her what she was doing still standing in the hall.

'If you'd hold the sleeve, I think I can pull my arm out of it,' he said with a thin thread of patience.

His struggle to remove the shirt was genuine and Susan walked into his room to help. She held the sleeve while he twisted his arm, grunting once with pain.

'Now all I have to do is work the other sleeve over my cast,' he muttered, tossing her a disgruntled look. 'And to think all this is because I was tired of dangling sleeves!'

'Let me help with that,' Susan offered, stepping around to his other side to ease the shirt off the cast. 'It will be easier, I think, if we take your arm out of the sling to begin with.'

Mitch slipped his arm out of the cradle sling. Together they worked the sleeve material over the plaster cast until his arm was free.

It was difficult for Susan not to look at his naked torso. His chest was as tanned as the rest of him, muscles rippling sinewy strong with curling tawny gold hair sprinkled over the center of his smooth chest. The flat stomach and slim waist belonged to an athlete.

'Shouldn't you be wearing an elastic support for those cracked ribs of yours?' she questioned, self-consciously turning away to drape his shirt over a chair.

'You mean my corset.' His mouth quirked mockingly. 'It became more of an irritant then a help, so I took it off.'

'I see,' she murmured, glancing in his direction without quite looking at him.

At this moment, his virility was like a bright fire on a cold Indiana winter night, drawing her irresistibly to its warmth. Susan forced her disturbed senses to the rear. She stood nervously before him, not wanting to leave and knowing she didn't dare stay. 'Would you like me to help you with your pajama top?'

A naughty light danced gleefully in his blue eyes. 'I don't mean to embarrass you, but I don't sleep in pajamas.'

'Oh,' she murmured, disconcerted by the image that sprang into her mind. Lowering her gaze she noticed the sling strap had become twisted around his neck. Without thinking, she reached upward to straighten it before Mitch slipped his arm into the cradle sling. Her fingers felt icily cold compared to the fire that seemed to burn beneath his skin.

The top of her head felt the caressing warmth of his breath near it. Her lashes veiled much of her disturbed state as she looked into his eyes. A mask seemed to have been pulled over the brilliant blue, yet the directness of his gaze compelled her not to glance away.

With a certainty that frightened her, she knew she wanted Mitch to kiss her. Her hands had completed their task, but they remained lightly touching the back of his neck. His hand was resting casually on the side of her waist.

'Susan.' There was a question in his husky, caressing voice.

'Yes?' she answered, her lips parting in invitation.

Mitch slowly lowered his head toward her, prolonging the moment when their lips met as if he expected her to deny the kiss at the last second and was allowing her time to protest.

A convulsive shudder quaked through Susan at the tentative possession. His mouth moved mobilely over hers, tasting the sweetness of her lips. The stiffness, the unnamed fear began to leave her body, melting under his gentle kiss.

The hardness of the plaster cast was behind her back while his right hand lightly caressed her waist and shoulder. When he released her mouth to begin an exploring search of her face and neck, Susan kept her face upturned, eyes closed by the magic in his touch.

A sigh of longing broke from her lips an instant before he claimed them again. This time it was with firm possession, a long, drugging kiss that stole her breath and awakened her senses that she had held in limbo.

Her hands twined themselves around his neck, not needing the pressure of his hands to mold herself against his length. Arching against him, she was subconsciously aware of his muscular thighs and the solidness of his bare chest. The knowledge added itself to the buffeting storm of emotions raging inside her, sensations that Susan had never experienced before.

Reeling under the turbulent winds that rocked her, she wasn't conscious of movement under Mitch's guiding hands. The action seemed part of the whirlwind that claimed her, the result of the hardening passion in his kiss.

Then there was a strange floating sensation. Her legs no longer needed to support her. Again his mouth began exploring the sensitive hollow of her throat, drawing tiny gasps of bewildered, sensuous pleasure from deep within. His fingers spread over the naked skin of her back, igniting fresh sparks with their caress. Absently Susan acknowledged that he must have loosened her blouse from her skirt.

'Now do you see what I mean, darling?' Mitch murmured against her throat.

Her lashes blinked with confusion at the smoldering blueness of his half-closed eyes.

'Mean about what?' Susan whispered blankly. The throbbing ache in her voice begged for the words to stop and the kisses to continue.

'Seventeen minutes. That's all it took,' he answered complacently.

'Seventeen minutes?' she repeated, trying to rise above the storm that had made everything so topsy-turvy.

'This is the way it should be, my beautiful one,' he stated decisively, and leaned his head forward to nuzzle her ear.

A frown puckered her forehead as the cyclonic upheaval began to recede. A stark white cloth was behind Mitch's head. In disbelief she stared at it, then at the maple headboard of the bed inches away.

'I could have you in bed with me in twenty minutes.' The words came back with slapping force. Mitch had said that in the kitchen not— seventeen minutes ago.

Horror washed over her head as she suddenly realized what he was talking about.

'How could you do this!' she breathed with fear-widened eyes.

'Do what?' he asked with mocking indifference.

'You tried to seduce me!' she accused. The pliancy was gone as she held herself rigid under his continued caress.

'If that had been my intention, darling, you would already have been seduced,' Mitch chuckled softly.

'How dare you!' she choked on a bubble of righteous indignation.

His arms tightened when she tried to pull away. Struggling and twisting, she succeeded in breaking away from his embrace, uncaring of the muffled cry of pain Mitch made as she accidentally hit his injured ribs.

'What's the matter with you?' he muttered as he tried to follow her.

'You can ask me that!' Frantically, she pushed the end of her blouse into the waistband of her skirt.

'Darling——'

'Don't you darling me!' snapped Susan.

'Keep your voice down,' he frowned, but with considerable amusement.

'I'll talk just as loudly as I please.' Yet she spoke in a softer and more angry tone.

'Susan,' Mitch murmured, in a coaxing, placating voice meant to soothe her growing temper.

'You lured me into your room deliberately just to prove your point, didn't you?' she accused.

'Not exactly,' he hedged. 'I suppose I could

have eventually fought my way out of that shirt, but I admit I did use it to persuade you to come in.'

'I suppose you're going to try to convince me now that it was a practical joke,' she hissed. 'You have a very warped sense of humor, Mitch Braden!'

He was standing in front of her now, easily within reaching distance, but his hand remained on his hip, a mocking kind of patience in his handsome features.

'My full name is Mitchum Alexander Braden,' he told her. 'My mother always liked to use all of it when she was really angry with me.'

'Well, I'm angry, too, Mitchum Alexander Braden!' she declared with some satisfaction. 'I think it was a mean, contemptible trick you played when you knew I'm engaged to Warren!'

'That is precisely my point in this,' Mitch drawled. 'You aren't in love with him. I tricked you because I was running out of time to prove that you don't love him. You have to realize it before you do something you'll live to regret, like marrying him.'

'You're quite wrong.'

'I am?' he said with challenging humor. 'Tell me how you love him so much that you can almost allow *me* to seduce you?'

'Did it ever occur to you that I might have been imagining Warren in your place?' Susan retorted with some fast thinking.

'No, it didn't occur to me, and it doesn't now,'

Mitch replied. 'You're only saying that to try to salvage some of your pride. Don't be stubborn by refusing to admit to yourself the truth of what I'm saying.'

'Truth! The truth is that I want you to leave me alone!'

'You're angry right now, Susan,' Mitch sighed. 'Think about what I've said, would you?'

His hand reached toward her and fell to his side as she took a hasty step away. Without saying another word, Susan turned around and walked swiftly from his room.

Several minutes later she was in her own bed, staring at the ceiling. How had she allowed herself to be tricked into that embarrassing situation? Nothing Mitch had said had been true. He had jumped to erroneous conclusions, she assured herself.

She was in love with Warren. She had loved him for almost two years. After that much time, a person didn't stop loving someone in one night.

'Not unless,' a little voice said, 'you never loved him in the beginning.'

'Impossible!' Susan whispered aloud, jamming a fist into her pillow and turning on her side.

CHAPTER NINE

'SUSAN, are you going to sleep until noon or are you going to get up?' Amy demanded impatiently, jiggling her sleeping sister's shoulder.

'W-what?' Groggily Susan blinked open her eyes, absently brushing away the hand on her shoulder.

'Mom has breakfast ready. Are you coming down or not?'

'Yes.' She snuggled deeper into her pillow. Then she realized the action would only bring more sleep and stretched out of her comfortable position. 'I'll get dressed and be right down.'

Amy waited until she saw her sister throw the covers off before she left the room. A gloomy sense of depression seemed to be clinging to Susan as she reached for the cranberry robe draped over a chair. As she slipped her arms into the sleeves, she remembered last night and the depression grew darker.

How was she going to face Mitch after the way she had behaved, she wondered, as she slid her feet into terrycloth slippers. Where had her common sense been? What could she say to him that would convince him it had all been a mistake?

Mistake! It had been a catastrophe. She simply had to convince him that she didn't want anything more to do with him. But how?

Plagued by her seemingly unsolvable dilemma, Susan ran a hand through her sleep-tousled hair. She stared sightlessly at the carpeted floor of the hallway as she made her way to the bathroom.

Opposite Mitch's room, her gaze nervously strayed to the open door. The room was empty. From downstairs, she could hear voices of her family and guessed that he was down there with them.

Breathing a sigh of relief that their moment of confrontation had been put off, Susan turned toward the open bathroom door. She stopped short inside its frame. Mitch was standing in front of the mirror above the sink, shirtless as he had been last night but wearing a pair of wheat tan pants instead of the blue checked.

Before she could recover from her surprise and retreat, the fingers of his right hand closed over her wrist and drew her into the room. When she pulled to free herself from his hold, he released her immediately. The movement of his hand continued fluidly to close the door.

'Good morning, beautiful,' he smiled lazily, his eyes moving possessively over her face. 'I didn't think it was possible, but you're even more beautiful first thing in the morning.'

'I imagine you've seen a lot of women "first thing in the morning"!' she snapped sarcastically, saying the first thing that came to her mind.

'I do believe you're jealous,' he chuckled. 'That's good.'

'That's absurd!' she denied with an impatient toss of her head away from his handsome face. 'You're so determined to see everything the way you want it to be that there isn't any use trying to explain things to you. Excuse me.'

'Wait.' His hand reached out again, checking her movement to leave. Susan stared pointedly at the fingers on her arm. 'Would you help me a second?'

She warily raised her eyes to his face.

Mitch smiled crookedly. 'No tricks, I promise.'

'What do you want?' she asked, still not trusting him.

'I've been trying for the last ten minutes to pour some after-shave lotion in my hand and I'm fast running out of patience,' he explained.

Her gaze found the uncapped bottle of after-shave lotion sitting on the counter beside the washbasin. That much of his statement seemed to be true.

He let go of her arm and reached for the bottle, tucking it in a precarious position between his cast and his body, cupping his right hand near the top of the bottle.

'You see what I mean,' he said as he tried to tip his body to one side to allow the liquid to run into his hand and nearly dropped the bottle in the process.

Sighing, Susan took the bottle from him and poured a small quantity in his hand, which he quickly rubbed over his freshly shaven face.

His gaze danced to her impassive expression. 'I thought you might have wanted to put it on. It would have given you a chance to slap my face.'

'Would it have done any good?' she asked cuttingly.

'You're still upset about last night, aren't you?' The crinkling lines around his eyes smoothed out as his expression became gently serious.

Her pulse began behaving erratically under his level gaze. 'I don't wish to discuss it with you.'

'I've backed you into a corner, haven't I, Susan?' he shrugged ruefully. 'And all I meant to do was to bring you out in the open where you could see things for yourself.'

His hand lightly caressed her cheek as he tucked a wayward strand of dark hair behind her ear. His hand remained there cupping the side of her head. Susan felt an inexplicable urge to turn her face into his hand and kiss his palm.

Why did he have to be so gentle? She could have withstood his mockery and his flattery. But this? Her eyes misted a liquid brown.

A thumb raised her chin. Too numbed by her inner bewilderment to protest, she remained motionless as his head bent toward her. His mouth lovingly caressed her trembling lips and that crazy whirlwind of emotions came sweeping over her again. It took all her strength to stand solidly in the face of it.

Finally, when Susan thought she could resist no longer, he raised his head, smiling lightly into her eyes with a tenderness as moving as his gentleness had been.

'When are you going to give Warren back his ring?' Mitch asked huskily.

Was there a faint unevenness to his breathing? Susan couldn't be certain. She stiffened away from the hand resting on her cheek.

'I'm not giving it back.' She lowered her gaze to the sling holding his arm. 'I'm going to marry him.'

'Susan, Susan,' Mitch sighed dispiritedly. 'When are you going to wake up?'

'When are you?' she demanded in a childishly hurt and confused voice. 'I keep telling you and telling you, but you won't listen. Why can't you leave me alone?'

'Is that what you really want me to do?' His eyes narrowed into piercing blue diamonds, cutting hard.

'Yes! Yes, it is!' Susan declared forcefully.

'All right.' His mouth tightened into an uncompromising line as he stepped away from her. 'If that's what you want, I will leave you alone.'

Without another word, Mitch walked out of the

bathroom leaving Susan standing there more bewildered and uncertain than she had been a moment ago.

And Mitch kept his word. He left Susan alone.

It was no small accomplishment when they both lived in the same house. Yet he succeeded. Whenever Susan entered a room, he found an excuse to leave. At the evening meal, he avoided addressing any comment to her, however trivially. Never once had she caught him looking at her.

If the family noticed the way they ignored each other, none of them said anything to Susan. For them, life seemed to be going very much as usual.

But not for Susan. She kept reminding herself how wonderful it was that she had finally made Mitch leave her alone. In truth, she was restless, on edge, and troubled. She blamed the state on Mitch's presence in the house. When he finally left, then everything would be all right. But she couldn't quite convince herself of that.

Her three dates with Warren since Mitch had begun ignoring her hadn't proved to be very enjoyable. Each time he embraced her, Susan began comparing her reactions to what she had felt with Mitch. It became impossible to respond to his kisses when she was mentally checking her pulse and respiration rate.

Warren didn't help matters by constantly chiding her for being so nervous and restless. She had come very close several times to telling him to shut up and leave her alone, too. The whole situation was becoming ridiculous in the extreme.

The names on the wedding list blurred into a jumble of lines. Susan shook her head to clear her vision and tried to find where she had left off before she had become lost in thought.

'Hi!' Amy flounced down on the sofa cushion beside Susan. 'What are you doing?'

'Going over the invitation list for the wedding,' she sighed, running the eraser end of her pencil down the names, not certain which was the last name she had checked.

She wasn't really in the mood to do it, but it was something that needed to be done and it filled the time until she went to bed.

'Are you going to invite Mitch?' Amy asked eagerly.

Susan paused, the muscles in her stomach knotting at the mention of his name. 'I don't think Mitch would be very interested in coming to my wedding,' she replied, avoiding a direct answer.

'You would come, wouldn't you, Mitch, if Susan invited you?' Amy's inquiry was directed toward the hallway arch.

Glancing up in surprise, Susan bit into her lower lip. Mitch was standing in its frame, lazily watching her with an almost mocking expression in his eyes.

'It would be very difficult to refuse a written invitation from Susan,' he said dryly. 'That would practically be a milestone.'

Her eyes bounced away from his face to the papers on her lap. The cast had been removed from his left arm. Without the cumbersome protective cast, Mitch looked more vitally attractive than she remembered.

Susan couldn't think of a single reply she could make to his comment. She didn't want him at her wedding. Even though she didn't think he would come, she still didn't want to invite him.

Fortunately Amy filled the silence.

'I'm going to be one of Susan's bridesmaids.' Amy had declared vigorously that she was much too old to be a flower girl. 'I'm going to wear a beautiful long gown of emerald green. And Mother said I could go to a beautician and have her fix my hair on top of my head.'

'Johnny Chambers had better watch out if you catch that bridal bouquet,' he teased.

'Oh, Mitch!' Amy giggled, her cheeks turning nearly as red as her hair.

Susan knew that Johnny Chambers was one of the boys in Amy's class at school and also the object of her latest crush. Mitch was still her idol, though.

Mitch leisurely wandered into the room, pausing beside the sofa where Susan sat. Her hand trembled nervously as she felt him looking over her shoulder.

'Is that the list of guests you're inviting to the wedding?' he asked after several long seconds had passed.

'Actually,' Susan didn't let her gaze wander from the handwritten lists, 'what it is is my list and Warren's list. I have to compare the two to make certain we haven't duplicated any names.'

'Amy!' her mother called from another room. 'You've left your record albums strewn all over the family room. Come in here and pick them up before they get broken.'

'Oh, Mother!' Amy grumbled, and slid off the couch.

Shifting her leg uneasily, Susan waited for Mitch to leave. He had avoided her so completely in the past week that she was apprehensive about his reasons for staying.

'Susan.' He was asking for her attention, but she refused to look at him.

'Yes,' she said absently as if she had forgotten he was there.

'Are you really going through with this wedding?'

'Of course,' she laughed, pretending she didn't understand why he had asked that question. 'It would certainly be a waste of time to compile all these names if there wasn't going to be a wedding, wouldn't it?' She knew some kind of deflating retort would be forthcoming, so she didn't give him a chance to respond. 'I see the doctor removed your cast this afternoon. It must really be a relief not to have that weight on your arm,' Susan commented with forced nonchalance.

Out of the corner of her eye, she saw him absently flex his left arm as if testing it. 'Yes, it is a relief.' Mitch allowed the change of subject. 'The doctor said it was healing almost perfectly, and it certainly does feel better.'

'In a couple of weeks you'll be as good as new,'

she observed brightly, still not letting her eyes stray from the paper on her lap.

'As good as new,' he agreed dryly. 'I'll be leaving next week, Susan.'

'So soon?' She flashed him a glance of surprise, meeting the watchfulness of his blue eyes. Then, feeling she had betrayed something, she immediately added, 'I imagine you're very eager to be on your way now that you've recovered.'

'Eager? I wouldn't say that,' he mocked. 'But I certainly don't have any reason not to meet the boys at Pocono now that the cast is off.'

'A-are you racing?' she frowned.

'I've entered in the Pocono 500 at the end of the month. The time trials start next week,' he told her.

A cold chill ran over her skin. She could hardly keep from shuddering. 'I—I'm sure you'll do very well,' she said. 'As Greg says, you're a very excellent driver.'

Mitch didn't reply to that rather inane comment. His head moved in a slight negative shake as if to say the situation was hopeless. In the next moment he was walking out of the room.

Be glad that he's leaving, Susan told herself. *Now everything will return to normal.* She could begin forgetting him. But there was an awful tightness in her throat.

When she mentioned Mitch's imminent departure to Warren the next night, he rejoiced openly with a scathing comment that it was about time. Susan's murmur of agreement was hollow. She tried, but she simply couldn't make herself be glad he was leaving.

Warren's exultation at the news forced her to hide the cloud of depression that had tagged along behind her ever since Mitch had told her.

Bright and early Wednesday morning was the time Mitch had chosen to leave, choosing the hour before Susan and her father left for work. Her mother cooked an enormous farewell breakfast, but most of the food Susan ate lodged itself somewhere between her throat and stomach.

She silently wished that Mitch had stolen away in the night, but he seemed determined to make his departure as big an impact on her life as his arrival had been.

Susan stayed in the kitchen helping her mother clear away the dishes rather than join Mitch's entourage. Her father, Greg, and Amy were all helping him pack the expensive blue sports car now parked in the driveway.

Finally there was no more to be done in the kitchen and Beth Mabry was urging her toward the outer door. Susan didn't want to take part in the lingering goodbye outside. She wished she were a child again so she could run away and hide. Instead she squared her shoulders and marched along beside her mother.

His few possessions were all stowed in the car. Mitch was leaning against the door when Susan and her mother joined the semicircle around him. His gaze touched her fleetingly before it casually moved away.

'Well,' Mitch drew a resigned breath and smiled as he straightened from the car and extended a hand to her father, 'I guess there isn't any reason to keep prolonging the moment when I have to say goodbye.'

'I wish you could, Mitch.' Simon Mabry gripped his hand firmly, a faint gruffness in his voice. 'We're going to miss you, all of us.'

'I can't say anything but thanks, and that doesn't seem like enough,' Mitch replied. He withdrew his hand and turned to her brother. 'Greg.'

Awkwardly Greg shook his hand. 'Good luck at Pocono. We'll be cheering for you.'

Amy's dark eyes were gazing at him soulfully when Mitch turned to her. She offered him her hand, a slight tremble in her chin.

'Goodbye, Mitch,' Amy said in a slightly strangled voice.

Mitch flashed one of those fulsome smiles that Susan had not seen in the last ten days. It was just as potent as it had always been and this time her sister was the object of his charm.

'May I kiss you goodbye, Amy?' he asked with an inquiring tilt of his head. 'I don't want Johnny Chambers to be the first.'

Amy's auburn head bobbed quickly in agreement, a sparkle of ecstatic disbelief in her eyes. Then Mitch was bending his head and tenderly brushing her sister's lips in a chaste kiss.

With her mother, Mitch didn't ask but kissed her lightly without speaking. Beth Mabry gave him a quick hug in return, a teary brightness appearing in her eyes.

'Thank you, Beth, for letting me be a part of your family for a while,' Mitch offered sincerely.

'We're going to miss you,' she reiterated her husband's statement.

The last one in the semicircle was Susan. She wanted to bolt and run when Mitch turned to her. For a long second he stood in front of her and said nothing, holding her troubled gaze with the compelling blueness of his.

The morning sun danced in his hair, brightening the shadowy brown. He looked so vigorous, so strong and so handsome that Susan felt her breath being ripped away. The image of him at this moment seemed to implant itself in her mind to be remembered and recalled for the rest of her life.

'And Susan,' he drawled, a faint smile turning up the corners of his mouth. 'I always try to save the best for last.'

The emotional scene leading up to this moment had eroded the control Susan had fought to attain. She had hoped to wish him a breezy goodbye and godspeed. But the genuinely affectionate exchanges that had gone before had erased the barrier. Still, she tried.

'Goodbye, Mitch.' She spoke in a low tone so her voice wouldn't tremble and politely offered him her hand.

Mitch ignored her outstretched hand. 'Aren't you going to kiss me goodbye, Susan?' he asked with complete seriousness, not even the faintest glimmer of wicked mockery in his eyes.

Self-consciously she glanced to the amused expressions of her parents. She appeared to be the only one taken aback by his question. Her hand fell uncertainly to her side.

'Warren won't mind,' Mitch added, 'not since you're kissing me goodbye. You never know, we might never see each other again. That's one of the risks in my profession.'

The blood rushed from her face at his words, the anguishing memory of his crash in the Indy 500 came vividly back. She swayed toward him, reeling from the stabbing pain in her midriff.

His hands closed over the soft flesh of her upper arms and drew her the rest of the way toward him. Her head was tilted back to gaze into the handsome features while her hands spread themselves on the solid wall of his chest. For an instant they were like two statues, motionless in the beginning of an embrace.

Drawing her up on tiptoe, Mitch lowered his head to meet her halfway. A quivering magic raced through her when his mouth claimed her lips, persuasively warm and ardent. A longing filled Susan for the enchanted spell to continue, her breath completely stolen and her heart thudding against her ribs. Almost with reluctance, he released her lips.

His back was to the others and he spoke in a low soft voice that carried its message only to her ears. 'You aren't going to forget me. I won't let you.' In a louder voice, for the benefit of the rest of the family, he said, 'Goodbye, Susan.'

Then she was released and he was moving away. The flesh of her arms was cold where his hands had been and the coldness began to penetrate to the bone. Only her mouth still tingled with warmth.

Her gaze was riveted to him, mesmerized by the mystical power he held over her that made her respond physically to his touch.

I'm engaged. I'm going to marry Warren. The words were almost a chant, spoken silently to ward off the bewitching effect Mitch had on her.

Susan marveled at the way he had dissociated himself from their kiss of a second ago. She was stunned by it and he was smiling cheerfully and bidding everyone a last goodbye as he slid behind the wheel of his sleek sports car.

When he reversed out of the drive, Mitch waved, but it was a wave that encompassed them all. Susan wasn't singled out for any last attention. She stood in the driveway with her family until he was out of sight, the hushed silence darkening the cloud of depression at her heels.

Susan was the first to turn away, hot tears in her eyes. 'I'll forget him,' she declared to herself. 'Maybe not tomorrow, but he's wrong. I'll forget him.'

It was a bold statement made in desperation. Her heart didn't believe a word of it, but her mind wouldn't listen to her heart. There were too many things it might have to admit if it did.

Yet when she arrived at the office that morning, Susan didn't say anything to Warren about Mitch leaving. She didn't think she would be able to listen to his caustic remarks about the Indy man. As often as she had tried, Susan couldn't despise Mitch as much as Warren did. Mitch had disrupted her life, but she couldn't bring herself to hate him for it.

CHAPTER TEN

'SUSAN! Warren is here. Are you ready yet?' her mother called from the bottom of the stairs.

Rising from the edge of the bed where she had sat for the last ten minutes in huddled silence, Susan walked slowly to the hallway door and then hesitated.

'I'll—I'll be down in a minute,' she answered.

Why hadn't she phoned him and said she wasn't feeling well? she asked herself for the hundredth time, as she walked to the mirror above the chest of drawers. It wasn't that she was actually sick. She simply didn't feel like going out tonight.

To be truthful, Susan hadn't felt like going out Saturday night or Thursday night or Tuesday night or either of the weekend nights before that. This Sunday evening was proving to be no different. The second Sunday since Mitch had left.

'That has nothing to do with it,' Susan whispered angrily the instant she had the thought.

But she was beginning to believe that it had more to do with it than she wanted. Every room in the house was haunted by Mitch's ghost. She could hardly bear Warren's embraces any more. They left her feeling vaguely revolted and sick. Warren hadn't changed, so she must have.

With a sigh, because that there was no sense putting off going downstairs, Susan turned away from the mirror and walked dispiritedly into the hallway and down the steps. The living room was empty and she guessed that her mother had invited Warren to wait in the family room where the others were.

Following the lower hallway, Susan paused in the open archway of the family room, her troubled eyes going to the man sitting with military erectness next to her father. A second later Warren glanced up, saw her and smiled.

'You look lovely, Susan,' he said warmly, but she felt nothing.

'I hope I didn't keep you waiting too long,' she said quickly.

'I didn't mind in the least,' Warren replied, rising to his feet. 'I planned——'

'Sssh!' Greg interrupted loudly, gesturing with his hand for Warren to be quiet while he frowned in deep concentration at the transistor radio in his hand.

'What is it?' Her father leaned forward eagerly. 'The results at Pocono?' At Greg's nod, Simon said, 'Turn it up.'

'—Snyder's victory today was marred by a disastrous crash on the hundred and seventy-fifth lap that involved seven cars. The leading cars were lapping the slower traffic when Binghamton lost control of his car in the turn and bumped into Braden, sending him to the wall. That started a chain reaction——'

'Oh, no!' Susan tried to muffle the cry with her hand, but it rang clearly in the hushed room. Warren stared at her stricken expression, a darkening cloud drawing blackly over his face. But she didn't see him.

'Turn it up!' cried Amy, reaching for the radio and bumping the station dial.

'Leave it alone!' Greg yelled, hurriedly turning the dial back to the station.

'—listed in critical condition. Now to the baseball scores,' the sportscaster said.

'Oh, Simon,' Beth Mabry glanced earnestly at her husband, 'you don't suppose it's Mitch? It couldn't be, could it?'

His gaze bounced away from hers as if unwilling to guess. 'Try another station, Greg,' her father urged.

Susan was rooted to the floor, frozen by the cold terror that held her motionless. If her heart was beating, she couldn't feel it, as she prayed that Mitch was all right.

Not even the shattering ring of the telephone in the living room could prod her into action. It was Amy who raced from the room, muttering that Cindy, her girl friend, had chosen a bad time to call. Warren touched Susan's arm.

'Are you ready?' he asked impatiently.

'Not now!' She looked at him blankly, stunned that he would want her to leave before she found out if Mitch was hurt. 'I can't leave now.'

'What——' Warren began with biting arrogance.

But Amy's voice interrupted him. 'Susan, it's for you. It's long distance.'

Susan crossed her arms, running her hands shakily over her elbows. 'Who is it, Amy?' she called back.

'Someone named Mike O'Brian. Do you know him?' was the answer.

Her eyes widened in instant recognition of the man Mitch had identified as his pit boss at the hospital. She pivoted sharply around and raced to the living room alcove where Amy stood holding the telephone receiver in her hand.

Susan took it and quickly put it to her ear. 'Hello?'

'This is Mike O'Brian, Susan,' the vaguely familiar voice answered on the other end. 'I don't know if you remember me, but I work——'

'Yes, yes I remember you,' she broke in nervously.

'I'm calling for Mitch.'

Susan interrupted again. 'Is he all right? We heard about the crash on the news a minute ago and—Is he all right?' she repeated desperately. Her fingers tightened on the receiver.

'Susan——' the man hesitated. 'He's asking for you.'

Fear rose to strangle her throat. 'How badly is . . . is he hurt?'

Her question was met by another moment of silence. 'I think it would be best,' Mike O'Brian answered slowly, choosing his words with care, 'if you could come right away, that is if you can come.'

'Of course I'll come. I'll leave right away,' Susan rushed, choking back a frightened sob.

'I'll tell him.'

'Mike, wait! What hospital——' But there was a click at the other end and the line went dead.

Slowly Susan replaced the receiver, turning to find the anxious faces of her family gathered around her. Behind them was Warren, a black mask stealing over his rugged features.

'Mitch? Is he——' Greg began, and stopped.

'I—I don't know how badly he's hurt.' Susan shook her head absently, trying to elude the nausea that made her want to faint. Her frightened brown eyes sought out her father. 'Mike said he was asking for me and wants me to come as soon as I can. I told him I would. Daddy,' her voice broke for a second, 'I don't know which hospital.'

He was instantly at her side, a supporting arm

curving around the back of her waist. 'Don't worry about it, honey. You'll be able to find that out when you get there. First let's get you there.'

'You don't actually intend to go to Pennsylvania, do you?' Warren accused.

For an instant, she could not honestly understand why he was objecting. Mitch needed her and her place was there. Then she realized what that meant.

'Yes, I am going,' she answered very calmly.

Her father, with his usual perception, sensed what was about to come and immediately began dispersing Susan's audience.

'Beth, go upstairs and pack Susan's things. Amy, give your mother a hand.' He tossed a set of car keys to Greg. 'Get my car out of the garage, Greg, and warm it up while I use the phone in the study to call the airlines and see how soon Susan can get a flight.'

During the flurry of orders, Warren continued to glare at Susan, angered that she would think of betraying him this way and arrogantly confident he could change her mind. Despite her fear for Mitch, Susan was feeling a crazy kind of peace. Nothing Warren could say or do would ever take it away from her.

'As your future husband, Susan, I'm asking you not to go,' he said crisply.

At his reference to their coming marriage, Susan glanced down at her tightly clasped hands, turning them slightly so she could see the rainbow sparkle of her engagement ring. She smiled faintly.

'I'm going.'

'You're my fiancée,' Warren reminded her tautly. 'I'm not going to stand by while you rush to another man's side.'

'I think you've missed the point.' Susan raised her head, serenely meeting the volcanic darkness of his eyes. 'I'm not asking you to stand by. I'm just wondering how I could have been so blind these past weeks.' She slipped the ring from her finger and held it out to him. 'I'm sorry, Warren, that we both had to find out this way.'

'You can't mean you're in love with this man!' he demanded incredulously, ignoring her outstretched hand.

'That's exactly what I mean.'

'But you're in love with me! You've told me that repeatedly. How can you suddenly say you're in love with someone else?' he accused angrily.

A gentle smile of understanding spread over Susan's mouth at Warren's outraged bewilderment. 'I was once warned that secretaries invariably become infatuated with their bosses, especially when they're men like you. I fell so heavily in love that I nearly missed the real thing.' It was so amazingly clear now that she marveled that she hadn't seen it before. A cold chill chased away the thought. 'I may be too late now.'

'I'm warning you, Susan, if I take that ring now, it's all over between us,' he stated icily. 'Don't expect to come running back to me if you discover that you're wrong.'

'I understand perfectly,' she nodded.

His mouth tightened into an ominous line. Then he reached out and snatched the ring from her fingers. Without another word he strode angrily toward the front door, slamming it loudly.

Her father appeared in the hallway arch, a bright twinkle in his eyes when he glanced at the front door. Turning to Susan, he winked broadly in approval and she couldn't help smiling back.

'There's a flight that will be leaving in fifty minutes,' Simon Mabry told her as he walked to the base of the stairs. 'Beth, do you have Susan's suitcase packed? We have to leave for the airport now if we want to catch the first flight.'

'I think so,' her mother called back, appearing seconds later at the top of the stairs with Amy right behind her. 'I do hope I haven't forgotten anything, Susan,' she said anxiously as she hurried down the steps carrying the overnight bag.

'We haven't time to go over it now,' her father decreed, taking the bag and motioning for Susan to follow him.

'Call us as soon as you can, Susan, and let us know how Mitch is,' her mother requested, hurrying out the front door behind them. 'And give him our love.'

'I will, Mom,' Susan promised.

The car was in the driveway, the motor running. Greg hopped from behind the wheel as Simon Mabry walked around the front of the car.

'Boy, was Warren mad when he left!' Greg declared in a slightly delighted tone. 'Did you ditch him, Susan?'

'Yes,' she said simply, opening the passenger door and sliding into the seat.

'Don't forget to phone!' Beth called to Susan as

Simon Mabry put the car in gear.

Susan nodded that she would.

'And tell Mitch he can recuperate at our house again!' Greg added.

They reversed out of the drive and headed down the residential street. As they turned on to the highway, Mr. Mabry glanced at his watch.

'I think we'll make it in plenty of time,' he assured Susan with a quick smile.

During all the turmoil, there had not been one question or comment from any of her family. Susan shifted self-consciously in her seat.

'Dad,' she began hesitantly, 'I think I should explain.'

'You don't need to,' he interrupted her. 'I think I'd already guessed which way the wind was blowing.'

'But how?' she frowned.

'If there's one thing more obvious than a couple gazing into each other's eyes, it's two people avoiding each other. And,' he breathed in with a faint shrug, 'that goodbye kiss Mitch gave you practically clinched it for me. He's one future son-in-law that I'm going to like.'

'Daddy,' chilling fear crept into her voice, 'he just has to be all right.'

'He will be.' It was almost a promise.

Everything had happened so fast that Susan hadn't been conscious of time. Now the interminable waiting had begun.

The jet plane might have had wings, but it couldn't travel fast enough for her. She alternated between cold dread that she was already too late,

377

that Mitch might have died before she was able to tell him she loved him, and clinging hope that love wouldn't let him slip away. The very fact that Mike O'Brian had avoided telling her how badly Mitch was injured made her imagine the worst.

Tears of relief pricked her eyes when the plane taxied to a stop at the terminal building. She knew she couldn't afford to panic.

First she had to find a telephone and discover which hospital Mitch was in and, she hoped, find out his condition. Then she would need to take a cab. She forced all other thoughts from her mind. She had to take one step at a time, she told herself as she impatiently followed the disembarking passengers ahead of her.

The gate area was filled with other passengers waiting to board the plane. Susan hurried to the counter to ask the airline attendant for the location of the nearest telephone. The words never were uttered as a man separated himself from the other waiting passengers and walked to her side.

The golden brown head tilted itself to one side, a bright glow in the blue eyes that crinkled at the corners. 'Hello, Susan,' Mitch said softly.

For a long second, Susan stared at him in disbelief. 'Mitch?' And he smiled. She took a hesitant step toward him. 'Wh—what are you doing here?'

The light in his eyes danced wickedly. 'I've been meeting every incoming plane that you could have possibly caught from Indianapolis.'

She took another step closer, wildly searching for any sign of concealed injury, cuts, bruises, anything. 'But I thought you were hurt? Mike. . . .'

'Mike never said I was hurt,' Mitch interrupted complacently. 'He only said I was asking for you.' His voice lowered to a husky caress. 'I've been asking for you for a long while. This time you finally heard me.'

'Do you mean this was all a trick?' Susan accused in astonishment. An anger began to build at all the unnecessary anguish she had gone through. 'You let me believe you were critically injured just to get me out here. I think that's cruel! It's—it's—'

'It's the mark of a desperate man,' Mitch answered quietly, reaching to take hold of the hand she was flinging wildly about. 'A man who's very much in love and who knows the woman he loves loves him, only he can't get her to admit it. And he's terrified she'll marry someone else. You do love me, don't you, beautiful?'

'Yes!' she snapped.

'What about Warren?' He turned her left hand slightly and saw her bare wedding finger.

'He was there when Mike telephoned,' Susan answered curtly. 'I gave him back his ring.'

'He must have been furious.' The grooves around his mouth deepened, those engaging, dimpling lines appearing in the lean cheeks.

'He was,' she admitted. Under the charm of his smile, she began to feel her anger fade. 'Oh, Mitch, what about the accident at the race? The radio said a car bumped yours and sent it into the wall.'

'That's true,' he agreed, cupping her cheek in his hand. 'But I just kissed the wall and continued on with the race. The other collisions occurred behind me. I didn't win, but I finished the race.'

379

Her love couldn't be held in check any longer and Susan rushed into his inviting arms. He held her against him, burying his head in her hair.

'I was so terrified,' Susan murmured against his chest. 'I was afraid I'd never be able to tell you that I love you.'

'Tell me,' he ordered, raising his head and forcing hers up with a thumb under her chin.

With her head tilted way back, Susan gazed adoringly into his face. 'I love you, Mitchum Alexander Braden.'

The blue eyes smouldered. 'Now, repeat after me: Will you marry me?'

'Yes,' she laughed gaily.

A smile flashed across his face as he shook his head. 'You're supposed to propose to me. I told your father you would.'

'When?' she asked with a doubting smile.

'About twenty minutes ago when the airline confirmed you were on this plane. I didn't want your family worrying about me, so I called,' Mitch told her lazily. 'Now, are you really going to make a liar out of me to your father?'

'Will you marry me?' she asked dutifully.

'I thought you'd never ask,' Mitch chuckled.

Unmindful of the other passengers in the terminal, he claimed his kiss to seal the bargain. At the moment, nothing and no one else existed except each other.

❧ FREE ❧
*Harlequin Reader Service Catalog**

A complete listing of all titles currently available in Harlequin Romance, Harlequin Presents, Classic Library and Superromance.

Special offers and exciting new books, too!

*Catalog varies each month.

Complete and mail this coupon today!

Choose from this great selection of early Harlequins—books that let you escape to the wonderful world of romance!*

982 **No Orchids by Request**
Essie Summers

984 **Island in the Dawn**
Averil Ives

1015 **Sweet Are the Ways**
Essie Summers

1048 **High Master of Clere**
Jane Arbor

1126 **Man of the Islands**
Henrietta Reid

1151 **Enchanted Autumn**
Mary Whistler

1156 **A Place Called Paradise**
Essie Summers

1162 **Island of Love**
Belinda Dell

1168 **Rose in the Bud**
Susan Barrie

1172 **Let Love Abide**
Norrey Ford

1173 **Red as a Rose**
Hilary Wilde

1175 **Moon over Madrid**
Fiona Finlay

1180 **Rose of the Desert**
Roumelia Lane

1181 **Dangerous Love**
Jane Beaufort

1183 **Never Call It Loving**
Majorie Lewty

1184 **The House of Oliver**
Jean S. MacLeod

1186 **Someone Else's Heart**
Barbara Allen

1187 **Sweet Adventure**
Mary Burchell

1195 **Spread Your Wings**
Ruth Clemence

1200 **Satin for the Bride**
Kate Starr

1203 **The Lucky One**
Marjorie Lewty

1204 **This Was Love**
Jean Curtis

1214 **The Marshall Family**
Mary Burchell

1215 **Soft Is the Music**
Jane Beech

1221 **Master of Melincourt**
Susan Barrie

1222 **Dark Confessor**
Elinor Davis

1237 **The Last of the Mallorys**
Kay Thorpe

1238 **White Rose of Love**
Anita Charles

1248 **Where Love Is**
Norrey Ford

1314 **Summer Island**
Jean S. MacLeod

*Some of these book were originally published under different titles.